-Level Chemistry for AQA

The Complete Course for AQA

Contents

Introduction

How Science Works

Unit 1

Section 1: Atomic Structure

Section 2: Amount of Substance

Section 3: Bonding and Periodicity

Section 4: Alkanes and Organic Chemistry

Unit 2

Section 1: Energetics

Section 2: Kinetics and Equilibria

Section 3: Reactions and Elements

Section 4: More Organic Chemistry

Investigative and Practical Skills

HOW SCIENCE WORKS

Exam Help

EXAM HELP

Reference

How to use this book

Learning Objectives

- These tell you exactly what you need to learn, or be able to do, for the exam.
- There's a specification reference at the bottom that links to the AQA specification.

Exam Tips

There are tips throughout the book to help with all sorts of things to do with answering exam questions.

Tips

These are here to help you understand the theory.

Learning Objectives:
- Know and understand the meaning of the term structural isomerism.
- Be able to draw the structures of chain, position and functional group isomers.

Specification Reference 3.1.5

Exam Tip
You don't always have to draw all of the bonds when you're drawing a molecule — writing CH_3 next to a bond is just as good as drawing out the carbon atom, three bonds and three hydrogen atoms. But if you're asked for a displayed formula you must draw out all of the bonds to get the marks.

Tip: Number the carbon atoms — it makes it easier to see where the longest carbon chain is and where side chains and atoms are attached:

2. Isomers

You can put the same atoms together in different ways to make completely different molecules. Two molecules that have the same molecular formula but are put together in a different way are isomers of each other.

Structural isomers

In structural isomers the atoms are connected in different ways. But they still have the same molecular formula. There are three types of structural isomers — chain isomers, position isomers and functional group isomers.

1. Chain isomers

Chain isomers have different arrangements of the carbon skeleton. Some are straight chains and others are branched in different ways.

Examples

There are different chain isomers of C_4H_{10}. The diagrams below show the straight chain isomer butane and a branched chain isomer methylpropane.

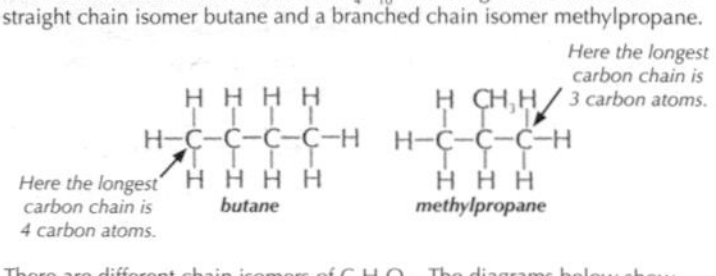

There are different chain isomers of $C_4H_8O_2$. The diagrams below show the straight chain isomer butanoic acid and a branched chain isomer methylpropanoic acid.

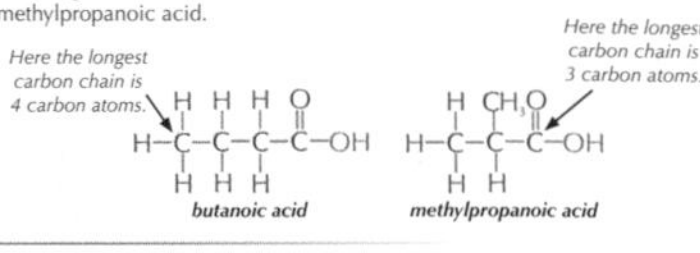

2. Positional isomers

Positional isomers have the same skeleton and the same atoms or groups of atoms attached. The difference is that the atom or group of atoms is attached to a different carbon atom.

Example

There are two position isomers of C_4H_9Cl. The chlorine atom is attached to different carbon atoms in each isomer.

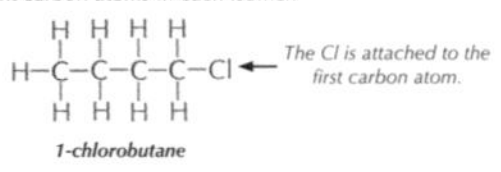

92 Unit 1: Section 4 Alkanes and Organic Chemistry

Bohr's model

There were quite a few other modifications to the model before we got to our currently accepted versions. Niels Bohr got pretty close though. Scientists realised that electrons in a 'cloud' around the nucleus of an atom, as Rutherford described, would quickly spiral down into the nucleus, causing the atom to collapse. Niels Bohr proposed a new model of the atom with four basic principles:

- Electrons only exist in fixed orbits (shells) and not anywhere in between.
- Each shell has a fixed energy.
- When an electron moves between shells electromagnetic radiation is emitted or absorbed.
- Because the energy of shells is fixed, the radiation will have a fixed frequency.

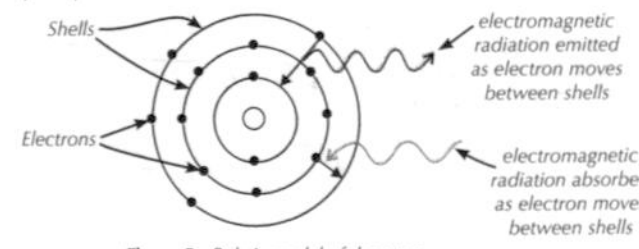

Figure 5: Bohr's model of the atom.

Figure 6: Rutherford and Bohr worked together at the University of Manchester.

The frequencies of radiation emitted and absorbed by atoms were already known from experiments. The Bohr model fitted these observations — it looked good.

The refined Bohr model

One of the things that makes a theory scientific is that it's 'falsifiable' — you can make predictions using the theory, then if you test the predictions and they turn out to be wrong, you know that the theory's wrong. Scientists discovered that not all the electrons in a shell had the same energy. This meant that the Bohr model wasn't quite right. So, they refined it to include sub-shells. The Bohr model also explained why some elements (the noble gases) are inert. Bohr said that the shells of an atom can only hold fixed numbers of electrons, and that an element's reactivity is due to its electrons. So, when an atom has full shells of electrons it's stable and does not react.

Examples

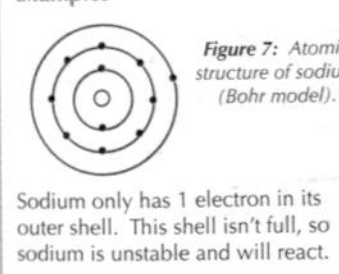

Figure 7: Atomic structure of sodium (Bohr model).

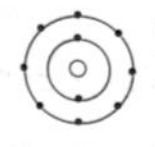

Sodium only has 1 electron in its outer shell. This shell isn't full, so sodium is unstable and will react.

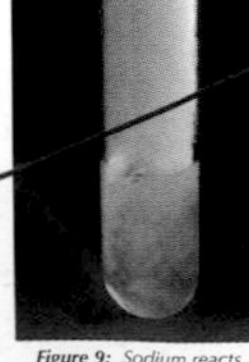

Figure 8: Atomic structure of neon (Bohr model).

Neon (a noble gas) has full shells of electrons. This means the atom is stable, so neon will not react.

Figure 9: Sodium reacts vigorously with water as it is unstable.

Loads of observations fitted in with the Bohr model, and the refined Bohr model was even better.

Unit 1: Section 1 Atomic Structure 9

How Science Works

- For AS Chemistry you need to know about How Science Works. There's a section on it at the front of the book.
- How Science Works is also covered throughout the book wherever you see this symbol.

HOW SCIENCE WORKS

Examples

These are here to help you understand the theory.

Exam Help

There's a section at the back of the book stuffed full of things to help with your exams.

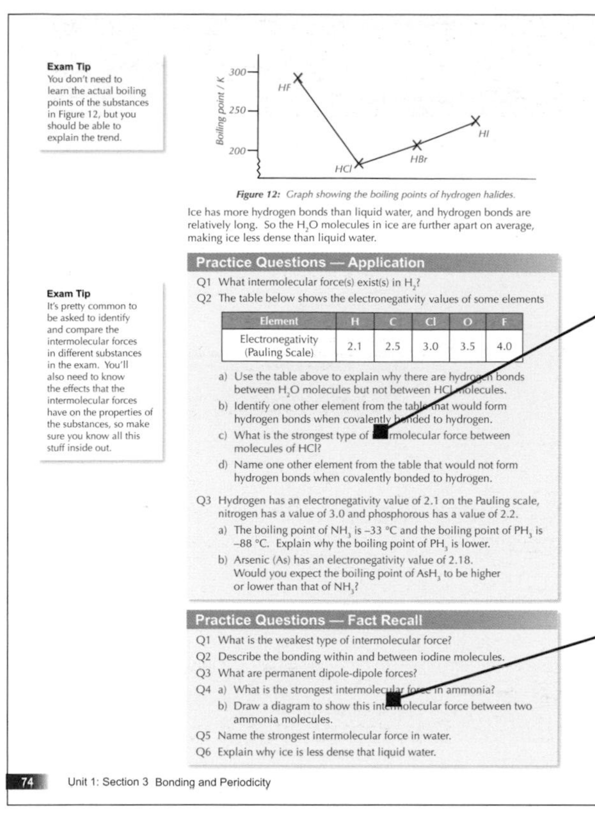

Exam Tip
You don't need to learn the actual boiling points of the substances in Figure 12, but you should be able to explain the trend.

Figure 12: Graph showing the boiling points of hydrogen halides.

Ice has more hydrogen bonds than liquid water, and hydrogen bonds are relatively long. So the H_2O molecules in ice are further apart on average, making ice less dense than liquid water.

Exam Tip
It's pretty common to be asked to identify and compare the intermolecular forces in different substances in the exam. You'll also need to know the effects that the intermolecular forces have on the properties of the substances, so make sure you know all this stuff inside out.

Practice Questions — Application

Q1 What intermolecular force(s) exist(s) in H_2?

Q2 The table below shows the electronegativity values of some elements

Element	H	C	Cl	O	F
Electronegativity (Pauling Scale)	2.1	2.5	3.0	3.5	4.0

a) Use the table above to explain why there are hydrogen bonds between H_2O molecules but not between HCl molecules.
b) Identify one other element from the table that would form hydrogen bonds when covalently bonded to hydrogen.
c) What is the strongest type of intermolecular force between molecules of HCl?
d) Name one other element from the table that would not form hydrogen bonds when covalently bonded to hydrogen.

Q3 Hydrogen has an electronegativity value of 2.1 on the Pauling scale, nitrogen has a value of 3.0 and phosphorous has a value of 2.2.
a) The boiling point of NH_3 is –33 °C and the boiling point of PH_3 is –88 °C. Explain why the boiling point of PH_3 is lower.
b) Arsenic (As) has an electronegativity value of 2.18. Would you expect the boiling point of AsH_3 to be higher or lower than that of NH_3?

Practice Questions — Fact Recall

Q1 What is the weakest type of intermolecular force?
Q2 Describe the bonding within and between iodine molecules.
Q3 What are permanent dipole-dipole forces?
Q4 a) What is the strongest intermolecular force in ammonia?
b) Draw a diagram to show this intermolecular force between two ammonia molecules.
Q5 Name the strongest intermolecular force in water.
Q6 Explain why ice is less dense that liquid water.

74 Unit 1: Section 3 Bonding and Periodicity

Practice Questions — Application

- Annoyingly, the examiners expect you to be able to apply your knowledge to new situations — these questions are here to give you plenty of practice at doing this.
- All the answers are in the back of the book (including any calculation workings).

Practice Questions — Fact Recall

- There are a lot of facts to learn for AS Chemistry — these questions are here to test that you know them.
- All the answers are in the back of the book.

Glossary

There's a glossary at the back of the book full of all the definitions you need to know for the exam, plus loads of other useful words.

Exam-style Questions

- Practising exam-style questions is really important — you'll find some at the end of each section.
- They're the same style as the ones you'll get in the real exams — some will test your knowledge and understanding and some will test that you can apply your knowledge.
- All the answers are in the back of the book, along with a mark scheme to show you how you get the marks.

Investigative and Practical Skills

- For AS-Chemistry you'll have to complete Unit 3 — Investigative and Practical Skills.
- There's a section at the back of the book with loads of stuff to help you plan, analyse and evaluate experiments.

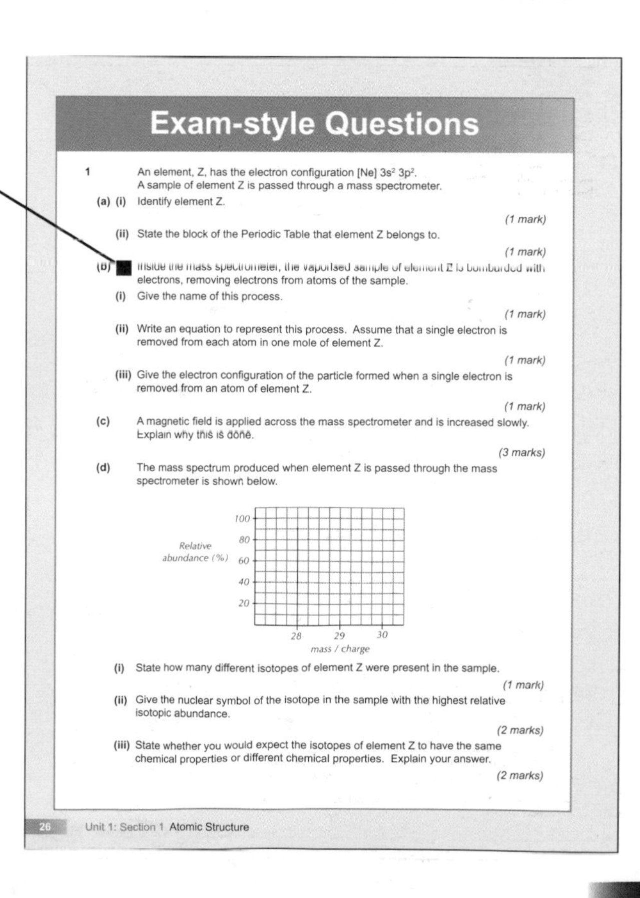

Exam-style Questions

1 An element, Z, has the electron configuration [Ne] $3s^2\ 3p^2$.
A sample of element Z is passed through a mass spectrometer.

(a) (i) Identify element Z. *(1 mark)*

(ii) State the block of the Periodic Table that element Z belongs to. *(1 mark)*

(b) Inside the mass spectrometer, the vaporised sample of element Z is bombarded with electrons, removing electrons from atoms of the sample.

(i) Give the name of this process. *(1 mark)*

(ii) Write an equation to represent this process. Assume that a single electron is removed from each atom in one mole of element Z. *(1 mark)*

(iii) Give the electron configuration of the particle formed when a single electron is removed from an atom of element Z. *(1 mark)*

(c) A magnetic field is applied across the mass spectrometer and is increased slowly. Explain why this is done. *(3 marks)*

(d) The mass spectrum produced when element Z is passed through the mass spectrometer is shown below.

(i) State how many different isotopes of element Z were present in the sample. *(1 mark)*

(ii) Give the nuclear symbol of the isotope in the sample with the highest relative isotopic abundance. *(2 marks)*

(iii) State whether you would expect the isotopes of element Z to have the same chemical properties or different chemical properties. Explain your answer. *(2 marks)*

26 Unit 1: Section 1 Atomic Structure

Published by CGP

Editors:
Katie Braid, Mary Falkner, Helen Ronan, Megan Tyler, Karen Wells, Dawn Wright.

Contributors:
Vicky Cunningham, Ian H. Davis, John Duffy, Emma Grimwood, Lucy Muncaster, Derek Swain,
Paul Warren, Chris Workman.

ISBN: 978 1 84762 791 9

With thanks to Chris Elliss and Chetna Gohil for the proofreading.
With thanks to Laura Jakubowski for the copyright research.
AQA Specification reference points are reproduced by permission of Assessment and Qualifications Alliance.

Groovy website: www.cgpbooks.co.uk

Printed by Elanders Ltd, Newcastle upon Tyne.
Jolly bits of clipart from CorelDRAW®

The Scientific Process

Science tries to explain how and why things happen. It's all about seeking and gaining knowledge about the world around us. Scientists do this by asking questions and suggesting answers and then testing them, to see if they're correct — this is the scientific process.

Developing and testing theories

A **theory** is a possible explanation for something. Theories usually come about when scientists observe something and wonder why or how it happens. (Scientists also sometimes form a **model** too — a simplified picture or representation of a real physical situation.) Scientific theories and models are developed and tested in the following way:

- Ask a question — make an observation and ask why or how whatever you've observed happens.
- Suggest an answer, or part of an answer, by forming a theory or a model (a possible explanation of the observations or a description of what you think is happening actually happening).
- Make a prediction or **hypothesis** — a specific testable statement, based on the theory, about what will happen in a test situation.
- Carry out tests — to provide evidence that will support the prediction or refute it.

Tip: A theory is only scientific if it can be tested.

Examples

Question: Why does sodium chloride dissolve in water?

Theory: Sodium chloride is made up of charged particles which are pulled apart by the polar water molecules (see p.59).

Hypothesis: Sodium chloride will dissolve in polar solvents but not in non-polar solvents.

Test: Add sodium chloride to polar solvents such as water and to non-polar solvents such as toluene. If it dissolves in the polar solvents but not in the non-polar solvents then the evidence would support the hypothesis.

Question: Why does changing the temperature affect the yield of a reversible reaction?

Theory: The equilibrium moves to counteract the change, favouring either the forward or reverse reaction, which increases the yield of this reaction and reduces the yield of the other.

Hypothesis: Increasing the temperature of an exothermic reversible reaction at equilibrium will decrease the yield, but for an endothermic reaction it will increase the yield.

Test: Measure the yield from exothermic and endothermic reversible reactions carried out at different temperatures. If the yield from the exothermic reactions decreases with increasing temperature, but the yield from the endothermic reactions increases with increasing temperature, then this evidence supports the hypothesis.

***Figure 1:** Sodium chloride dissolving in water.*

Tip: The results of one test can't prove that a theory is true — they can only suggest that it's true. They can however disprove a theory — show that it's wrong.

PHILOSOPHICAL
TRANSACTIONS:
GIVING SOME
ACCOMPT
OF THE PRESENT
Undertakings, Studies, and Labours
OF THE
INGENIOUS
IN MANY
CONSIDERABLE PARTS
OF THE
WORLD.

Vol I.
For Anno 1665, and 1666.

In the SAVOY,
Printed by T. N. for John Martyn at the Bell, a little without Temple-Bar, and James Allestry in Duck-Lane, Printers to the Royal Society.

Figure 2: The first scientific journal, 'Philosophical Transactions of the Royal Society', published in 1665.

Tip: Scientific research is often funded by companies who have a vested interest in its outcomes. Scientists are ethically obliged to make sure that this does not bias their results.

Tip: Once an experimental method is found to give good evidence it becomes a protocol — an accepted method to test that particular thing that all scientists can use.

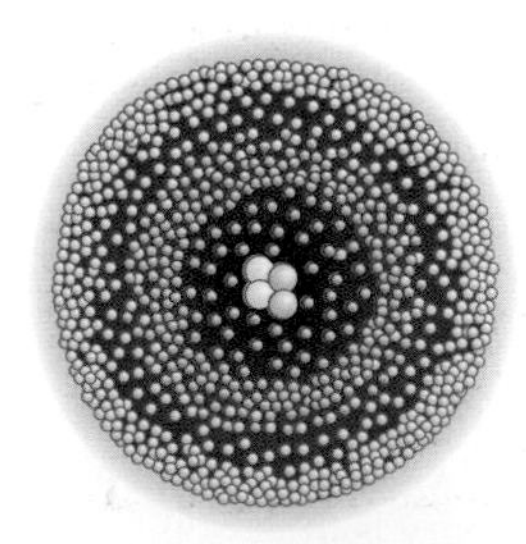

Figure 3: The quantum model of an atom — one of the current theories of atomic structure.

Communicating results

The results of testing a scientific theory are published — scientists need to let others know about their work. Scientists publish their results in scientific journals. These are just like normal magazines, only they contain scientific reports (called papers) instead of the latest celebrity gossip.

Scientists use standard terminology when writing their reports. This way they know that other scientists will understand them. For instance, there are internationally agreed rules for naming organic compounds, so that scientists across the world will know exactly what substance is being referred to (see pages 88 and 95-97).

Scientific reports are similar to the lab write-ups you do in school. And just as a lab write-up is reviewed (marked) by your teacher, reports in scientific journals undergo **peer review** before they're published. The report is sent out to peers — other scientists who are experts in the same area. They go through it bit by bit, examining the methods and data, and checking it's all clear and logical. Thorough evaluation allows decisions to be made about what makes a good methodology or experimental technique. Individual scientists may have their own ethical codes (based on their humanistic, moral and religious beliefs), but having their work scrutinised by other scientists helps to reduce the effect of personal bias on the conclusions drawn from the results.

When the report is approved, it's published. This makes sure that work published in scientific journals is of a good standard. But peer review can't guarantee the science is correct — other scientists still need to reproduce it. Sometimes mistakes are made and bad work is published. Peer review isn't perfect but it's probably the best way for scientists to self-regulate their work and to publish quality reports.

Validating theories

Other scientists read the published theories and results, and try to test the theory themselves. This involves repeating the exact same experiments, using the theory to make new predictions, and then testing them with new experiments. This is known as **validation**. If all the experiments in the world provide evidence to back it up, the theory is thought of as scientific 'fact' (for now). If new evidence comes to light that conflicts with the current evidence the theory is questioned all over again. More rounds of testing will be carried out to try to find out where the theory falls down. This is how the scientific process works — evidence supports a theory, loads of other scientists read it and test it for themselves, eventually all the scientists in the world agree with it and then bingo, you get to learn it.

Example

The structure of the atom

It took years and years for the current model of the atom to be developed and accepted — this is often the case with the scientific process.

Dalton's theory in the early 1800s, that atoms were solid spheres, was disputed by the results of Thomson's experiments at the end of that century. As a result, Thomson developed the 'plum pudding' model of the atom, which was proven wrong by Rutherford's alpha scattering experiments in 1909. Rutherford's 'nuclear model' has since been developed and modified further to create the currently accepted model of the atom we use today — but scientists are still searching for more accurate models (see pages 8-10).

How do theories evolve?

Our currently accepted theories have survived this 'trial by evidence'. They've been tested over and over again and each time the results have backed them up. But they never become totally indisputable fact. Scientific breakthroughs or advances could provide new ways to question and test the theory, which could lead to changes and challenges to it. Then the testing starts all over again. This is the tentative nature of scientific knowledge — it's always changing and evolving.

Tip: Sometimes data from one experiment can be the starting point for developing a new theory.

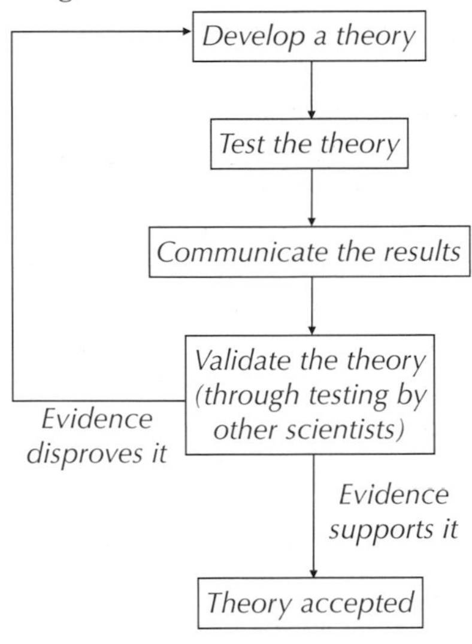

Figure 4: *Flow diagram summarising the scientific process.*

Example

CFCs and the ozone layer

When CFCs were first used in fridges in the 1930s, scientists thought they were problem-free — well, why not? There was no evidence to say otherwise. It was decades before anyone found out that CFCs were actually making a whopping great hole in the ozone layer (see page 163).

A couple of scientists developed a theory that CFCs were destroying ozone in the stratosphere, and this was tested, shared and validated by other scientists worldwide. The rigour of the scientific process meant that there was strong enough evidence against CFCs that governments could impose bans and restrictions in order to protect the ozone layer.

Figure 5: *Dumped fridges containing CFCs.*

Collecting evidence

1. Evidence from lab experiments

Results from controlled experiments in laboratories are great. A lab is the easiest place to control **variables** so that they're all kept constant (except for the one you're investigating). This means you can draw meaningful conclusions.

Tip: There's more on controlling variables and drawing conclusions from lab experiments on pages 204 and 207 in the Practical and Investigative Skills section.

Example

Reaction rates

If you're investigating how temperature affects the rate of a reaction you need to keep everything but the temperature constant. This means controlling things like the pH of the solution, the concentration of the solution, etc. Otherwise there's no way of knowing if it's the change in temperature that's affecting the rate, or some other changing variable.

Figure 6: Tap water can be chlorinated, but it's hard to design a fair and ethical test to measure its true effects.

2. Investigations outside the lab

There are things you can't study in a lab. And outside the lab controlling the variables is tricky, if not impossible.

Examples

Are increasing CO_2 emissions causing climate change?

There are other variables which may have an effect, such as changes in solar activity. You can't easily rule out every possibility. Also, climate change is a very gradual process. Scientists won't be able to tell if their predictions are correct for donkey's years.

Does drinking chlorinated tap water increase the risk of developing certain cancers?

There are always differences between groups of people. The best you can do is to have a well-designed study using matched groups — choose two groups of people (those who drink tap water and those who don't) which are as similar as possible (same mix of ages, same mix of diets etc.). But you still can't rule out every possibility. Taking newborn identical twins and treating them identically, except for making one drink gallons of tap water and the other only pure water, might be a fairer test, but it would present huge ethical problems.

Science and decision-making

Tip: Don't get mixed up — it's not the scientists who make the decisions, it's society. Scientists just produce evidence to help society make the decisions.

Lots of scientific work eventually leads to important discoveries that could benefit humankind and improve everyone's quality of life. But there are often risks attached (and almost always financial costs). Society (that's you, me and everyone else) must weigh up the information in order to make decisions — about the way we live, what we eat, what we drive, and so on. Information can also be used by politicians to devise policies and laws. However, there is not always enough information available for society and politicians to be certain about the decisions made. The scientific evidence we do have can also be overshadowed by other influences such as personal bias and beliefs, public opinion, and the media. Decisions are also affected by social, ethical and economic factors.

Examples

Disinfecting water

Chlorine is added to water in small quantities to disinfect it. Some studies link drinking chlorinated water with certain types of cancer (see page 142). But the risks from drinking water contaminated by nasty bacteria are far, far greater. There are other ways to get rid of bacteria in water, but they're heaps more expensive.

Fuels for cars

Scientific advances mean that non-polluting hydrogen-fuelled cars can be made. They're better for the environment, but are really expensive. Also, it'd cost a fortune to adapt the existing filling stations to store hydrogen.

Figure 7: A hydrogen powered car being refuelled as part of a study into the use of hydrogen fuels.

Developing drugs

Pharmaceutical drugs are really expensive to develop, and drug companies want to make money. So they put most of their efforts into developing drugs that they can sell for a good price. Society has to consider the cost of buying new drugs — the NHS can't afford the most expensive drugs without sacrificing something else.

Unit 1 Section 1: Atomic Structure

1. The Atom

Atoms are the basis of all of chemistry. You learned about them at GCSE and they're here again at AS-Level. They're super important.

Learning Objectives:
- Be able to describe the properties of protons, neutrons and electrons in terms of relative charge and relative mass.
- Understand the importance of these particles in the structure of the atom.
- Be able to recall the meaning of mass number (A) and atomic (proton) number (Z).
- Be able to explain the existence of isotopes.

Specification Reference 3.1.1

The structure of the atom

All elements are made of **atoms**. Atoms are made up of 3 types of particle — **protons**, **neutrons** and **electrons**. Figure 1 shows how they are arranged in the atom.

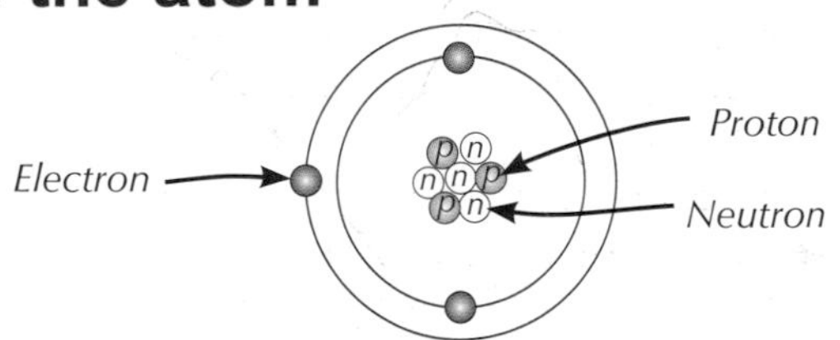

Figure 1: *The atom.*

Electrons have 1– charge. They whizz around the nucleus in orbitals. The orbitals take up most of the volume of the atom. Most of the mass of the atom is concentrated in the **nucleus**. The diameter of the nucleus is rather titchy compared to the whole atom. The nucleus is where you find the protons and neutrons. The mass and charge of these subatomic particles is really small, so relative mass and relative charge are used instead. Figure 2 shows the relative masses and charges of protons, neutrons and electrons.

Subatomic particle	Relative mass	Relative charge
Proton	1	1+
Neutron	1	0
Electron, e^-	$\frac{1}{2000}$	1–

Figure 2: *Relative masses and charges of subatomic particles.*

Tip: The mass of an electron is negligible compared to a proton or a neutron — this means you can usually ignore it.

Nuclear symbols

You can figure out the number of protons, neutrons and electrons from the nuclear symbol.

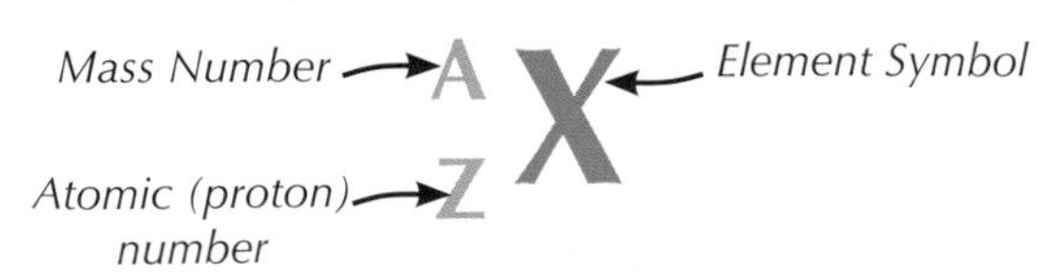

Figure 3: *Nuclear symbol.*

Tip: You can find the symbols and atomic numbers for each element using the Periodic Table. The other number in the periodic table isn't the mass number though — it's the relative atomic mass, which is a bit different. (See page 11 for more on relative atomic mass.)

Mass number

This is the total number of protons and neutrons in the nucleus of an atom.

Atomic (proton) number

This is the number of protons in the nucleus of an atom — it identifies the element. All atoms of the same element have the same number of protons. Sometimes the atomic number is left out of the nuclear symbol, e.g. ^{7}Li. You don't really need it because the element's symbol tells you its value.

Atoms and ions

For neutral atoms, which have no overall charge, the number of electrons is the same as the number of protons. The number of neutrons is just mass number minus atomic number, i.e. 'top minus bottom' in the nuclear symbol. Figure 4 shows some examples.

Nuclear symbol	Atomic number, Z	Mass number, A	Protons	Electrons	Neutrons
$^{7}_{3}Li$	3	7	3	3	7 – 3 = 4
$^{80}_{35}Br$	35	80	35	35	80 – 35 = 45
$^{24}_{12}Mg$	12	24	12	12	24 – 12 = 12

Figure 4: *Calculating the number of neutrons in atoms.*

Ions have different numbers of protons and electrons. Negative ions have more electrons than protons and positive ions have fewer electrons than protons. It kind of makes sense if you think about it.

Tip: Ions are easy to spot — they've always got a $^+$ or a $^-$ next to them. If they've got a $^+$ it means they've lost electrons, if it's a $^-$ then they've gained electrons. If there's a number next to the sign it means more than one electron has been lost or gained. For example, $^{3+}$ means 3 electrons have been lost, $^{2-}$ means that 2 have been gained.

Examples

Br^- is a negative ion

The negative charge means that there's 1 more electron than there are protons. Br has 35 protons (see table above), so Br^- must have 36 electrons. The overall charge = + 35 – 36 = –1.

Mg^{2+} is a positive ion

The 2+ charge means that there's 2 fewer electrons than there are protons. Mg has 12 protons (see table above), so Mg^{2+} must have 10 electrons. The overall charge = +12 – 10 = +2.

Isotopes

Isotopes of an element are atoms with the same number of protons but different numbers of neutrons.

Examples

Chlorine-35 and chlorine-37 are examples of isotopes. They have different mass numbers which means they have different numbers of neutrons. The atomic numbers are the same. Both isotopes have 17 protons and 17 electrons.

Chlorine-35: $^{35}_{17}Cl$

35 – 17 = 18 neutrons

Chlorine-37: $^{37}_{17}Cl$

37 – 17 = 20 neutrons

Here's another example — naturally occurring magnesium consists of 3 isotopes.

^{24}Mg (79%)	^{25}Mg (10%)	^{26}Mg (11%)
12 protons	12 protons	12 protons
12 neutrons	13 neutrons	14 neutrons
12 electrons	12 electrons	12 electrons

Figure 5: *Subatomic particles in Mg isotopes.*

Tip: You can show isotopes in different ways. For example, the isotope of magnesium with 12 neutrons can be shown as:

Magnesium-24,

^{24}Mg or $^{24}_{12}Mg$

It's the number and arrangement of electrons that decides the chemical properties of an element. Isotopes have the same configuration of electrons, so they've got the same chemical properties. Isotopes of an element do have slightly different physical properties though, such as different densities, rates of diffusion, etc. This is because physical properties tend to depend more on the mass of the atom.

Practice Questions — Application

Q1 Aluminium has the nuclear symbol: $^{27}_{13}Al$

a) How many protons does an atom of aluminium have?

b) How many electrons does an atom of aluminium have?

c) How many neutrons does an atom of aluminium have?

Q2 A potassium atom has 19 electrons and 20 neutrons.

a) How many protons does a potassium ion have?

b) What is the mass number of a potassium atom?

c) Write the nuclear symbol for potassium.

d) Potassium ions have a charge of 1+. How many electrons does a potassium ion have?

Q3 Calcium has the nuclear symbol: $^{40}_{20}Ca$
It forms Ca^{2+} ions.

a) How many electrons does a Ca^{2+} ion have?

b) How many neutrons does a Ca^{2+} ion have?

Q4 Element A has 41 protons and 52 neutrons.

a) Write the nuclear symbol for element A.

b) Write the nuclear symbol of a different isotope of element A.

Q5 This question relates to the atoms or ions A to D:

A $^{16}_{8}O^{2-}$ B $^{17}_{7}N$ C $^{20}_{10}Ne$ D $^{18}_{8}O$

Identify the similarity for each of the following pairs.

a) A and C.

b) A and D.

c) B and C.

d) B and D.

e) Which two of the atoms or ions are isotopes of each other? Explain your reasoning.

Practice Questions — Fact Recall

Q1 Name the three types of particle found in an atom.

Q2 Give the relative masses of these particles.

Q3 State where in the atom each of these particles would be found.

Q4 What is mass number?

Q5 What is atomic number?

Q6 How can you work out the number of neutrons an atom has?

Q7 What are isotopes?

Q8 Why do isotopes have the same chemical properties?

Q9 Explain why isotopes can have different physical properties.

2. Atomic Models

Learning Objectives:

- Know that early models of atomic structure predicted that atoms and ions with noble gas electron arrangements should be stable.
- Appreciate that there are various models to illustrate atomic structure.

Specification Reference 3.1.1

The model of the atom is useful for understanding loads of ideas in chemistry. But it's just a model, and the accepted model of the atom has changed throughout history.

Dalton's and Thomson's models

The model of the atom you're expected to know (the one on page 5) is one of the currently accepted ones. But in the past, completely different models were accepted, because they fitted the evidence available at the time. As scientists did more experiments, new evidence was found and the models were modified to fit it.

At the start of the 19th century John Dalton described atoms as solid spheres (see Figure 1) and said that different spheres made up the different elements. In 1897 J J Thomson concluded from his experiments that atoms weren't solid and indivisible. His measurements of charge and mass showed that an atom must contain even smaller, negatively charged particles — electrons. The 'solid sphere' idea of atomic structure had to be changed. The new model was known as the 'plum pudding model' — see Figure 2.

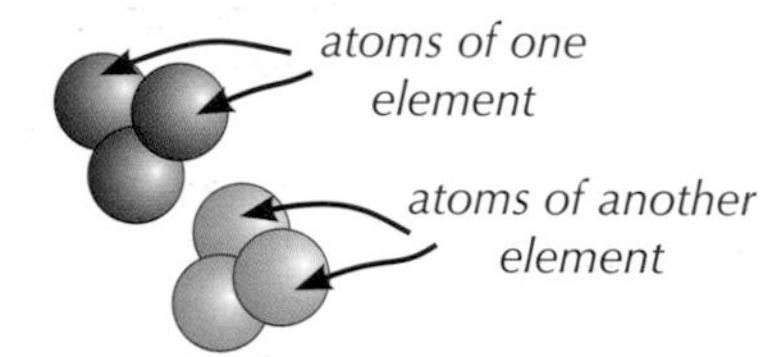

Figure 1: *Dalton's model of the atom.*

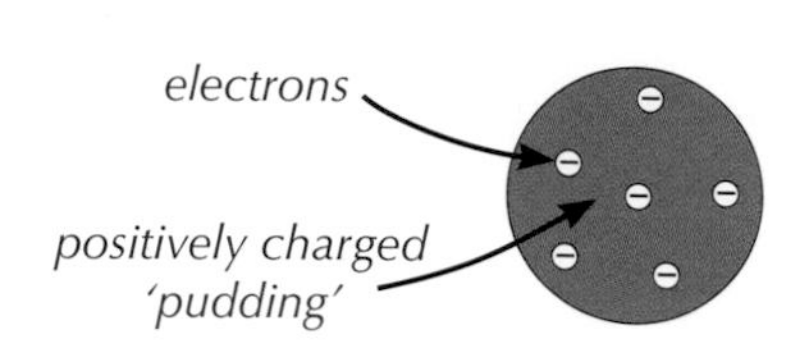

Figure 2: *Thomson's model of the atom.*

Rutherford's model

HOW SCIENCE WORKS

In 1909 Ernest Rutherford and his students Hans Geiger and Ernest Marsden conducted the famous gold foil experiment. They fired alpha particles (which are positively charged) at an extremely thin sheet of gold. From the plum pudding model, they were expecting most of the alpha particles to be deflected very slightly by the positive 'pudding' that made up most of an atom. In fact, most of the alpha particles passed straight through the gold atoms, and a very small number were deflected backwards. So the plum pudding model couldn't be right. So Rutherford came up with a model that could explain this new evidence — the nuclear model of the atom. In this, there's a tiny, positively charged nucleus at the centre, surrounded by a 'cloud' of negative electrons — most of the atom is empty space.

Figure 3: *Rutherford and Thomson worked together at Cambridge University.*

A few alpha particles are deflected very strongly by the nucleus.

Most of the alpha particles pass through empty space.

Figure 4: *Rutherford's model of the atom.*

This is nearly always the way scientific knowledge develops — new evidence prompts people to come up with new, improved ideas. Then other people go through each new, improved idea with a fine-tooth comb as well — modern 'peer review' (see page 2) is part of this process.

Bohr's model

HOW SCIENCE WORKS

There were quite a few other modifications to the model before we got to our currently accepted versions. Niels Bohr got pretty close though. Scientists realised that electrons in a 'cloud' around the nucleus of an atom, as Rutherford described, would quickly spiral down into the nucleus, causing the atom to collapse. Niels Bohr proposed a new model of the atom with four basic principles:

- Electrons only exist in fixed orbits (shells) and not anywhere in between.
- Each shell has a fixed energy.
- When an electron moves between shells electromagnetic radiation is emitted or absorbed.
- Because the energy of shells is fixed, the radiation will have a fixed frequency.

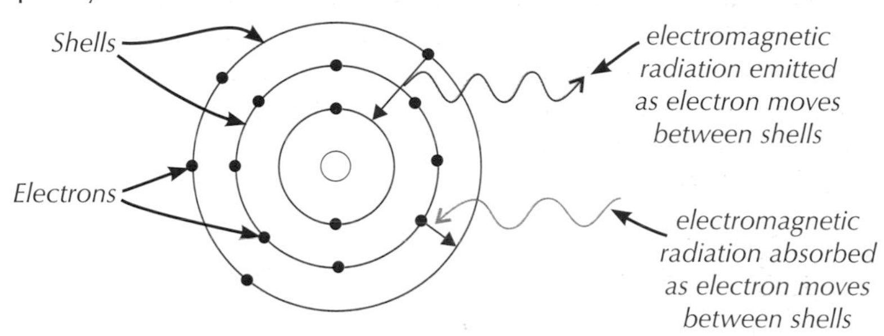

Figure 5: *Bohr's model of the atom.*

Figure 6: *Rutherford and Bohr worked together at the University of Manchester.*

The frequencies of radiation emitted and absorbed by atoms were already known from experiments. The Bohr model fitted these observations — it looked good.

The refined Bohr model

HOW SCIENCE WORKS

One of the things that makes a theory scientific is that it's 'falsifiable' — you can make predictions using the theory, then if you test the predictions and they turn out to be wrong, you know that the theory's wrong. Scientists discovered that not all the electrons in a shell had the same energy. This meant that the Bohr model wasn't quite right. So, they refined it to include sub-shells. The Bohr model also explained why some elements (the noble gases) are inert. Bohr said that the shells of an atom can only hold fixed numbers of electrons, and that an element's reactivity is due to its electrons. So, when an atom has full shells of electrons it's stable and does not react.

Examples

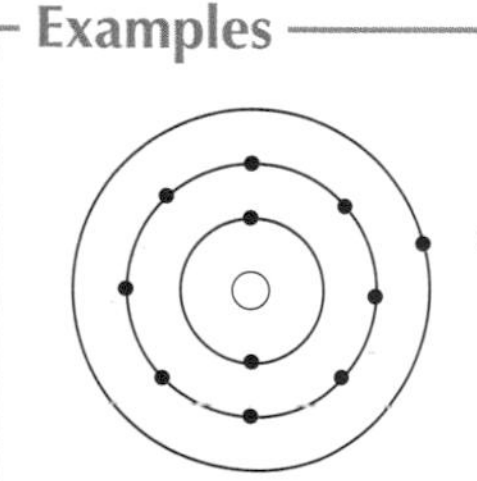

Figure 7: *Atomic structure of sodium (Bohr model).*

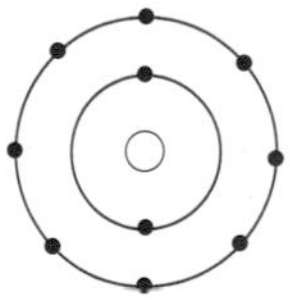

Figure 8: *Atomic structure of neon (Bohr model).*

Sodium only has 1 electron in its outer shell. This shell isn't full, so sodium is unstable and will react.

Neon (a noble gas) has full shells of electrons. This means the atom is stable, so neon will not react.

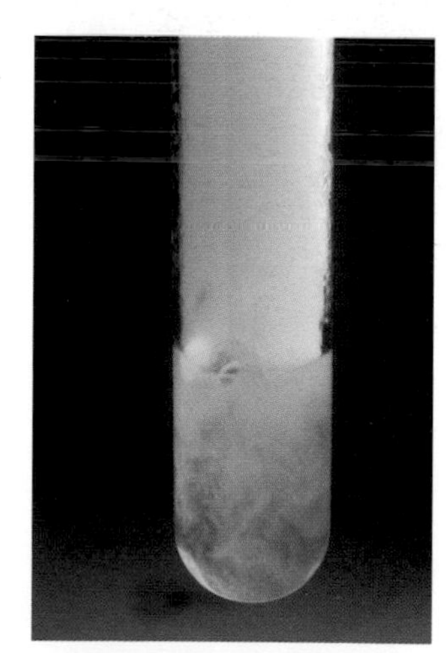

Figure 9: *Sodium reacts vigorously with water as it is unstable.*

Loads of observations fitted in with the Bohr model, and the refined Bohr model was even better.

Other atomic models

We now know that the refined Bohr model is not perfect — but it's still widely used to describe atoms because it is simple and explains many observations from experiments, like bonding and ionisation energy trends. The most accurate model we have today involves complicated quantum mechanics — see Figure 10. Basically, you can never know where an electron is or which direction it's going in at any moment, but you can say how likely it is to be at a certain point in the atom. Oh, and electrons can act as waves as well as particles. But you don't need to worry about that.

Tip: Even though some of these models are outdated now you still need to learn about them. So make sure you know what each model is like and who came up with it.

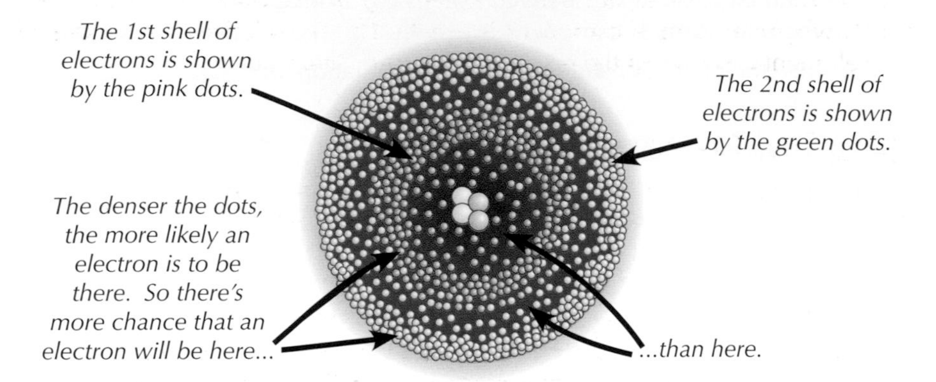

Figure 10: *The quantum model of an atom.*

The quantum model might be more accurate, but it's a lot harder to get your head round and visualise. It does explain some observations that can't be accounted for by the Bohr model though. So scientists use whichever model is most relevant to whatever they're investigating.

Practice Questions — Fact Recall

Q1 Describe how J J Thomson's model of the atom was different from Dalton's model.

Q2 What name was given to J J Thomson's model of the atom?

Q3 Name the scientists who conducted the gold foil experiment in 1909.

Q4 Explain how the gold foil experiment provided evidence that Thomson's model was wrong.

Q5 Describe Rutherford's model of the atom.

Q6 Describe the main features of Bohr's model of the atom.

Q7 Is the refined Bohr model a true representation of the structure of the atom?

3. Relative Mass

The actual mass of an atom is very, very tiny. Don't worry about exactly how tiny for now, but it's far too small to weigh. So, the mass of one atom is compared to the mass of a different atom. This is its relative mass. You need to know about relative atomic mass, relative isotopic mass and relative molecular mass.

Learning Objective:

- Be able to define relative atomic mass (A_r) and relative molecular mass (M_r) in terms of ^{12}C. (Relative formula mass is the term used for ionic compounds.)

Specification Reference 3.1.2

Relative atomic mass

The relative atomic mass, A_r, is the average mass of an atom of an element on a scale where an atom of carbon-12 is exactly 12. The relative atomic mass of each element is shown in the periodic table (see Figure 1).

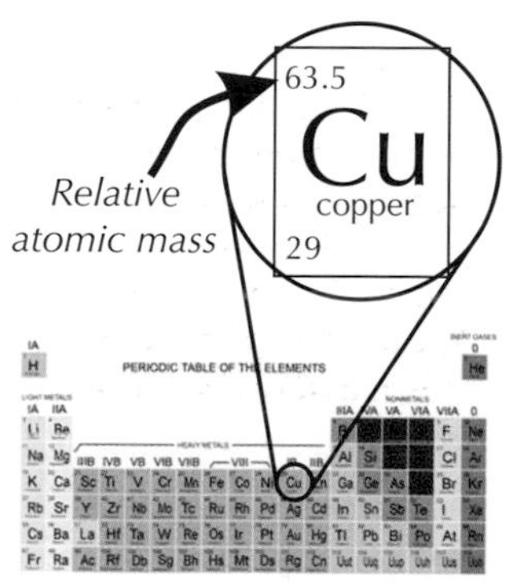

Figure 1: Location of relative atomic masses on the periodic table.

Relative isotopic mass

Relative isotopic mass is the mass of an atom of an isotope of an element on a scale where an atom of carbon-12 is exactly 12.

Calculating relative atomic mass

Relative isotopic mass is usually a whole number (at AS level anyway). Relative atomic mass is an average, so it's not usually a whole number.

Example

A natural sample of chlorine contains a mixture of ^{35}Cl and ^{37}Cl so the relative isotopic masses are 35 and 37. 75% of the sample is ^{35}Cl and 25% is ^{35}Cl. You need to take these percentages into account when you're working out the relative atomic mass.

$$\text{Relative atomic mass} = \frac{(75 \times 35) + (25 \times 37)}{100}$$

isotopic masses × percentages (numerator)

total percentage (75% ^{37}Cl + 25% ^{35}Cl) (denominator)

Relative atomic mass = 35.5

Relative molecular mass

The relative molecular mass, M_r, is the average mass of a molecule on a scale where an atom of carbon-12 is exactly 12. To find the M_r, just add up the relative atomic mass values of all the atoms in the molecule.

Examples

Calculating the relative molecular mass of C_2H_6O.

In one molecule of C_2H_6O there are 2 atoms of carbon, 6 of hydrogen and 1 of oxygen. The relative atomic masses (A_r) of each atom are shown in Figure 2.

$$M_r \text{ of } C_2H_6O = (2 \times 12) + (6 \times 1) + (1 \times 16) = 46.$$

2 C atoms (2), *A_r of C* (12), *6 H atoms* (6), *A_r of H* (1), *1 O atom* (1), *A_r of O* (16)

Atom	A_r
Carbon (C)	12.0
Hydrogen (H)	1.0
Oxygen (O)	16.0
Calcium (Ca)	40.1
Fluorine (F)	19.0

Figure 2: Table of relative atomic masses.

Calculating the relative molecular mass of C_4H_{10}.

In one molecule of C_4H_{10} there are 4 atoms of carbon and 10 of hydrogen.

$$M_r \text{ of } C_4H_{10} = (4 \times 12) + (10 \times 1) = 58.$$

Relative formula mass

Relative formula mass is the average mass of a formula unit on a scale where an atom of carbon-12 is exactly 12. It's used for compounds that are ionic (or giant covalent, such as SiO_2). To find the relative formula mass, just add up the relative atomic masses (A_r) of all the ions in the formula unit.

Tip: Relative molecular mass and relative formula mass are basically the same thing — it's just that ionic compounds aren't made of molecules so they can't have a molecular mass. You work them out the same way though.

Examples

Calculating the relative formula mass of CaF_2.

In CaF_2 there is one Ca^{2+} ion and two F^- ions. The A_r of ions is the same as the A_r of atoms of that element — the electrons make no difference to the mass.

A_r of Ca (there's only one calcium ion)

$$M_r \text{ of } CaF_2 = 40.1 + (2 \times 19) = 78.1$$

2 ions of F^- *A_r of F*

Calculating the relative formula mass of $CaCO_3$.

In $CaCO_3$ there is one Ca^{2+} ion and one CO_3^{2-} ion. The CO_3^{2-} ion contains 1 carbon atom and 3 oxygen atoms, so the A_r values of all these atoms need to be included in the calculation.

$$M_r \text{ of } CaCO_3 = 40.1 + 12 + (3 \times 16) = 100.1$$

Practice Questions — Application

Q1 Find the relative atomic mass of the following elements:
- a) Rubidium
- b) Mercury
- c) Zinc

Q2 Find the relative molecular mass of the following compounds:
- a) NH_3
- b) CO_2
- c) $C_2H_4O_6N_2$

Q3 Find the relative formula mass of the following compounds:
- a) $CaCl_2$
- b) $MgSO_4$
- c) NaOH

Q4 A sample of tungsten is 0.1% ^{180}W, 26.5% ^{182}W, 14.3% ^{183}W, 30.7% ^{184}W and 28.4% ^{186}W. Calculate the A_r of tungsten.

Q5 A sample of zirconium is 51.5% ^{90}Zr, 11.2% ^{91}Zr, 17.1% ^{92}Zr, 17.4% ^{94}Zr and 2.8% ^{96}Zr. Calculate the A_r of zirconium.

Exam Tip

It's really important that you can calculate relative molecular mass (and relative formula mass). It crops up in loads of different calculations so you need to be really confident that you can do it correctly.

Practice Questions — Fact Recall

Q1 What is relative atomic mass?

Q2 What is relative molecular mass?

Q3 What is relative formula mass?

4. Mass Spectrometry

Mass spectrometry — using a machine called a mass spectrometer to get a graph called a mass spectrum. And then interpreting it. More details below...

Learning Objectives:

- Understand the principles of a simple mass spectrometer, limited to ionisation, acceleration, deflection and detection.
- Know that mass spectrometers give accurate information about relative isotopic mass and the relative abundance of isotopes.
- Be able to interpret simple mass spectra of elements and calculate relative atomic mass from isotopic abundance of mononuclear ions.
- Know that mass spectrometry can be used to identify elements (e.g. in space probes).
- Know that mass spectrometry can be used to determine relative molecular mass.

Specification Reference 3.1.1

Measuring atomic mass

You can use a mass spectrometer to find out loads of stuff. It can tell you the relative atomic mass, relative molecular mass, relative isotopic abundance, molecular structure and your horoscope for the next fortnight. There are 5 things that happen when a sample is squirted into a mass spectrometer.

1. Vaporisation

The sample is turned into gas (vaporised) using an electrical heater.

2. Ionisation

The gas particles are bombarded with high-energy electrons to ionise them. Electrons are knocked off the particles, leaving positive ions.

3. Acceleration

The positive ions are accelerated by an electric field.

4. Deflection

The positive ions' paths are altered with a magnetic field. Lighter ions have less momentum and are deflected more than heavier ions. For a given magnetic field, only ions with a particular mass/charge ratio make it to the detector.

5. Detection

The magnetic field strength is slowly increased. As this happens, different ions (ones with a higher mass/charge ratio) can reach the detector. As ions hit the detector they cause a current to flow. The bigger the current produced the more of that isotope was present in the sample. A mass spectrum is produced.

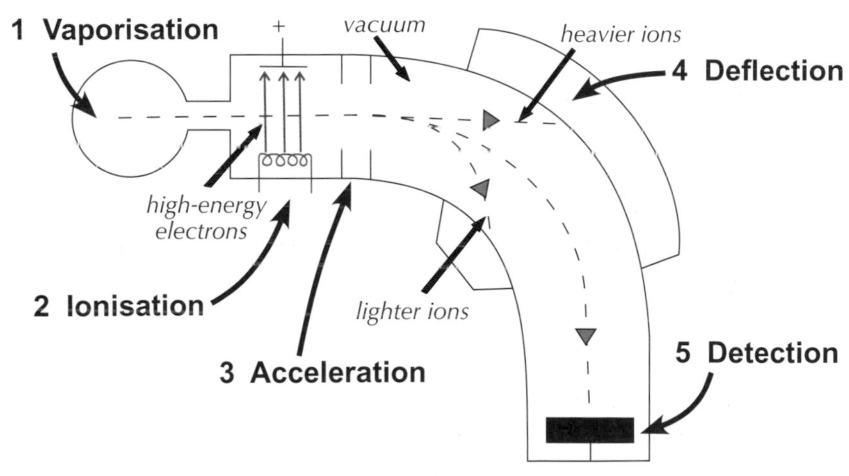

Figure 1: *Diagram of how a mass spectrometer works.*

Figure 2: *A mass spectrometer.*

Interpreting mass spectra

A **mass spectrum** is a type of chart produced by a mass spectrometer. It shows information about the sample that was passed through the mass spectrometer. If the sample is an element, each line will represent a different isotope of the element (see Figure 4). The y-axis gives the abundance of ions, often as a

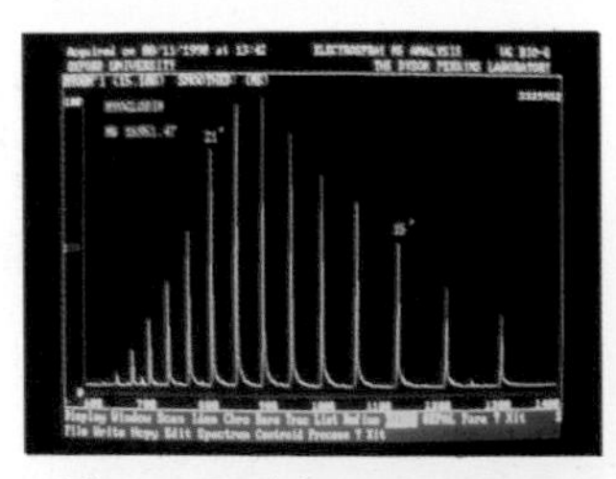

Figure 3: Mass spectrum of myoglobin.

percentage. For an element, the height of each peak gives the relative **isotopic abundance** (the amount of each isotope present in a sample). The x-axis units are given as a 'mass/charge' ratio. Since the charge on the ions is mostly 1+, you can often assume the x-axis is simply the relative isotopic mass.

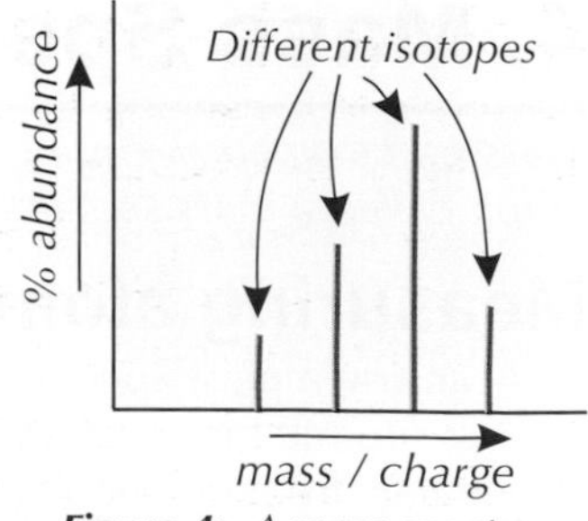

Figure 4: A mass spectrum.

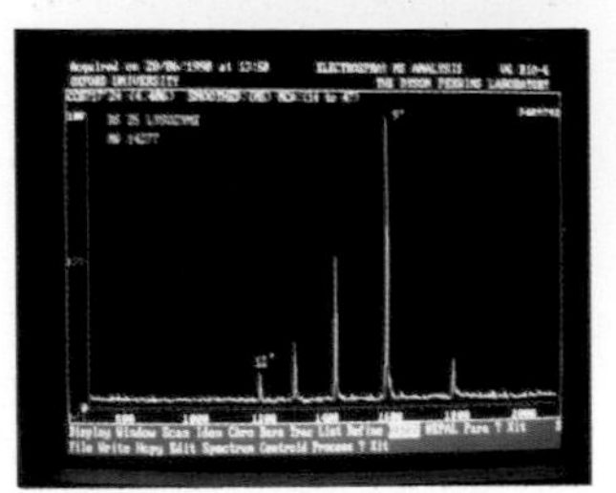

Figure 5: Mass spectrum of the enzyme lysozyme.

Tip: Mass/charge is often shown as m/z.

Example

The mass spectrum produced when a sample of chlorine is passed through a mass spectrometer is shown below.

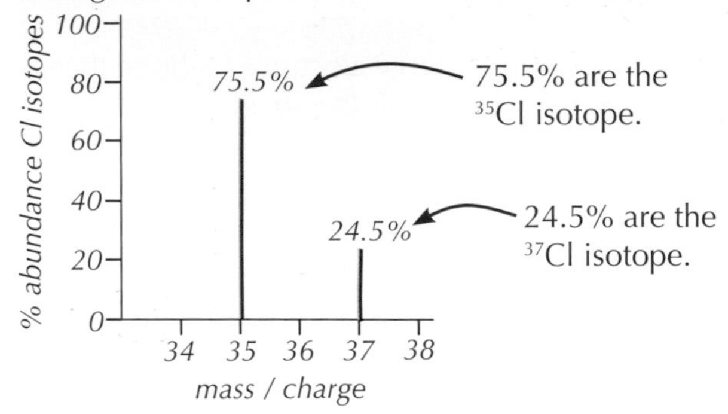

There are two peaks so there are two isotopes of chlorine.

One peak has a mass/charge ratio of 35, so the relative isotopic mass of one isotope is 35. (As chlorine ions have a charge of 1+ (Cl^+) and $35 \div 1 = 35$.)

The other peak has a mass/charge ratio of 37, so the relative isotopic mass of the other isotope is 37.

So, from the mass spectrum you can tell that there are two isotopes present, ^{35}Cl and ^{37}Cl. 75.5% of the sample is ^{35}Cl. 24.5% of the sample is ^{37}Cl.

Practice Questions — Application

Q1 The mass spectrum for a sample of copper is shown below.

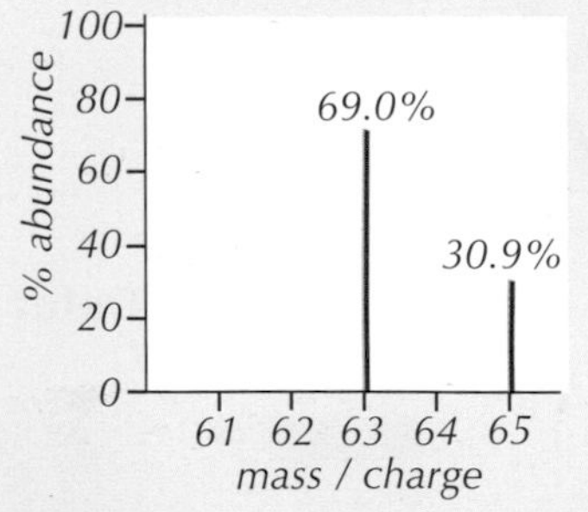

a) How many isotopes of copper were in the sample?

b) Give the relative isotopic mass of each isotope.

c) Give the relative isotopic abundance of each isotope.

Q2 The mass spectrum for a sample of sulfur is shown on the right.

a) How many isotopes were in the sample?

b) Give the relative isotopic mass of each isotope.

c) Give the relative isotopic abundance of each isotope.

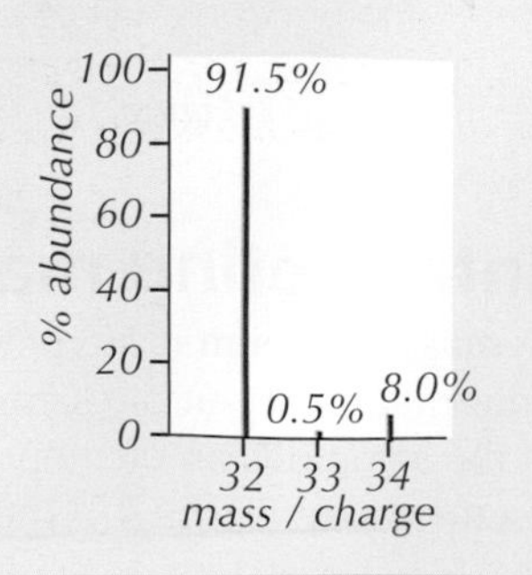

Calculating relative atomic mass

You need to know how to calculate the relative atomic mass (A_r) of an element from the mass spectrum.

- Step 1: For each peak, read the % relative isotopic abundance from the y-axis and the relative isotopic mass from the x-axis. Multiply them together to get the total mass for each isotope.
- Step 2: Add up these totals.
- Step 3: Divide by 100 (since percentages were used).

Figure 6: *The Phoenix Mars lander probe. Mass spectrometry is a good way to identify elements and molecules (it's kind of like fingerprinting). For instance, small mass spectrometers have been used in probes to find out what the Martian atmosphere is made of.*

Example

Here's how to calculate A_r for magnesium, using the mass spectrum below.

Step 1:

Total mass of 1st isotope: $79 \times 24 = 1896$

Total mass of 2nd isotope: $10 \times 25 = 250$

Total mass of 3rd isotope: $11 \times 26 = 286$

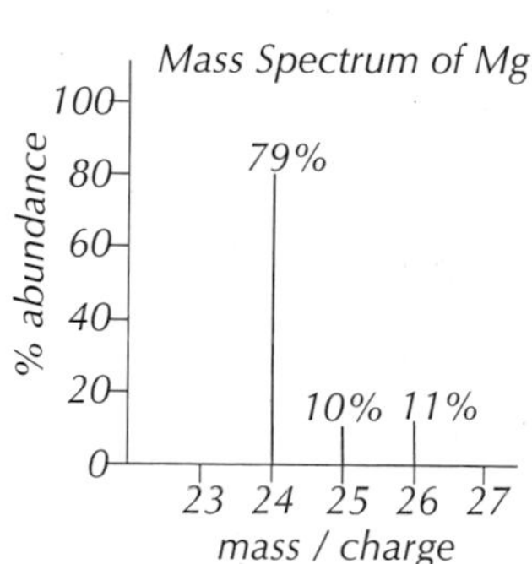

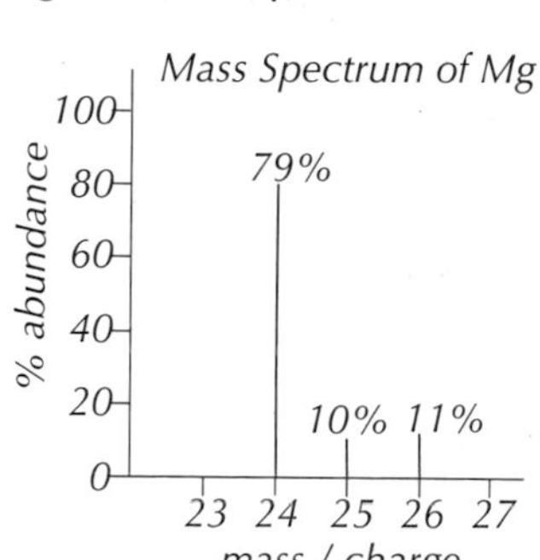

Step 2:

$1896 + 250 + 286 = 2432$

Step 3:

$2432 \div 100 = 24.32$

So A_r (Mg) ≈ 24.3

If the relative abundance is not given as a percentage, the total abundance may not add up to 100. In this case, don't panic. Just do steps 1 and 2 as above, but then divide by the total relative abundance instead of 100.

Example

Here's how to calculate A_r for neon, using the mass spectrum below.

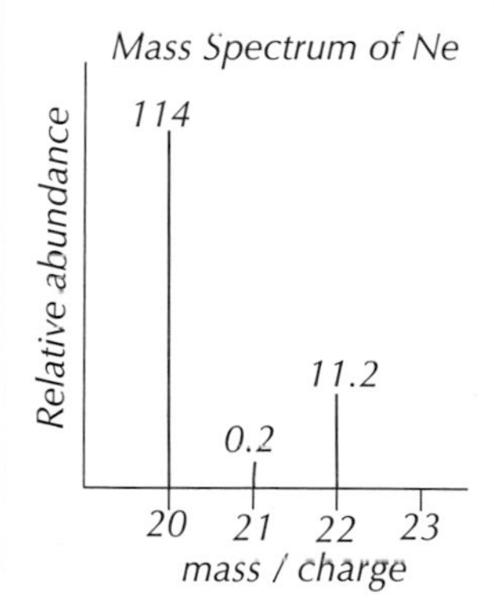

Step 1:

Total mass of 1st isotope: $114 \times 20 = 2280$

Total mass of 2nd isotope: $0.2 \times 21 = 4.2$

Total mass of 3rd isotope: $11.2 \times 22 = 246.4$

Step 2:

$2280 + 4.2 + 246.4 = 2530.6$

Step 3:

$2530.6 \div (114 + 0.2 + 11.2) = 20.18...$

So A_r (Ne) ≈ 20.18

total relative abundance

Practice Questions — Application

Q1 Use the mass spectrum on the right to calculate the A_r of bromine.

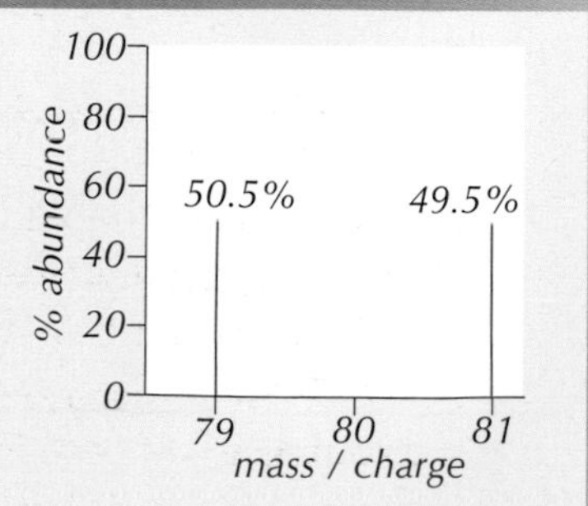

Exam Tip
Remember to check whether the y axis shows relative abundance or percentage abundance before you start your calculation.

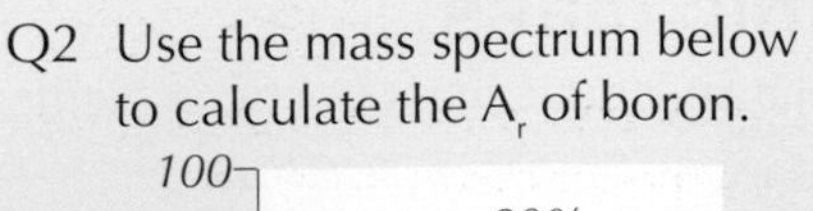
Q2 Use the mass spectrum below to calculate the A_r of boron.

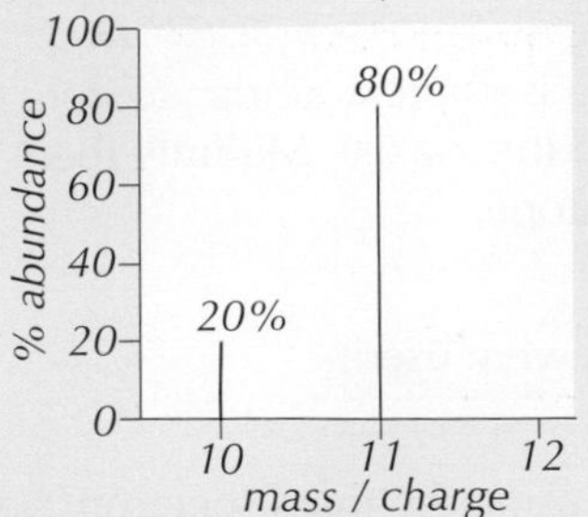

Q3 Use the mass spectrum below to calculate the A_r of rubidium.

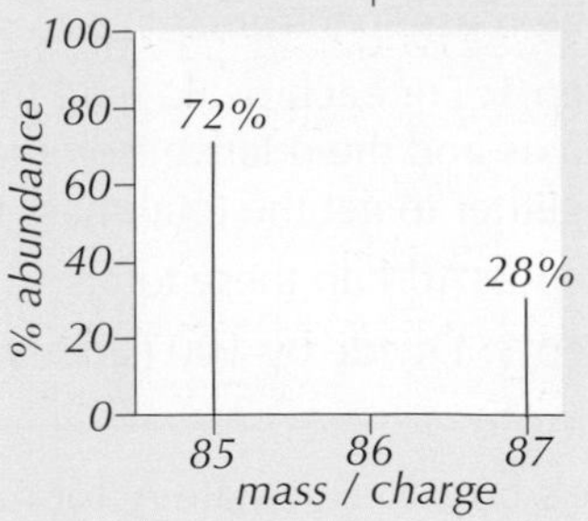

Q4 Use the mass spectrum below to calculate the A_r of lithium.

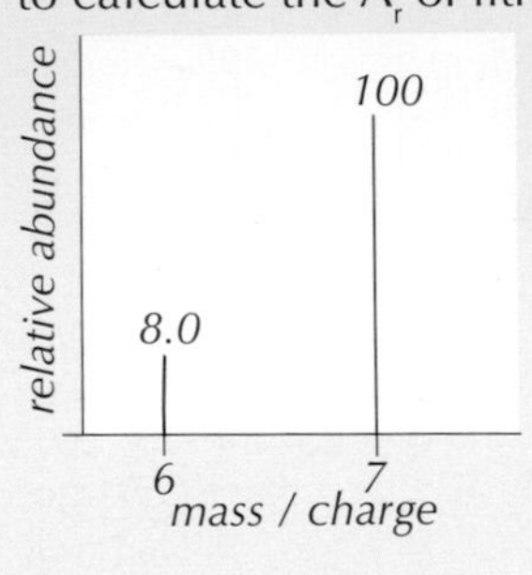

Q5 Use the mass spectrum below to calculate the A_r of gallium.

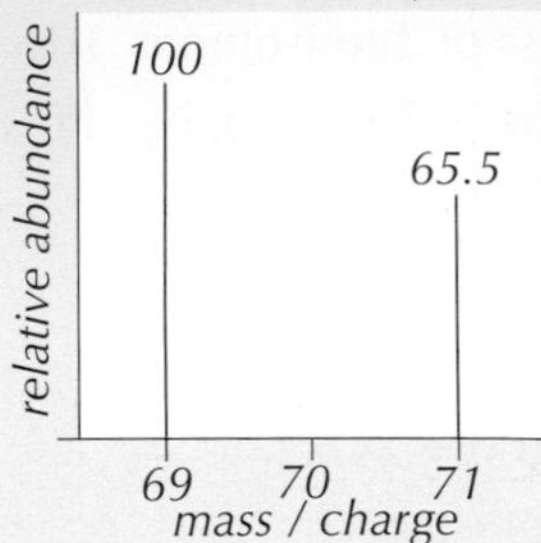

Calculating relative molecular mass

You can also get a mass spectrum for a molecular sample. A molecular ion, $M^+(g)$, is formed when the bombarding electrons remove 1 electron from the molecule. This gives the peak in the spectrum with the highest mass (furthest to the right, ignoring isotopes). The mass of M^+ gives M_r for the molecule. But it's not that simple — bombarding with electrons makes some molecules break up into fragments. These all show up on the mass spectrum, making a fragmentation pattern. Fragmentation patterns are actually pretty cool because you can use them to identify molecules and even their structure. There's more about fragmentation patterns on pages 192-195.

Example

The mass spectrum of ethanol (CH_3CH_2OH) is shown below.

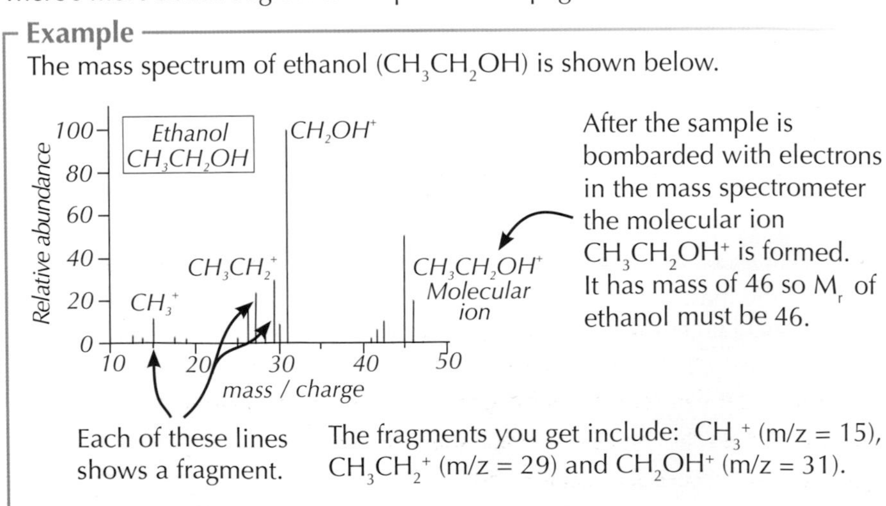

After the sample is bombarded with electrons in the mass spectrometer the molecular ion $CH_3CH_2OH^+$ is formed. It has mass of 46 so M_r of ethanol must be 46.

Each of these lines shows a fragment.

The fragments you get include: CH_3^+ (m/z = 15), $CH_3CH_2^+$ (m/z = 29) and CH_2OH^+ (m/z = 31).

Practice Questions — Application

Q1 Give the formula of the molecular ions formed when the compounds listed below are passed through a mass spectrometer.

a) CH_3CH_2COOH

b) C_3H_6O

c) CH_3OH

Q2 The mass spectrum of an acid is shown below. What is the relative molecular mass of the acid?

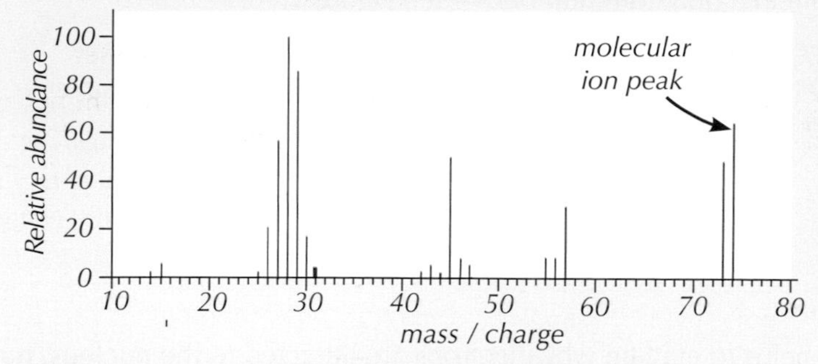

Q3 The mass spectrum of a ketone is shown below. What is the relative molecular mass of the ketone?

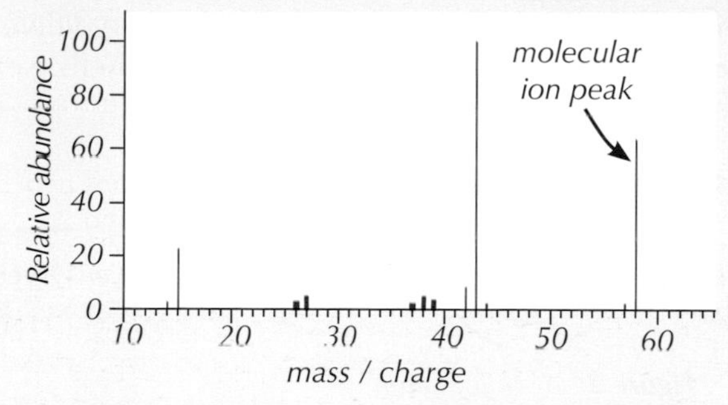

Q4 The mass spectrum of methanol is shown below. What is the relative molecular mass of methanol?

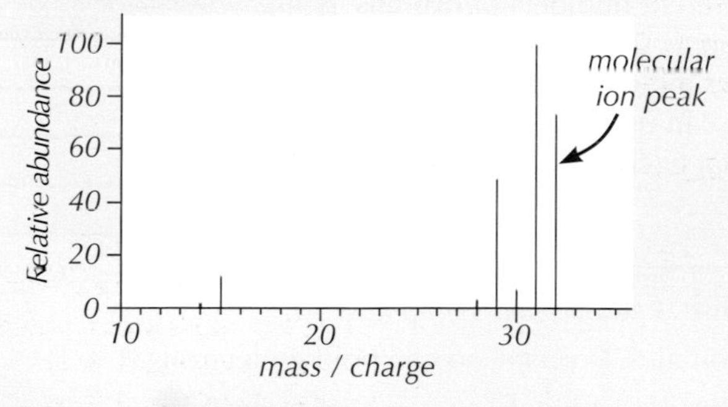

Practice Questions — Fact Recall

Q1 Name the five stages that happen in a mass spectrometer.

Q2 What does the x-axis of a mass spectrum show?

Q3 How is a molecular ion formed?

Q4 What information does the mass / charge value of the molecular ion give?

5. Electronic Structure

Learning Objectives:

- Know the electron configurations of atoms and ions up to Z = 36 in terms of levels and sub-levels (orbitals) s, p and d.
- Be able to classify an element as s, p or d block according to its position in the Periodic Table.

Specification Reference 3.1.1, 3.1.4

Electronic structure is all about how electrons are arranged in atoms.

Electron shells

In the currently accepted model of the atom, electrons have fixed energies. They move around the nucleus in certain regions of the atom called **shells** or **energy levels**. Each shell is given a number called the principal quantum number. The further a shell is from the nucleus, the higher its energy and the larger its principal quantum number — see Figure 1.

1st electron shell.
Principle quantum number = 1
This shell has the lowest energy.

2nd electron shell.
Principle quantum number = 2

3rd electron shell.
Principle quantum number = 3
This shell has the highest energy.

***Figure 1**: A sodium atom.*

This model helps to explain why electrons are attracted to the nucleus, but are not drawn into it and destroyed. Experiments show that not all the electrons in a shell have exactly the same energy. The atomic model explains this — shells are divided up into **sub-shells**. Different electron shells have different numbers of sub-shells, which each have a different energy. Sub-shells can be s sub-shells, p sub-shells, d sub-shells or f sub-shells.

Tip: Don't get confused by notation like 2s or 4f. The letter shows what type of sub-shell it is, the number shows what shell it's in. So 3p means a p sub-shell in the 3rd electron shell.

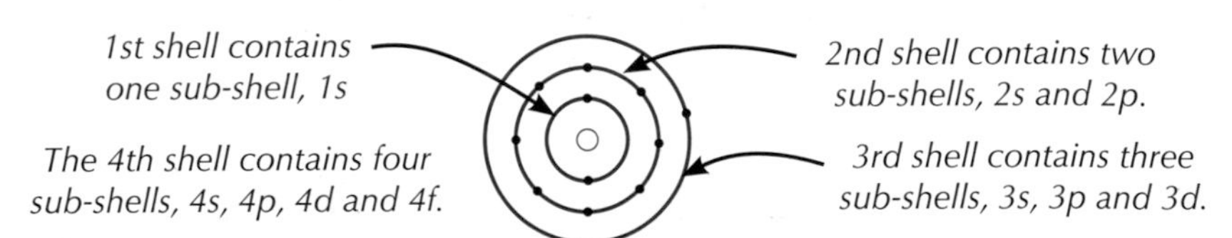

***Figure 2**: A sodium atom.*

The sub-shells have different numbers of **orbitals** which can each hold up to 2 electrons. The table on the right shows the number of orbitals in each sub-shell. You can use it to work out the number of electrons that each shell can hold.

Sub-shell	Number of orbitals
s	*1*
p	*3*
d	*5*
f	*7*

Example

The third shell contains 3 sub-shells: 3s, 3p and 3d.

- An s sub-shell contains 1 orbital, so can hold 2 electrons (1 × 2).
- A p sub-shell contains 3 orbitals, so can hold 6 electrons (3 × 2).
- A d sub-shell contains 5 orbitals, so can hold 10 electrons (5 × 2).

So the total number of electrons the third shell can hold is 2 + 6 + 10 = 18

Exam Tip
Make sure you learn how many electrons each electron shell can hold — you won't get far with electronic structures if you don't know these numbers.

The table on the right shows the number of electrons that the first four electron shells can hold.

Shell	Sub-shells	Total number of electrons
1st	*1s*	*2 = 2*
2nd	*2s 2p*	*2 + (3 × 2) = 8*
3rd	*3s 3p 3d*	*2 + (3 × 2) + (5 × 2) = 18*
4th	*4s 4p 4d 4f*	*2 + (3 × 2) + (5 × 2) + (7 × 2) = 32*

Showing electron configurations

The number of electrons that an atom or ion has, and how they are arranged, is called its **electron configuration**. Electron configurations can be shown in different ways. For example, an atom of neon has 10 electrons — two electrons are in the 1s sub-shell, two are in the 2s sub-shell and six are in the 2p sub-shell. You can show this electron configuration in three different ways...

1. Sub-shell notation

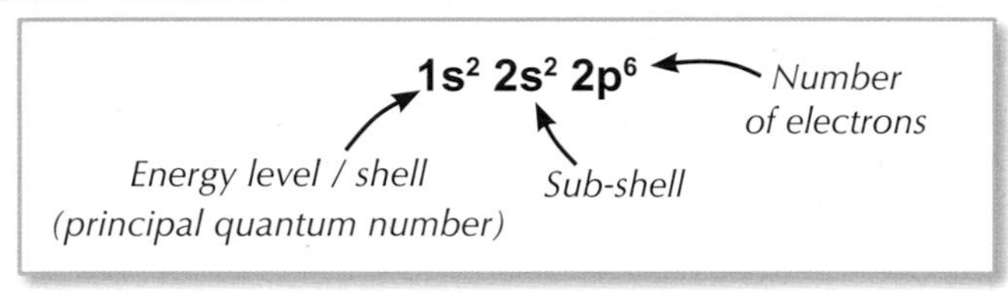

2. Arrows in boxes

Each of the boxes represents one orbital. Each of the arrows represents one electron. The up and down arrows represent the electrons spinning in opposite directions. Two electrons can only occupy the same orbital if they have opposite spin.

1s 2s 2p

3. Energy level diagrams

These show the energy of the electrons in different orbitals, as well as the number of electrons and their arrangement.

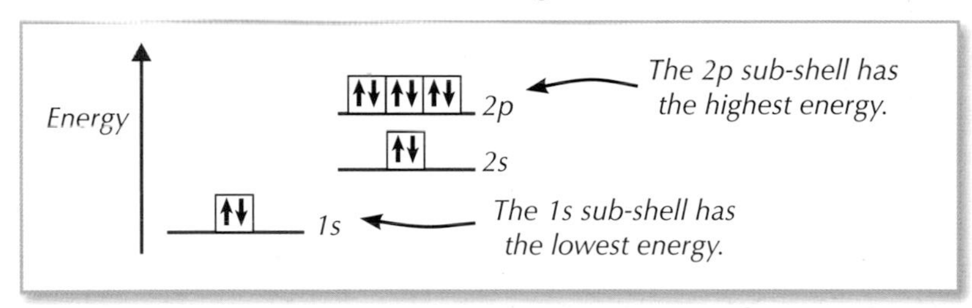

Exam Tip
You need to know how to show electron configurations using sub-shell notation, arrows in boxes and energy level diagrams — any of them could come up in the exam.

Working out electron configurations

You can figure out most electronic configurations pretty easily, so long as you know a few simple rules:

Rule 1

Electrons fill up the lowest energy sub-shells first.

Example

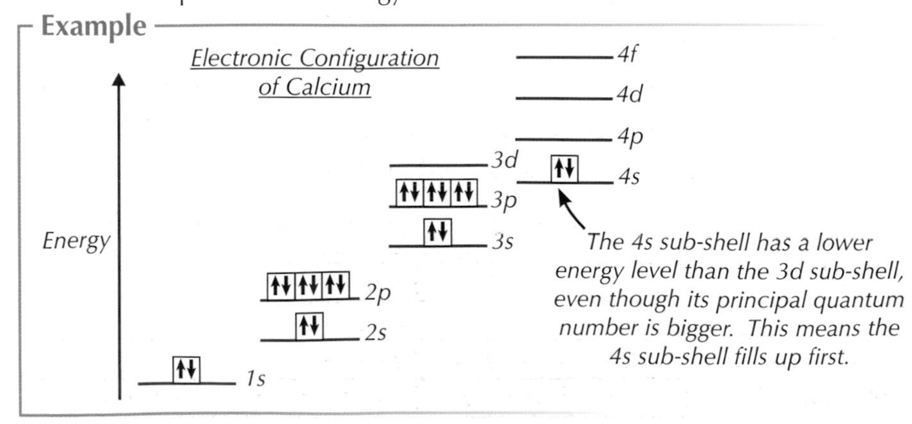

Tip: Even though the 4s sub-shell fills up before the 3d sub-shell, the 3d electrons are usually shown first when you write the configurations down. So the electron configuration of Ca is usually shown as:

$1s^2\ 2s^2\ 2p^6\ 3s^2\ 3p^6\ 4s^2$

and the electron configuration of Sc is:

$1s^2\ 2s^2\ 2p^6\ 3s^2\ 3p^6\ 3d^1\ 4s^2$

Rule 2

Electrons fill orbitals singly before they start sharing.

Examples

	1s	2s	2p		1s	2s	2p
Nitrogen	↑↓	↑↓	↑ ↑ ↑	*Oxygen*	↑↓	↑↓	↑↓ ↑ ↑

Rule 3

For the configuration of ions from the s and p blocks of the periodic table, just add or remove the electrons to or from the highest energy occupied sub-shell.

Examples

Mg atom: $1s^2\ 2s^2\ 2p^6\ 3s^2$ Cl atom: $1s^2\ 2s^2\ 2p^6\ 3s^2\ 3p^5$

Mg^{2+} ion: $1s^2\ 2s^2\ 2p^6$ Cl^- ion: $1s^2\ 2s^2\ 2p^6\ 3s^2\ 3p^6$

Tip: Elements with their outer electrons in an s sub-shell are called s block elements. Elements with their outer electrons in a p sub-shell are called p block elements.

Shortened electron configurations

Noble gas symbols in square brackets, such as [Ar], are sometimes used in electron configurations. For example, calcium ($1s^2\ 2s^2\ 2p^6\ 3s^2\ 3p^6\ 4s^2$) can be written as $[Ar]4s^2$, where $[Ar] = 1s^2\ 2s^2\ 2p^6\ 3s^2\ 3p^6$.

Exam Tip

Writing electron configurations using noble gas symbols can save you loads of time. Just make sure you've got your head round sub-shell notation before you start to use it — otherwise you're likely to get confused. And if a question asks you to give the full configuration then make sure that's what you do.

Practice Questions — Application

Q1 Use sub-shell notation to show the full electron configurations of the elements listed below.

a) Lithium

b) Titanium

c) Gallium

d) Nitrogen

Q2 Draw arrows in boxes to show the electron configurations of the elements listed below.

a) Calcium

b) Nickel

c) Sodium

d) Oxygen

Q3 Draw energy level diagrams to show the electron configurations of the elements listed below.

a) Magnesium

b) Argon

c) Carbon

d) Arsenic

Q4 Use sub-shell notation to show the electron configurations of the ions listed below.

a) Na^+

b) O^{2-}

c) Al^{3+}

d) Cl^-

Q5 Which elements have the electron configurations given below?

a) $[Ar]3d^{10}\ 4s^2\ 4p^5$

b) $[Ne]3s^2\ 3p^3$

c) $[Ne]3s^2\ 3p^6\ 3d^3\ 4s^2$

Electron configuration of transition metals

Chromium (Cr) and copper (Cu) are badly behaved. They donate one of their 4s electrons to the 3d sub-shell. It's because they're happier with a more stable full or half-full d sub-shell.

So, the electron configuration of a Cr atom is: $1s^2\ 2s^2\ 2p^6\ 3s^2\ 3p^6\ 3d^5\ 4s^1$ (not ending in $3d^4\ 4s^2$ as you'd expect).

And the electron configuration of a Cu atom is: $1s^2\ 2s^2\ 2p^6\ 3s^2\ 3p^6\ 3d^{10}\ 4s^1$ (rather than finishing with $3d^9\ 4s^2$).

Here's another weird thing about transition metals — when they become ions, they lose their 4s electrons before their 3d electrons.

Example

The electron configuration of an Fe atom is: $1s^2\ 2s^2\ 2p^6\ 3s^2\ 3p^6\ 3d^6\ 4s^2$

To become an Fe^{3+} ion it loses three electrons — two 4s electrons and one 3d electron. So the electron configuration of an Fe^{3+} ion is : $1s^2\ 2s^2\ 2p^6\ 3s^2\ 3p^6\ 3d^5$

Exam Tip

The electron configurations of chromium and copper don't follow the normal rules. Make sure you learn these two exceptions — they're really important.

Electronic structure and chemical properties

The number of outer shell electrons decides the chemical properties of an element. You can use the Periodic Table to help you work them out.

- The s block elements (Groups 1 and 2) have 1 or 2 outer shell electrons. These are easily lost to form positive ions with an inert gas configuration. E.g. Na — $1s^2\ 2s^2\ 2p^6\ 3s^1 \rightarrow Na^+$ — $1s^2\ 2s^2\ 2p^6$ (the electronic configuration of neon).
- The elements in Groups 5, 6 and 7 (in the p block) can gain 1, 2 or 3 electrons to form negative ions with an inert gas configuration. E.g. O — $1s^2\ 2s^2\ 2p^4 \rightarrow O^{2-}$ — $1s^2\ 2s^2\ 2p^6$. Groups 4 to 7 can also share electrons when they form covalent bonds.
- Group 0 (the inert gases) have completely filled s and p sub-shells and don't need to bother gaining, losing or sharing electrons — their full sub-shells make them inert.

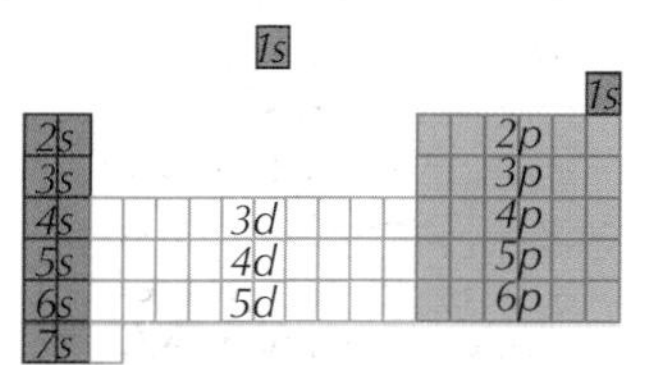

Figure 3: Elements can be classified as s block elements, p block elements or d block elements depending on where they are in the Periodic Table and which sub-shell their outer electrons are in.

Practice Questions — Application

Q1 Give the full electron configuration of Cr^{2+} using sub-shell notation.

Q2 Give the full electron configuration of Ni^{2+} using sub-shell notation.

Q3 Give the full electron configuration of V^{3+} using sub-shell notation.

Practice Questions — Fact Recall

Q1 How many orbitals does a p sub-shell contain?

Q2 How many electrons can a p sub-shell hold?

Q3 How many electrons can the 3rd electron shell hold in total?

Q4 What does "electron configuration" mean?

Q5 Which electron shells are filled up first?

1s ↑↓ 2s ↑↓ 2p ↑↓ | |

Q6 The electron configuration shown here is wrong. Explain why.

Q7 What is the electron configuration of a chromium atom?

Q8 The electron configuration of copper is $1s^2\ 2s^2\ 2p^6\ 3s^2\ 3p^6\ 3d^{10}\ 4s^1$. Why isn't it $1s^2\ 2s^2\ 2p^6\ 3s^2\ 3p^6\ 3d^9\ 4s^2$?

Q9 Describe the ions that Group 5, 6 and 7 elements form.

6. Ionisation Energies

More stuff on electron configurations coming up. The title may be ionisation energies, but it's still all about electrons and how they're arranged.

Learning Objectives:

- Know the meaning of the term ionisation energy.
- Understand how ionisation energies in Period 3 (Na-Ar) and in Group 2 (Be-Ba) give evidence for electron arrangement in sub-levels and in levels.
- Understand the reasons for the trends in first ionisation energy of the elements Na-Ar.

Specification Reference 3.1.1, 3.1.4

Ionisation

When electrons have been removed from an atom or molecule, it's been ionised. The energy you need to remove the first electron is called the **first ionisation energy** (or often just ionisation energy).

> The first ionisation energy is the energy needed to remove 1 electron from each atom in 1 mole of gaseous atoms to form 1 mole of gaseous 1+ ions.

You can write equations for this process — here's the equation for the first ionisation of oxygen:

$O(g) \rightarrow O^+(g) + e^-$ 1st ionisation energy = +1314 kJ mol^{-1}

Here are a few rather important points about ionisation energies:

- You must use the gas state symbol, (g), because ionisation energies are measured for gaseous atoms.
- Always refer to 1 mole of atoms, as stated in the definition, rather than to a single atom.
- The lower the ionisation energy, the easier it is to form an ion.

Exam Tip
Make sure you learn the definition of first ionisation energy — it's a really common exam question and a dead easy way to get marks.

Factors affecting ionisation energy

A high ionisation energy means there's a high attraction between the electron and the nucleus. There are three things that can affect ionisation energy:

1 Nuclear charge

The more protons there are in the nucleus, the more positively charged the nucleus is and the stronger the attraction for the electrons.

2 Distance from nucleus

Attraction falls off very rapidly with distance. An electron close to the nucleus will be much more strongly attracted than one further away.

3 Shielding

As the number of electrons between the outer electrons and the nucleus increases, the outer electrons feel less attraction towards the nuclear charge. This lessening of the pull of the nucleus by inner shells of electrons is called shielding (or screening).

Tip: You can only really see the effect of nuclear charge on ionisation energy if you're looking at atoms with outer electrons that are the same distance from the nucleus and with equal shielding effects.

This only really happens when you're looking at elements in the same period of the Periodic Table.

Example

There are only two electrons between the nucleus and the outer electron in a lithium atom.

There are ten electrons between the nucleus and the outer electron in a sodium atom — the shielding effect is greater.

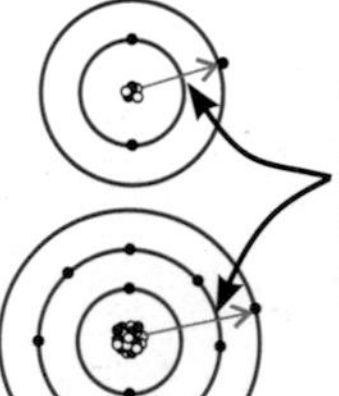

The distance between the nucleus and the electron being removed is greater in the sodium atom.

Figure 1: *A lithium atom and a sodium atom.*

This means that lithium has a higher first ionisation energy (519 kJ mol^{-1}) than sodium (496 kJ mol^{-1}). (The shielding and the distance from the nucleus have a bigger effect than the nuclear charge in this example.)

Second ionisation energy

The second ionisation energy is the energy needed to remove an electron from each ion in 1 mole of gaseous 1+ ions, for example:

$O^{+}(g) \rightarrow O^{2+}(g) + e^{-}$ 2nd ionisation energy = +3388 kJ mol^{-1}

Just like first ionisation energy, the value of second ionisation energy depends on nuclear charge, the distance of the electron from the nucleus and the shielding affect of inner electrons. Second ionisation energies are greater than first ionisation energies because the electron is being removed from a positive ion (and not an atom), which will require more energy. The electron configuration of the atom will also play a role in how much larger the second ionisation energy is than the first.

Example

The first electron removed from lithium is in the second shell ($2s^1$) and the second is in the first shell ($1s^2$). So, the electron being removed during the second ionisation is closer to the nucleus and will experience a stronger nuclear attraction than the electron that is removed during the first ionisation. This means that the second ionisation energy of lithium is much higher than the first.

Tip: The third ionisation energy is the energy needed to remove an electron from a 2+ ion. Third ionisation energies are greater than second ionisation energies — there's a greater attraction between a 2+ ion and its electrons than between a 1+ ion and its electrons.

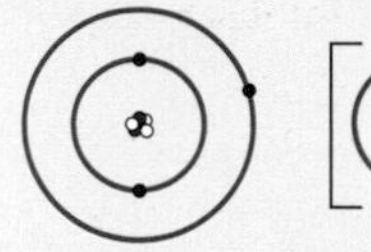

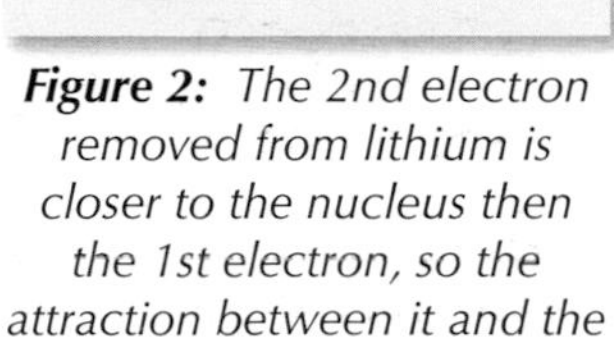

Figure 2: *The 2nd electron removed from lithium is closer to the nucleus then the 1st electron, so the attraction between it and the nucleus is greater.*

Ionisation energy trends

Ionisation trends down Group 2

First ionisation energy decreases down Group 2. This provides evidence that electron shells really do exist. If each element down Group 2 has an extra electron shell compared to the one above, the extra inner shells will shield the outer electrons from the attraction of the nucleus. Also, the extra shell means that the outer electrons are further away from the nucleus, so the nucleus's attraction will be greatly reduced. It makes sense that both of these factors will make it easier to remove outer electrons, resulting in a lower ionisation energy.

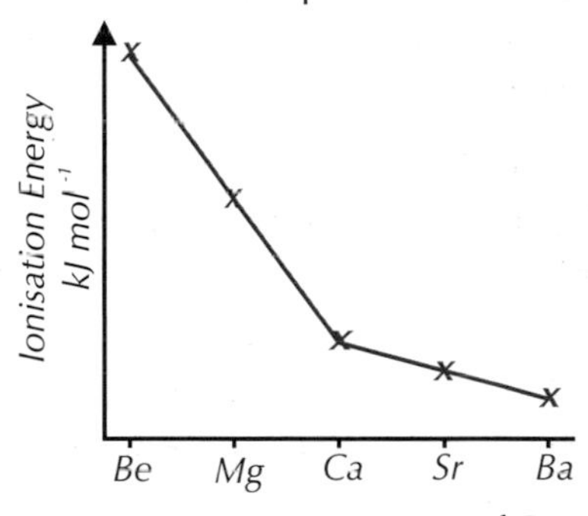

Figure 3: *First ionisation energies of Group 2.*

Ionisation trends across periods

The graph below shows the first ionisation energies of elements in Period 3. As you move across a period, the general trend is for the ionisation energies to increase — i.e. it gets harder to remove the outer electrons. This can be explained because the number of protons is increasing, which means a stronger nuclear attraction. All the extra electrons are at roughly the same energy level, even if the outer electrons are in different orbital types. This means there's generally little extra shielding effect or extra distance to lessen the attraction from the nucleus. But, there are small drops between Groups 2 and 3, and 5 and 6. Tell me more I hear you cry. Well, alright then...

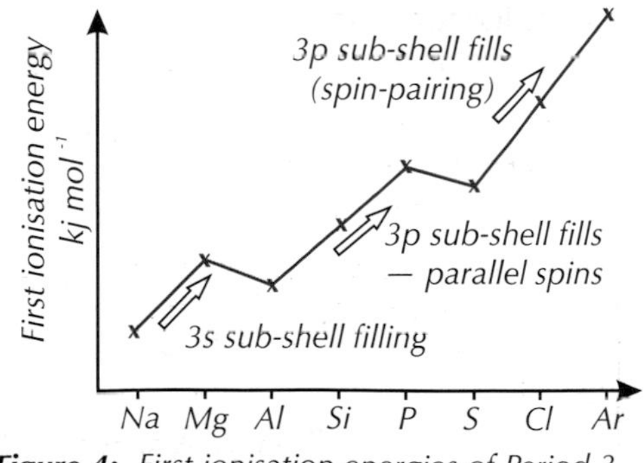

Figure 4: *First ionisation energies of Period 3.*

Exam Tip

You could get asked to state or explain the trend in ionisation energy down a group or across a period. You could also be asked to explain why the ionisation energy for one element is higher or lower than it is for another element.

The drop between Groups 2 and 3 shows sub-shell structure.

Example

Mg	$1s^2 2s^2 2p^6 3s^2$	1st ionisation energy = 738 kJ mol^{-1}
Al	$1s^2 2s^2 2p^6 3s^2 3p^1$	1st ionisation energy = 578 kJ mol^{-1}

- Aluminium's outer electron is in a 3p orbital rather than a 3s. The 3p orbital has a slightly higher energy than the 3s orbital, so the electron is, on average, to be found further from the nucleus.
- The 3p orbital has additional shielding provided by the $3s^2$ electrons.

Both these factors together are strong enough to override the effect of the increased nuclear charge, resulting in the ionisation energy dropping slightly. This pattern in ionisation energies provides evidence for the theory of electron sub-shells.

Tip: Writing out or drawing the electronic configurations of elements can help you work out why their ionisation energies are what they are. For example, drawing

will show you that the electron being removed is paired, so there will be repulsion. Drawing

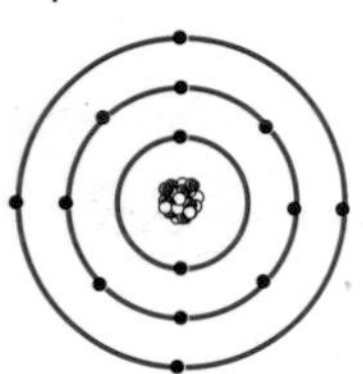

will show you how much shielding there is.

The drop between Groups 5 and 6 is due to electron repulsion.

Example

P	$1s^2 2s^2 2p^6 3s^2 3p^3$	1st ionisation energy = 1012 kJ mol^{-1}
S	$1s^2 2s^2 2p^6 3s^2 3p^4$	1st ionisation energy = 1000 kJ mol^{-1}

The shielding is identical in the phosphorus and sulfur atoms, and the electron is being removed from an identical orbital.

In phosphorus's case, the electron is being removed from a singly-occupied orbital. But in sulfur, the electron is being removed from an orbital containing two electrons.

Phosphorus: [Ne] 3s: ↑↓ 3p: ↑ ↑ ↑   *Sulfur:* [Ne] 3s: ↑↓ 3p: ↑↓ ↑ ↑

The repulsion between two electrons in an orbital means that electrons are easier to remove from shared orbitals. Yup, yet more evidence for the electronic structure model.

Practice Questions — Application

Q1 Write an equation for the first ionisation energy of chlorine.

Q2 Sketch a graph showing the first ionisation energies of the elements in Period 2.

Q3 The first ionisation energy of nitrogen is 1402 kJ mol^{-1}. The first ionisation energy of oxygen is 1314 kJ mol^{-1}. Explain why there is a difference between these ionisation energies.

Q4 The first ionisation energy of beryllium is 900 kJ mol^{-1}. The first ionisation energy of boron is 801 kJ mol^{-1}. Explain why there is a difference between these ionisation energies.

Practice Questions — Fact Recall

Q1 Define first ionisation energy.

Q2 How does the number of protons affect the first ionisation energy?

Q3 Give two other factors that affect the first ionisation energy.

Q4 What happens to the first ionisation energy of elements in Group 2 as you go down the group?

Q5 What is the general trend in first ionisation energy across a period?

Section Summary

Make sure you know...

- The structure of the atom — including the location, relative masses and charges of protons, neutrons and electrons.
- What nuclear symbols, mass numbers (A) and proton numbers (Z) are.
- What atoms, ions and isotopes are.
- The different models of the structure of the atom.
- What relative atomic mass (A_r) is.
- How to calculate relative atomic mass.
- What relative isotopic mass is.
- What relative molecular mass (M_r) and relative formula mass are.
- How to calculate relative molecular mass or relative formula mass of a substance.
- How a mass spectrometer works, including the main steps of vaporisation, ionisation, acceleration, deflection and detection.
- What information a mass spectrometer can give you.
- How to interpret a mass spectrum.
- How to calculate the relative atomic mass of an element from a mass spectrum.
- How to calculate the relative molecular mass of a compound from a mass spectrum.
- How electrons are arranged in levels and sub-levels within an atom.
- What orbitals there are (e.g. s, p d orbitals) in each level.
- How many electrons each orbital and sub-shell can hold.
- How to show electron configurations using sub-shell notation, arrows in boxes and energy level diagrams.
- How to work out electron configurations of the first 36 elements of the Periodic Table, including the electron configurations of chromium and copper.
- What ionisation energy is.
- How to write equations to show ionisation energies.
- The factors that affect ionisation energy.
- The trend in ionisation energy down Group 2, and the reasons for this trend.
- How ionisation energy changes across Period 3, and the reasons for these changes.
- How changes in ionisation energy give evidence for electron arrangement in levels and sub-levels.

Exam-style Questions

1 An element, Z, has the electron configuration [Ne] $3s^2$ $3p^2$.
A sample of element Z is passed through a mass spectrometer.

(a) (i) Identify element Z.

(1 mark)

(ii) State the block of the Periodic Table that element Z belongs to.

(1 mark)

(b) Inside the mass spectrometer, the vaporised sample of element Z is bombarded with electrons, removing electrons from atoms of the sample.

(i) Give the name of this process.

(1 mark)

(ii) Write an equation to represent this process. Assume that a single electron is removed from each atom in one mole of element Z.

(1 mark)

(iii) Give the electron configuration of the particle formed when a single electron is removed from an atom of element Z.

(1 mark)

(c) A magnetic field is applied across the mass spectrometer and is increased slowly. Explain why this is done.

(3 marks)

(d) The mass spectrum produced when element Z is passed through the mass spectrometer is shown below.

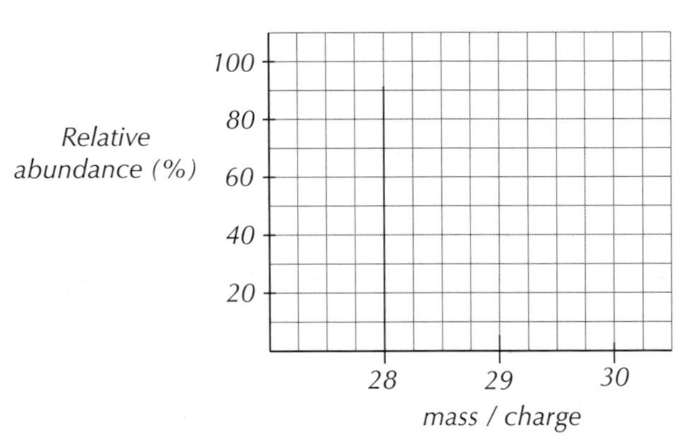

(i) State how many different isotopes of element Z were present in the sample.

(1 mark)

(ii) Give the nuclear symbol of the isotope in the sample with the highest relative isotopic abundance.

(2 marks)

(iii) State whether you would expect the isotopes of element Z to have the same chemical properties or different chemical properties. Explain your answer.

(2 marks)

2 The table below shows the first ionisation energies of some of the elements in Period 3.

Element	Na	Mg	Al	Si	P	S	Cl
First ionisation energy kJ mol^{-1}	496	738	578		1012		1251

(a) (i) State the general trend in first ionisation energy across Period 3.

(1 mark)

(ii) Explain why the first ionisation energy of aluminium is lower than the first ionisation energy of magnesium.

(3 marks)

(b) (i) Suggest a value for the first ionisation energy of silicon.

(1 mark)

(ii) Using your understanding of electron configuration, explain why you suggested the value you gave in **(b)** part **(i)**.

(3 marks)

(c) (i) Suggest a value for the first ionisation energy of sulfur.

(1 mark)

(ii) Using your understanding of electron configuration, explain why you suggested the value you gave in **(c)** part **(i)**.

(2 marks)

3 Vanadium and copper are both transition metals.

(a) (i) Give the electron configuration of vanadium.

(1 mark)

(ii) When vanadium is ionised it can form V^{2+} and V^{3+} ions.
Give the electron configurations of these ions

(2 marks)

(b) (i) Give the electron configuration of copper and explain why it deviates from the normal rules of electron configuration.

(2 marks)

(ii) Give the name of one other element that has an electron configuration that deviates from the normal rules.

(1 mark)

(c) Identify the transition metal with the electron configuration $1s^2\ 2s^2\ 2p^6\ 3s^2\ 3p^6\ 3d^6\ 4s^2$.

(1 mark)

(d) A transition metal is ionised to form a 2+ ion. The ion has the electron configuration $1s^2\ 2s^2\ 2p^6\ 3s^2\ 3p^6\ 3d^5$. Identify the transition metal.

(1 mark)

4 The relative isotopic masses and relative abundances of element X were identified using mass spectrometry. The isotopes and their relative abundances are shown in the table below.

Isotope	Relative abundance
^{20}X	90.48
^{21}X	0.27
^{22}X	9.25

(a) Calculate the relative atomic mass of element X.

Identify element X.

State the number of protons, neutrons and electrons in an atom of each isotope of element X.

(6 marks)

(b) Isotopes of an element, such as the isotopes of element X, have the same proton number but different mass numbers.

Define the term *mass number (A)* of an atom.

Define the term *proton number (Z)* of an atom.

State and explain whether it is the mass number or the proton number of an element that affects its physical properties the most.

(4 marks)

(c) The first ionisation energy of element Z is 2080.7 kJ mol^{-1}. Atoms of another element, element A, contain 24 more electrons than atoms of element Z.

Define the term *first ionisation energy*.

Using your understanding of the factors that affect ionisation energy, state how you would expect the first ionisation energy of element A to be different from element Z. Explain your answer.

(5 marks)

1. The Mole

Amount of substance is a really important idea in chemistry. It's all about working out exactly how much of a chemical you have and what amount of it is reacting with other chemicals. Then you can use that information in all sorts of calculations to do with things like mass, concentration and volume.

Learning Objectives:
- Understand the concept of a mole as applied to electrons, atoms, molecules, ions, formulas and equations.
- Understand the concept of the Avogadro constant.
- Be able to calculate concentrations and volumes for reactions in solutions, limited to examples for which the equations are given.

Specification Reference 3.1.2

What is a mole?

Amount of substance is measured using a unit called the **mole** (mol for short) and given the symbol n. One mole is roughly 6×10^{23} particles (Avogadro's constant). It doesn't matter what the particles are. They can be atoms, molecules, electrons, ions, penguins — anything.

Examples

In the reaction $C + O_2 \rightarrow CO_2$:

1 atom of carbon reacts with 1 molecule of oxygen to make 1 molecule of carbon dioxide, so 1 mole of carbon reacts with 1 mole of oxygen to make 1 mole of carbon dioxide.

In the reaction $2Mg + O_2 \rightarrow 2MgO$:

2 atoms of magnesium react with 1 molecule of oxygen to make 2 molecules of magnesium oxide, so 2 moles of magnesium react with 1 mole of oxygen molecules to make 2 moles of magnesium oxide.

Figure 1: 1 mole of carbon.

Molar mass

Molar mass, M, is the mass of one mole of something. But the main thing to remember is that molar mass is just the same as the relative molecular mass, M_r (or relative formula mass). The only difference is you stick a 'g mol^{-1}' for grams per mole on the end.

Examples

Find the molar mass of $CaCO_3$.

Relative formula mass, M_r, of $CaCO_3 = 40 + 12 + (3 \times 16) = 100$

So the molar mass, M, is 100 g mol^{-1} (i.e. 1 mole of $CaCO_3$ weighs 100 g).

Find the molar mass of $Ni(OH)_2$.

Relative formula mass, M_r, of $Ni(OH)_2 = 58.7 + (2 \times (16 + 1)) = 92.7$

So the molar mass, M, is 92.7 g mol^{-1} (i.e. 1 mole of $Ni(OH)_2$ weighs 92.7 g).

Tip: Remember, to find relative formula mass, all you need to do is add up the relative atomic masses of all the atoms in the formula (see page 12). So, keep a periodic table handy...

Calculations with moles

There's a formula that connects the molar mass of a substance to the number of moles of the substance that you have. It looks like this:

$$\text{Number of moles} = \frac{\text{mass of substance}}{\text{molar mass}}$$

Exam Tip
This formula crops up in all sorts of chemistry calculations — you'll definitely need to know it off by heart for your exams.

Examples

How many moles of aluminium oxide are present in 5.1 g of Al_2O_3?

Molar mass of Al_2O_3 = (2 × 27.0) + (3 × 16.0) = 102 g mol^{-1}

Number of moles of Al_2O_3 = $\frac{5.1}{102}$ = 0.05 moles

How many moles of calcium bromide are present in 39.98 g of $CaBr_2$?

Molar mass of $CaBr_2$ = 40.1 + (2 × 79.9) = 199.9 g mol^{-1}

Number of moles of $CaBr_2$ = $\frac{39.98}{199.9}$ = 0.2 moles

Tip: The molar mass of a compound is the same as its M_r — so this formula links moles and relative molecular mass too.

You can also rearrange the formula and use it to work out either the mass of a substance or its relative molecular mass:

Examples

What is the mass of 2 moles of NaF?

Rearrange the formula to find mass (multiply both sides by molar mass):

mass of substance = number of moles × molar mass

Molar mass of NaF = 23 + 19 = 42 g mol^{-1}

Mass of 2 moles of NaF = 2 × 42 = 84 g

0.05 moles of a compound weigh 2.6 g. Find its relative molecular mass.

Rearrange the formula to find molar mass:

molar mass = mass ÷ number of moles

Molar mass = 2.6 ÷ 0.05 = 52 g mol^{-1}. So, relative molecular mass = 52.

Tip: If it helps you to remember how to rearrange the equation, you could use this formula triangle:

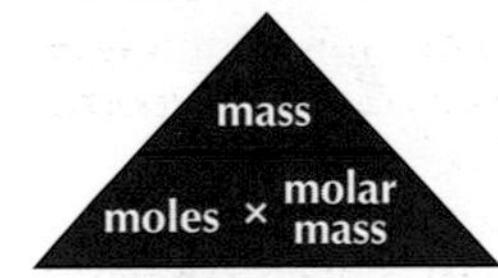

Just cover the thing you want to calculate to find the right formula.

(For example, if you cover mass it will tell you that to calculate mass you multiply moles by molar mass.)

Practice Questions — Application

Q1 Look at this balanced equation: $4Na + O_2 \rightarrow 2Na_2O$
How many moles of Na_2O are produced when 6 moles of Na react with 1.5 moles of O_2?

Q2 Find the molar mass of:
a) F_2
b) $CaCl_2$
c) $MgSO_4$

Q3 How many moles of sodium nitrate are present in 212.5 g of $NaNO_3$?

Q4 How many moles of zinc chloride are present in 15.5 g of $ZnCl_2$?

Q5 What is the mass of 2 moles of NaCl?

Q6 What is the mass of 0.6 moles of $CrCl_3$?

Q7 What is the mass of 0.25 moles of $MgCO_3$?

Q8 1.5 moles of a mystery compound weighs 66 g. Find its molar mass.

Moles and concentration

The concentration of a solution is how many moles are dissolved per 1 dm^3 of solution. The units are mol dm^{-3} (or M).

Here's the formula to find the number of moles.

$$\text{Number of moles} = \frac{\text{Concentration} \times \text{Volume (in cm}^3)}{1000}$$

$$\text{Or: Number of moles} = \text{Concentration} \times \text{Volume (in dm}^3)$$

You need to be able to use these formulas to do calculations in the exam.

Tip: 1 dm^3 is the same as 1000 cm^3 or 1 litre.

Exam Tip
You need to know all of the formulas in this section by heart — so look out for the formula boxes, and learn them.

Tip: This is another formula that you can stick in a formula triangle if it helps you:

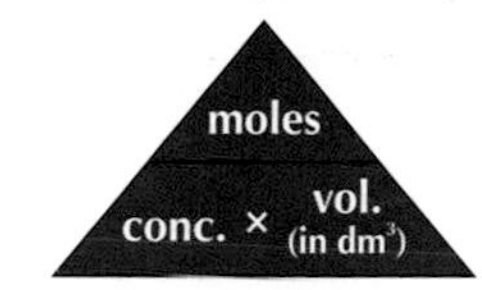

Examples

How many moles of lithium chloride are present in 25 cm^3 of a 1.2 mol dm^{-3} solution of LiCl?

$$\text{Number of moles} = \frac{\text{concentration} \times \text{volume (in cm}^3)}{1000}$$

$$= \frac{1.2 \times 25}{1000} = 0.03 \text{ moles}$$

A solution of Fe_2O_3 contains 0.2 moles of iron(III) oxide in 0.4 dm^3. What is the concentration of the solution?

Rearrange the formula to find concentration (divide both sides by volume):

$$\text{concentration} = \frac{\text{number of moles}}{\text{volume (in dm}^3)}$$

$$= \frac{0.2}{0.4} = 0.5 \text{ mol dm}^{-3}$$

A 0.5 mol dm^{-3} solution of zinc sulfate contains 0.08 moles of $ZnSO_4$. What volume does the solution occupy?

Rearrange the formula to find volume (divide both sides by volume):

$$\text{volume (in dm}^3) = \frac{\text{number of moles}}{\text{concentration}}$$

$$= \frac{0.08}{0.5} = 0.16 \text{ dm}^3$$

Exam Tip
Remember to watch out for the units in this type of calculation. Double check whether the volume you've been given is in cm^3 or dm^3.

You might be asked to combine a concentration calculation with a molar mass calculation. This just means using both formulas, one after the other.

Example

What mass of sodium hydroxide needs to be dissolved in 50 cm^3 of water to make a 2 M solution?

First look at the question and see what information it gives you. You've got concentration and volume — so you can work out number of moles.

$$\text{Number of moles} = \frac{2 \times 50}{1000} = 0.1 \text{ moles of NaOH}$$

Then you can use this to work out the mass using the equation number of moles = mass ÷ molar mass

Molar mass, M, of NaOH = 23 + 16 + 1 = 40 g mol^{-1}

Mass = number of moles × M = 0.1 × 40 = 4 g

Practice Questions — Application

Q1 How many moles of potassium phosphate are present in 50 cm^3 of a 2 mol dm^{-3} solution?

Q2 How many moles of sodium chloride are present in 0.5 dm^3 of a 0.08 mol dm^{-3} solution?

Q3 How many moles of silver nitrate are present in 30 cm^3 of a 0.7 M solution?

Q4 A solution contains 0.25 moles of copper bromide in 0.5 dm^3. What is the concentration of the solution?

Q5 A solution contains 0.08 moles of lithium chloride in 0.75 dm^3. What is the concentration of the solution?

Q6 A solution contains 0.1 moles of iron oxide in 36 cm^3. What is the concentration of the solution?

Q7 A solution of calcium chloride contains 0.46 moles of $CaCl_2$. The concentration of the solution is 1.8 mol dm^{-3}. What volume does the solution occupy?

Q8 A solution of copper sulfate contains 0.01 moles of $CuSO_4$. The concentration of the solution is 0.55 mol dm^{-3}. What volume does the solution occupy?

Q9 The molecular formula of sodium oxide is Na_2O. What mass of sodium oxide would you have to dissolve in 75 cm^3 of water to make a 0.8 M solution?

Q10 The molecular formula of cobalt bromide is $CoBr_2$. What mass of cobalt bromide would you have to dissolve in 30 cm^3 of water to make a 0.5 M solution?

Q11 A solution is made by dissolving 4.08 g of a compound in 100 cm^3 of pure water. The solution has a concentration of 1.2 mol dm^{-3}. What is the molar mass of the compound?

Practice Questions — Fact Recall

Q1 a) How many particles are there in a mole?

b) What's the name for this special number?

Q2 What is the molar mass of a chemical?

Q3 What's the formula that links molar mass and number of moles?

Q4 How many cm^3 are there in one dm^3?

Q5 Name two units that you could use to describe concentration.

Q6 What's the formula that links number of moles and concentration? (Write it out twice, once using each volume measurement.)

2. Gases and the Mole

Lots of things in chemistry relate back to how many moles of a substance you have. And that includes how much volume a gas takes up.

Learning Objective:

- Be able to recall the ideal gas equation $pV = nRT$ and be able to apply it to simple calculations in S.I. units for ideal gases.

Specification Reference 3.1.2

Gas Volume

If temperature and pressure stay the same, one mole of any gas always has the same volume. At room temperature and pressure (r.t.p.), this happens to be 24 dm^3, (r.t.p is 298 K (25 °C) and 100 kPa).

Here are two formulas for working out the number of moles in a volume of gas. Don't forget — only use them for r.t.p.

$$\text{number of moles} = \frac{\text{volume in dm}^3}{24}$$

$$\text{Or: number of moles} = \frac{\text{volume in cm}^3}{24\ 000}$$

You need to be able to use these formulas to find number of moles and gas volumes.

Examples

How many moles are there in 6 dm^3 of oxygen gas at r.t.p.?

Number of moles = 6 ÷ 24
= 0.25 moles of oxygen molecules

What volume, in cm^3, does 0.02 moles of hydrogen gas occupy at r.t.p.?

Rearrange the formula to find volume (multiply both sides by 24 000):

Volume = number of moles × 24 000
= 0.02 × 24 000 = 480 cm^3

Exam Tip

Keep a close eye on the units in questions like these. You don't want to lose marks just because you didn't check whether you needed the formula for dm^3 or cm^3 before you started.

Practice Questions — Application

Q1 How many moles are there in 2.4 dm^3 of carbon dioxide gas at r.t.p.?

Q2 How many moles are there in 0.65 dm^3 of carbon monoxide gas at r.t.p.?

Q3 How many moles are there in 3120 cm^3 of chlorine gas at r.t.p.?

Q4 How many moles are there in 250 cm^3 of sulfur dioxide gas at r.t.p.?

Q5 What volume, in dm^3, does 0.21 moles of hydrogen chloride gas occupy at r.t.p.?

Q6 What volume, in dm^3, does 1.1 moles of fluorine gas occupy at r.t.p.?

Q7 What volume, in cm^3, does 0.028 moles of argon gas occupy at r.t.p.?

Q8 What volume, in cm^3, does 0.072 moles of nitrogen dioxide gas occupy at r.t.p.?

The ideal gas equation

In the real world (and AQA exam questions), it's not always room temperature and pressure. The **ideal gas equation** lets you find the number of moles in a certain volume at any temperature and pressure:

Tip: You don't need to worry about what the gas constant is for AS level. Just make sure you learn the ideal gas equation off by heart.

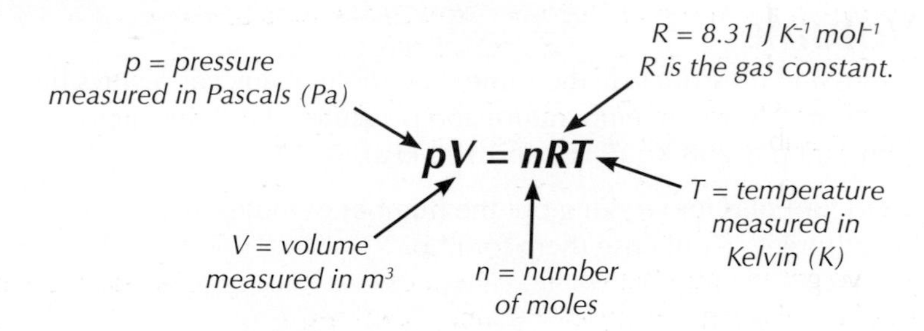

You could be asked to find any of the values in the equation. Its the same old idea — just rearrange the equation and put in the numbers you know.

Examples

How many moles are there in 0.06 m³ of hydrogen gas, at 283 K and 50 000 Pa?

Rearrange the equation to find number of moles (divide both sides by RT):

$$n = \frac{pV}{RT} = \frac{50000 \times 0.06}{8.31 \times 283} = 1.28 \text{ moles}$$

At what pressure would 0.4 moles of argon gas occupy 0.01 m³ at 298 K?

Rearrange the equation to find pressure (divide both sides by V):

$$p = \frac{nRT}{V} = \frac{0.4 \times 8.31 \times 298}{0.01} = 99\ 055 \text{ Pa}$$

Tip: There's more about converting units in the exam help section on pages 215-216.

If you're given the values in different units from the ones used in the ideal gas equation you'll need to convert them to the right units first.

- You might be given pressure in kPa (kilopascals). To convert from kPa to Pa you multiply by 1000 (e.g. 2 kPa = 2000 Pa).
- You might be given temperature in °C. To convert from °C to K you add 273 (e.g. 25 °C = 298 K).
- You might be given volume in cm³ or dm³. To convert from cm³ to m³ you multiply by 10^{-6}. To convert from dm³ to m³ you multiply by 10^{-3}. ($1 \text{ m}^3 = 1 \times 10^{-6} \text{ cm}^3 = 1 \times 10^{-3} \text{ dm}^3$)

Tip: All of these units are S.I. units. That means they're part of an agreed system of measurements used by scientists all over the world.

Example

What volume would 2 moles of argon gas occupy at 27 °C and 100 kPa?

First put all the values you have into the right units:
T = 27 °C = (27 + 273) K = 300 K
p = 100 kPa = 100 000 Pa
Now rearrange the equation to find volume (divide both sides by pressure):

$$V = \frac{nRT}{p} = \frac{2 \times 8.31 \times 300}{100\ 000} = 0.05 \text{ m}^3$$

Tip: There's no need to worry about units for number of moles (it doesn't have any units) or R (it always has the same units).

You might be asked to combine an ideal gas equation calculation with another type of calculation.

Example

At a temperature of 60 °C and a pressure of 250 kPa, a gas occupied a volume of 1100 cm³ and had a mass of 1.6 g. Find its relative molecular mass.

You've been given temperature, pressure and volume, so you need to find the number of moles:

$$n = \frac{pV}{RT} = \frac{(250 \times 10^3) \times (1.1 \times 10^{-3})}{8.31 \times 333} = 0.1 \text{ moles}$$

Now you've got the number of moles, you can calculate molar mass using the formula molar mass = mass ÷ number of moles.

Molar mass = mass ÷ number of moles = 1.6 ÷ 0.1 = 16 g mol^{-1}.

So the relative molecular mass is also 16.

Tip: There's a 10^3 and a 10^{-3} in this formula because the numbers have been put into standard form. There's more about standard form on page 212.

Tip: This is the formula from page 30 again. Remember that molar mass is the same as relative molecular mass.

Practice Questions — Application

Q1 How many moles are there in 0.04 m³ of oxygen gas at a temperature of 350 K and a pressure of 70 000 Pa?

Q2 What volume would 0.65 moles of carbon dioxide gas occupy at a temperature of 280 K and a pressure of 100 000 Pa?

Q3 How many moles are there in 0.55 dm³ of nitrogen gas at a temperature of 35 °C and a pressure of 90 000 Pa?

Q4 At a pressure of 110 000 Pa, 0.05 moles of hydrogen gas occupied a volume of 1200 cm³. What was the temperature in °C?

Q5 What volume would 0.75 moles of helium gas occupy at a temperature of 22 °C and a pressure of 75 kPa?

Q6 At a temperature of 300 K and a pressure of 80 kPa a gas had a volume of 1.5 dm³ and a mass of 2.6 g. Find its relative molecular mass.

Q7 A student had a sample of neon gas, Ne. They heated it to 44 °C. At this temperature the gas had a volume of 0.003 m³. If the pressure was 100 kPa, what was the mass of the neon gas?

Practice Questions — Fact Recall

Q1 What is the formula for calculating the number of moles in a volume of gas in dm³ at r.t.p.?

Q2 What is the formula for calculating the number of moles in a volume of gas in cm³ at r.t.p.?

Q3 Write out the ideal gas equation. Say what the terms mean and give the standard units that each is measured in.

Learning Objectives:

- Be able to balance equations for unfamiliar reactions when reactants and products are specified.
- Be able to write balanced equations (full and ionic) for reactions studied.

Specification Reference 3.1.2

3. Balancing Equations

Balancing equations is one of those topics that gets everywhere in chemistry. You'll have done this before, so it should look a bit familiar. Make sure you've got your head round it now though, because you'll definitely need it again.

How to balance equations

Balanced equations have the same number of each atom on both sides. They're.. well... you know... balanced. You can only add more atoms by adding whole compounds. You do this by putting a number in front of a compound or changing one that's already there. You can't mess with formulas — ever (e.g. you can change H_2O to $2H_2O$, but never to H_4O).

Examples

Balance the equation $H_2SO_4 + NaOH \rightarrow Na_2SO_4 + H_2O$.

First you need to count how many of each atom you have on each side.

$$H_2SO_4 + NaOH \rightarrow Na_2SO_4 + H_2O$$

H = 3 Na = 1	*H = 2 Na = 2*
O = 5 S = 1	*O = 5 S = 1*

The left side needs 2 Na's, so try changing NaOH to 2NaOH:

$$H_2SO_4 + 2NaOH \rightarrow Na_2SO_4 + H_2O$$

H = 4 Na = 2	*H = 2 Na = 2*
O = 6 S = 1	*O = 5 S = 1*

Now the right side needs 4 H's, so try changing H_2O to $2H_2O$:

$$H_2SO_4 + 2NaOH \rightarrow Na_2SO_4 + 2H_2O$$

H = 4 Na = 2	*H = 4 Na = 2*
O = 6 S = 1	*O = 6 S = 1*

Both sides have the same number of each atom — the equation is balanced.

Balance the equation $C_2H_6 + O_2 \rightarrow CO_2 + H_2O$.

First work out how many of each atom you have on each side.

$$C_2H_6 + O_2 \rightarrow CO_2 + H_2O$$

C = 2 H = 6	*C = 1 H = 2*
O = 2	*O = 3*

The right side needs 2 C's, so try $2CO_2$. It also needs 6 H's, so try $3H_2O$.

$$C_2H_6 + O_2 \rightarrow 2CO_2 + 3H_2O$$

C = 2 H = 6	*C = 2 H = 6*
O = 2	*O = 7*

The left side needs 7 O's, so try $3\frac{1}{2}O_2$ (you can use ½ to balance equations).

$$C_2H_6 + 3\tfrac{1}{2}O_2 \rightarrow 2CO_2 + 3H_2O$$

C = 2 H = 6	*C = 2 H = 6*
O = 7	*O = 7*

This balances the equation.

Tip: Always do a quick check to make sure your final equation balances.

Balancing ionic equations

In ionic equations, only the reacting particles are included. You don't have to worry about the rest of the stuff. First you make sure that both sides have the same number of atoms — just like a normal equation. Then you balance the charges by adding extra electrons.

Examples

Balance the ionic equation $H_2O_2 \rightarrow O_2 + H^+$

Work out how many of each atom you have on each side.

$$H_2O_2 \rightarrow O_2 + H^+$$

O = 2   H = 2 | O = 2   H = 1

The right side needs 2 H's, so try $2H^+$:

$$H_2O_2 \rightarrow O_2 + 2H^+$$

O = 2   H = 2 | O = 2   H = 2

Now you need to balance the charges:

charges on left side	charges on right side
0	*(2 × 1+) = 2+*

The right side needs two extra electrons.
So the balanced ionic equation is: $H_2O_2 \rightarrow O_2 + 2H^+ + 2e^-$

Balance the ionic equation $Cr_2O_7^{2-} + H^+ + e^- \rightarrow Cr^{3+} + H_2O$

Again, first work out how many of each atom you have on each side.

$$Cr_2O_7^{2-} + H^+ + e^- \rightarrow Cr^{3+} + H_2O$$

Cr = 2   O = 7   H = 1 | Cr = 1   O = 1   H = 2

The right side needs 2 Cr's, so try $2Cr^{3+}$. It also needs 7 O's, so try $7H_2O$.

$$Cr_2O_7^{2-} + H^+ + e^- \rightarrow 2Cr^{3+} + 7H_2O$$

Cr = 2   O = 7   H = 1 | Cr = 2   O = 7   H = 14

The left side needs 14 H's, so try $14H^+$.

$$Cr_2O_7^{2-} + 14H^+ + e^- \rightarrow 2Cr^{3+} + 7H_2O$$

Cr = 2   O = 7   H = 14 | Cr = 2   O = 7   H = 14

Now the charges just need balancing:

charges on left side	charges on right side
(2–) + (14 × 1+) + (1–) = 11+	*(2 × 3+) = 6+*

The left side needs five additional electrons.
The balanced ionic equation is: $Cr_2O_7^{2-} + 14H^+ + 6e^- \rightarrow 2Cr^{3+} + 7H_2O$

Tip: The extra electrons are just there to balance charge — they're not atoms, so you don't need to include them in the atom balancing bit.

Tip: When you balance the charges, don't forget to multiply the charge by the number in front. One H^+ ion on its own has a charge of 1+, but 14 H^+ ions together carry a total charge of 14+.

Practice Questions — Application

Q1 Balance these equations:

a) $Mg + HCl \rightarrow MgCl_2 + H_2$

b) $S_8 + F_2 \rightarrow SF_6$

c) $Ca(OH)_2 + H_2SO_4 \rightarrow CaSO_4 + H_2O$

d) $Na_2CO_3 + HCl \rightarrow NaCl + CO_2 + H_2O$

e) $C_4H_{10} + O_2 \rightarrow CO_2 + H_2O$

Q2 Balance these ionic equations:

a) $Ag \rightarrow Ag^{2+}$

b) $Br_2 \rightarrow Br^-$

c) $CrO_4^{2-} + H_2O \rightarrow CrO_2^- + OH^-$

d) $MnO_4^- + H^+ \rightarrow Mn^{2+} + H_2O$

Learning Objectives:

- Be able to calculate reacting masses from balanced equations.
- Be able to calculate reacting volumes of gases.

Specification Reference 3.1.2

4. Equations and Calculations

Once you've made sure that an equation is balanced, you can use it to calculate all sorts of things — like how much product a reaction will make...

Calculating masses

You can use the balanced equation for a reaction to work out how much product you will get from a certain mass of reactant.

Here are the steps to follow:

1. Write out the balanced equation for the reaction.
2. Work out how many moles of the reactant you have.
3. Use the **molar ratio** from the balanced equation to work out the number of moles of product that will be formed from this much reactant.
4. Calculate the mass of that many moles of product.

Tip: The ratio of the moles of each reactant and product in a balanced chemical equation is called the molar ratio.

Here's a nice juicy example to help you get to grips with the method:

Example

Calculate the mass of iron(III) oxide produced if 28 g of iron is burnt in air.

1. Write out the balanced equation: $2Fe_{(s)} + 1\frac{1}{2}O_{2\,(g)} \rightarrow Fe_2O_{3\,(s)}$
2. Work out how many moles of iron you have:
   M_r of Fe = 55.8
   Moles = mass ÷ M_r = 28 ÷ 55.8 = 0.5 moles of iron
3. The molar ratio of Fe : Fe_2O_3 is 2 : 1. This means that for every 2 moles of Fe that you have, you will produce 1 mole of Fe_2O_3.
   But you only have 0.5 moles of Fe here.
   So you will produce: 0.5 ÷ 2 = 0.25 moles of Fe_2O_3
4. Now find the mass of 0.25 moles of Fe_2O_3:
   M_r of Fe_2O_3 = (2 × 55.8) + (3 × 16) = 159.6
   Mass = moles × M_r = 0.25 × 159.6 = 40 g of iron(III) oxide

Tip: Look — it's that moles = mass ÷ M_r formula yet again...

You can use similar steps to work out how much of a reactant you had at the start of a reaction when you're given a certain mass of product:

Tip: <u>Reactants</u> are the chemicals you start with that get used up during a reaction. <u>Products</u> are the chemicals that are formed during a reaction.

Example

Hydrogen gas can react with nitrogen gas to give ammonia (NH_3). Calculate the mass of hydrogen needed to produce 6.8 g of ammonia.

1. $N_{2\,(g)} + 3H_{2\,(g)} \rightarrow 2NH_{3\,(g)}$
2. M_r of NH_3 = 14 + (3 × 1) = 17
   Moles = mass ÷ M_r = 6.8 ÷ 17 = 0.4 moles of NH_3
3. From the equation: the molar ratio of NH_3 : H_2 is 2 : 3.
   So to make 0.4 moles of NH_3, you must need to start with (0.4 ÷ 2) × 3 = 0.6 moles of H_2
4. M_r of H_2 = 2 × 1 = 2
   Mass = moles × M_r = 0.6 × 2 = 1.2 g of hydrogen

Practice Questions — Application

Q1 3.3 g of zinc is dissolved in hydrochloric acid, producing zinc chloride ($ZnCl_2$) and hydrogen gas.
   a) Write a balanced equation for this reaction.
   b) Calculate the number of moles of zinc in 3.3 g.
   c) How many moles of zinc chloride does the reaction produce?
   d) What mass of zinc chloride does the reaction produce?

Q2 A student burns some ethene gas (C_2H_4) in oxygen, producing carbon dioxide gas and 15 g of water.
   a) Write a balanced equation for this reaction.
   b) Calculate the number of moles of water in 15 g.
   c) How many moles of ethene did the student begin with?
   d) What mass of ethene did the student begin with?

Q3 Calculate the mass of barium carbonate ($BaCO_3$) produced if 4.58 g of barium chloride ($BaCl_2$) is reacted with sodium carbonate (Na_2CO_3).

Figure 1: Zinc dissolving in hydrochloric acid.

Calculating gas volumes

It's pretty handy to be able to work out how much gas a reaction will produce, so that you can use large enough apparatus. Or else there might be a rather large bang. The first three steps of this method are the same as the method on the last page. Once you've found the number of moles of product, the final step is to put that number into one of the gas equations that you saw on pages 33-34.

Examples

What volume of hydrogen gas is produced when 15 g of sodium is reacted with excess water at r.t.p.?

1. $2Na_{(s)} + 2H_2O_{(l)} \rightarrow 2NaOH_{(aq)} + H_{2(g)}$
2. M_r of Na = 23
   number of moles = mass ÷ M_r
   = 15 ÷ 23 = 0.65 moles of sodium
3. From the equation: the molar ratio of Na : H_2 is 2 : 1.
   So 0.65 moles of Na must produce (0.65 ÷ 2) = 0.33 moles of H_2.

At room temperature and pressure 1 mole of gas takes up 24 dm^3.
Volume in dm^3 = number of moles × 24
= 0.33 × 24 = 7.9 dm^3 of hydrogen gas

What volume of carbon dioxide is produced when 10 g of calcium carbonate reacts with excess hydrochloric acid at r.t.p.?

1. $CaCO_{3(s)} + 2HCl_{(aq)} \rightarrow CaCl_{2(aq)} + CO_{2(g)} + H_2O_{(l)}$
2. M_r of $CaCO_3$ = 40.1 + 12 + (3 × 16) = 100.1
   number of moles = mass ÷ M_r
   = 10 ÷ 100.1 = 0.1 moles of calcium carbonate
3. From the equation: the molar ratio of $CaCO_3$: CO_2 is 1 : 1.
   So 0.1 moles of $CaCO_3$ must produce 0.1 moles of CO_2.

At room temperature and pressure 1 mole of gas takes up 24 dm^3.
Volume in dm^3 = number of moles × 24
= 0.1 × 24 = 2.4 dm^3 of carbon dioxide

Tip: 'Excess water' just means that all of the sodium will react.

Exam Tip
If you're given a calculation with a gas that isn't at r.t.p., you'll have to use the ideal gas equation to calculate the volume of the gas instead.

State symbols

State symbols are put after each compound in an equation. They tell you what state of matter things are in:

s = solid, l = liquid, g = gas, aq = aqueous (solution in water).

Exam Tip
Make sure you include state symbols for the equation you write in the exam.

Example

$$CaCO_{3\,(s)} + 2HCl_{(aq)} \rightarrow CaCl_{2\,(aq)} + H_2O_{(l)} + CO_{2\,(g)}$$

solid *aqueous* *aqueous* *liquid* *gas*

Practice Questions — Application

Q1 Give the state symbols that you would use in an equation to show the state of the following substances.

a) a solution of magnesium chloride in water
b) a piece of magnesium metal
c) a measured amount of water
d) a solution of sodium nitrate in water
e) ethane gas
f) copper oxide powder

Q2 9 g of water is split apart to produce hydrogen gas and oxygen gas.

a) Write a balanced equation for this reaction.
b) Calculate the number of moles of water in 9 g.
c) How many moles of oxygen gas does the reaction produce?
d) What volume of oxygen gas will the reaction produce at r.t.p.?

Q3 7 g of zinc sulfide (ZnS) is burnt in oxygen. This produces solid zinc oxide (ZnO) and sulfur dioxide gas (SO_2).

a) Write a balanced equation for this reaction.
b) Calculate the number of moles of zinc sulfide in 7 g.
c) How many moles of sulfur dioxide gas does the reaction produce?
d) What volume of sulfur dioxide gas will the reaction produce at r.t.p.?

Q4 A sample of hexane gas (C_6H_{14}) is cracked to give butane gas (C_4H_{10}) and ethene gas (C_2H_4). The mass of butane produced is 3 g.

a) Write a balanced equation for this reaction.
b) Calculate the number of moles of butane in 3 g.
c) How many moles of hexane gas were present in the sample?
d) What volume would this many moles of hexane gas occupy at a temperature of 308 K and a pressure of 100 000 Pa?

Q5 Magnesium metal will react with steam to produce solid magnesium oxide and hydrogen gas. Calculate the volume of steam needed to create 10 g of MgO at 100 °C and 101 325 Pa.

5. Titrations

You can do a titration to find the concentration of an acid or an alkali. You'll almost certainly be asked to do one at some point during AS chemistry. And there are some more calculations to learn too.

Learning Objective:

- Be able to calculate concentrations and volumes for reactions in solutions, limited to titrations of monoprotic acids and bases and examples for which the equations are given.

Specification Reference 3.1.2

Neutralisation

When an acid reacts with an alkali you get a salt and water. This is called a neutralisation reaction.

Example

$$\underset{acid}{H_2SO_{4\,(aq)}} + \underset{alkali}{2NaOH_{(aq)}} \rightarrow \underset{salt}{Na_2SO_{4\,(aq)}} + \underset{water}{2H_2O_{(l)}}$$

Performing titrations

Titrations allow you to find out exactly how much acid is needed to neutralise a quantity of alkali. You measure out some alkali using a pipette (see Figure 2) and put it in a flask, along with some indicator, e.g. phenolphthalein. Add the acid to the alkali using a burette (see Figure 2) — open the tap to run acid into the alkali a little bit at a time. Every time you add some more acid, give the flask a swirl to make sure that the acid and the alkali are properly mixed.

First of all, do a rough titration to get an idea where the end point is. The end point of the titration is the exact point at which the indicator changes colour — at this point the amount of acid added is just enough to neutralise the alkali. Now do an accurate titration. Run the acid in to within 2 cm^3 of the end point, then add the acid dropwise (a drop at a time). If you don't notice exactly when the solution changed colour you've overshot and your result won't be accurate. Record the amount of acid used to neutralise the alkali. It's best to repeat this process a few times, making sure you get the same answer each time. This will make sure your results are reliable.

Tip: Phenolphthalein is clear in acidic solutions and pink in alkaline ones. You might see other indicators (e.g. methyl orange) used in titrations too.

Tip: You can also do titrations the other way round — adding alkali to acid.

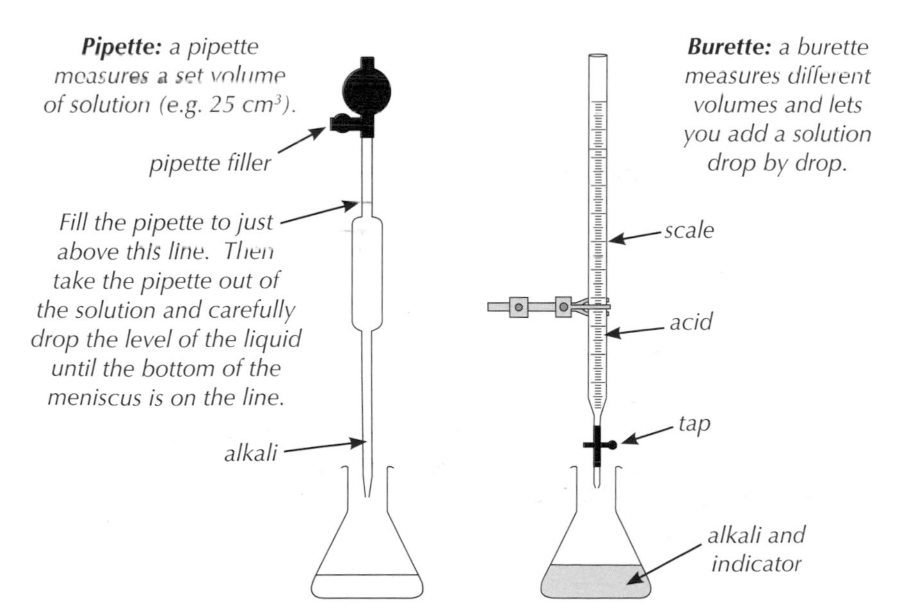

Figure 2: *The apparatus needed for a titration.*

Figure 1: *A student doing a titration. She is adding acid from the burette to the alkali in the flask. The alkali looks pink because it contains phenolphthalein.*

Calculating concentrations

You need to be able to use the results of a titration to calculate the concentration of acids and alkalis. There's more on concentration calculations on page 31.

Exam Tip
At AS Level you'll only have to do calculations like this for monoprotic acids. Monoprotic acids are acids that can only release one H^+ from each molecule, like HCl and HNO_3.

Examples

25 cm³ of 0.5 M HCl was used to neutralise 35 cm³ of NaOH solution. Calculate the concentration of the sodium hydroxide solution in mol dm⁻³.

First write a balanced equation and decide what you know and what you need to know:

$$HCl + NaOH \rightarrow NaCl + H_2O$$

	HCl	NaOH
Volume:	*25 cm³*	*35 cm³*
Concentration:	*0.5 M*	*?*

You know the volume and concentration of the HCl, so first work out how many moles of HCl you have:

$$\text{Number of moles HCl} = \frac{\text{concentration} \times \text{volume (cm}^3)}{1000}$$

$$= \frac{0.5 \times 25}{1000} = 0.0125 \text{ moles}$$

From the equation, you know 1 mole of HCl neutralises 1 mole of NaOH.

So 0.0125 moles of HCl must neutralise 0.0125 moles of NaOH.

Now it's a doddle to work out the concentration of NaOH.

$$\text{Concentration of NaOH} = \frac{\text{moles of NaOH} \times 1000}{\text{volume (cm}^3)}$$

$$= \frac{0.0125 \times 1000}{35} = 0.36 \text{ mol dm}^{-3}$$

Here's an example where it's an alkali being added to an acid instead.

40 cm³ of 0.25 M KOH was used to neutralise 22 cm³ of HNO_3 solution. Calculate the concentration of the nitric acid in mol dm⁻³.

Tip: Remember, when you're using units of concentration, M and mol dm⁻³ are the same thing.

Write out the balanced equation and the information that you have:

$$HNO_3 + KOH \rightarrow KNO_3 + H_2O$$

	HNO_3	KOH
Volume:	*22 cm³*	*40 cm³*
Concentration:	*?*	*0.25 M*

You know the volume and concentration of the KOH, so now work out how many moles of KOH you have:

$$\text{Number of moles KOH} = \frac{\text{concentration} \times \text{volume (cm}^3)}{1000}$$

$$= \frac{0.25 \times 40}{1000} = 0.01 \text{ moles}$$

From the equation, you know 1 mole of KOH neutralises 1 mole of HNO_3.

So 0.01 moles of KOH must neutralise 0.01 moles of HNO_3.

$$\text{Concentration of } HNO_3 = \frac{\text{moles of } HNO_3 \times 1000}{\text{volume (cm}^3)}$$

$$= \frac{0.01 \times 1000}{22} = 0.45 \text{ mol dm}^{-3}$$

Practice Questions — Application

Q1 28 cm³ of 0.75 M hydrochloric acid (HCl) was used to neutralise 40 cm³ of potassium hydroxide (KOH) solution.

a) Write a balanced equation for this reaction.

b) Calculate the number of moles of HCl used to neutralise the solution.

c) How many moles of KOH were neutralised by the HCl?

d) What was the concentration of the KOH solution?

Q2 15.3 cm³ of 1.5 M sodium hydroxide (NaOH) was used to neutralise 35 cm³ of nitric acid (HNO_3).

a) Write a balanced equation for this reaction.

b) Calculate the number of moles of NaOH used to neutralise the nitric acid.

c) How many moles of HNO_3 were neutralised by the NaOH?

d) What was the concentration of the HNO_3 solution?

Q3 12 cm³ of 0.5 M HCl solution was used to neutralise 24 cm³ of LiOH solution. What was the concentration of the LiOH solution?

Calculating volumes

You can use a similar method to find the volume of acid or alkali that you need to neutralise a solution. You'll need to use the number of moles = (concentration × volume (cm³)) ÷ 1000 formula again, but this time rearrange it to find the volume:

$$\text{volume (cm}^3) = \frac{\text{number of moles} \times 1000}{\text{concentration}}$$

Example

20.4 cm³ of a 0.5 M solution of sodium carbonate reacts with 1.5 M nitric acid. Calculate the volume of nitric acid required to neutralise the sodium carbonate.

Like before, first write a balanced equation for the reaction and decide what you know and what you want to know:

$$Na_2CO_3 + 2HNO_3 \rightarrow 2NaNO_3 + H_2O + CO_2$$

	Na_2CO_3	HNO_3
Volume:	*20.4 cm³*	*?*
Concentration:	*0.5 M*	*1.5 M*

Now work out how many moles of Na_2CO_3 you've got:

$$\text{Number of moles } Na_2CO_3 = \frac{\text{concentration} \times \text{volume (cm}^3)}{1000}$$

$$= \frac{0.5 \times 20.4}{1000} = 0.0102 \text{ moles}$$

1 mole of Na_2CO_3 neutralises 2 moles of HNO_3, so 0.0102 moles of Na_2CO_3 neutralises 0.0204 moles of HNO_3.

Now you know the number of moles of HNO_3 and the concentration, you can work out the volume:

$$\text{Volume of } HNO_3 = \frac{\text{number of moles} \times 1000}{\text{concentration}}$$

$$= \frac{0.0204 \times 1000}{1.5} = 13.6 \text{ cm}^3$$

Tip: All of these calculations are just like the moles, concentration and volume ones back on page 31. You just apply the same method to titrations.

Figure 3: A titration where an alkali is being added to an acid. The indicator in the flask is phenolphthalein, so the solution starts clear and turns pink at the endpoint.

And here's an example where you're finding the volume of alkali used.

Example

18.2 cm³ of a 0.8 M solution HCl reacts with 0.3 M LiOH. Calculate the volume of lithium hydroxide required to neutralise the hydrochloric acid.

Write out the balanced equation and the information that you have:

$$HCl + LiOH \rightarrow LiCl + H_2O$$

	HCl	LiOH
Volume:	*18.2 cm³*	*?*
Concentration:	*0.8 M*	*0.3 M*

Now work out how many moles of HCl you've got:

$$\text{Number of moles HCl} = \frac{\text{concentration} \times \text{volume (cm}^3\text{)}}{1000}$$

$$= \frac{0.8 \times 18.2}{1000} = 0.0146 \text{ moles}$$

1 mole of HCl neutralises 1 moles of LiOH, so 0.0146 moles of HCl neutralises 0.0146 moles of LiOH.

Now use this to work out the volume:

$$\text{Volume of LiOH} = \frac{\text{number of moles} \times 1000}{\text{concentration}}$$

$$= \frac{0.0146 \times 1000}{0.3} = 48.7 \text{ cm}^3$$

Practice Questions — Application

Q1 18.8 cm³ of a 0.2 M solution of nitric acid (HNO_3) reacts with 0.45 M lithium hydroxide (LiOH) solution.

a) Write a balanced equation for this reaction.

b) Calculate the number of moles of HNO_3 present in the acid added.

c) How many moles of LiOH were in the sample of the alkali?

d) What volume of LiOH was required to neutralise the HNO_3 solution?

Q2 37.3 cm³ of a 0.42 M solution of potassium hydroxide (KOH) reacts with 1.1 M ethanoic acid (CH_3COOH) solution.

a) Write a balanced equation for this reaction.

b) Calculate the number of moles of KOH present in the alkali added.

c) How many moles of CH_3COOH were in the sample of the acid?

d) What volume of CH_3COOH was required to neutralise the KOH solution?

Q3 14 cm³ of a 1 M NaOH solution reacts with a 0.5 M HCl solution. What volume of HCl was required to neutralise the NaOH solution?

Practice Questions — Fact Recall

Q1 Name the piece of equipment that you would use to measure out a set volume of alkali or acid for a titration.

Q2 Name the piece of equipment that you would use to add liquid drop by drop to the flask during a titration.

Q3 When you are doing a titration, why do you swirl the flask after adding each drop?

Q4 What is the 'end point' of a titration?

6. Formulas

Now for a few pages about chemical formulas. A formula tells you what atoms are in a compound. Useful, I think you'll agree.

Learning Objectives:

- Understand the concept of, and the relationship between, empirical and molecular formulas.
- Be able to calculate empirical formulas from data giving percentage composition by mass.

Specification Reference 3.1.2

Empirical and molecular formulas

You need to know what's what with empirical and molecular formulas. The **empirical formula** gives just the smallest whole number ratio of atoms in a compound. The **molecular formula** gives the actual numbers of atoms in a molecule. The molecular formula is made up of a whole number of empirical units. There's a bit more on this on pages 89-90.

Example

This molecule is butane:

```
   H  H  H  H
   |  |  |  |
H—C—C—C—C—H
   |  |  |  |
   H  H  H  H
```

Butane contains 4 carbon (C) atoms and 10 hydrogen (H) atoms. So its molecular formula is C_4H_{10}.

Butane's empirical formula is C_2H_5. This means that the ratio of carbon atoms to hydrogen atoms in the molecule is 2:5. That's as much as you can simplify it.

If you know the empirical formula and the molecular mass of a compound, you can calculate its molecular formula. Just follow these steps:

1. Find the empirical mass (that's just the mass of the empirical formula).
2. Divide the molecular mass by the empirical mass. This tells you how many multiples of the empirical formula are in the molecular formula.
3. Multiply the empirical formula by that number to find the molecular formula.

Here are a couple of examples to show you how it works.

Example

A molecule has an empirical formula of $C_4H_3O_2$, and a molecular mass of 166 g. Work out its molecular formula.

1. Find the empirical mass — add up by the relative atomic mass values of all the atoms in the empirical formula.

3 H atoms · *A_r of H*

empirical mass = (4 × 12) + (3 × 1) + (2 × 16) = 83 g

4 C atoms · *A_r of C* · *2 O atoms* · *A_r of O*

2. Divide the molecular mass by the empirical mass. The molecular mass is 166 g, so there are (166 ÷ 83) = 2 empirical units in the molecule.
3. The molecular formula is the empirical formula × 2, so the molecular formula = $C_8H_6O_4$.

Tip: Empirical mass is just like relative formula mass (see page 12).

Example

The empirical formula of glucose is CH_2O. Its relative molecular mass is 180. Find its molecular formula.

1. Find the empirical mass of glucose.
   empirical mass = $(1 \times 12) + (2 \times 1) + (1 \times 16) = 30$ g
2. Divide the molecular mass by the empirical mass. The molecular mass is 180, so there are $(180 \div 30) = 6$ empirical units in the molecule.
3. Molecular formula = $C_6H_{12}O_6$.

Practice Questions — Application

Q1 A molecule has the empirical formula C_4H_9, and a molecular mass of 171 g. Find its molecular formula.

Q2 A molecule has the empirical formula $C_3H_5O_2$, and a relative molecular mass of 146. Find its molecular formula.

Q3 A molecule has the empirical formula C_2H_6O, and a molecular mass of 46 g. Find its molecular formula.

Q4 A molecule has the empirical formula $C_4H_6Cl_2O$, and a relative molecular mass of 423. Find its molecular formula.

Tip: There's more on finding the empirical formulas of organic compounds on page 90.

Calculating empirical formulas

You need to know how to work out empirical formulas from the percentages of the different elements. Follow these steps each time:

1. Assume you've got 100 g of the compound — you can turn the percentages straight into masses. Then you can work out how many moles of each element are in 100 g of the compound.
2. Divide each number of moles by the smallest number of moles you found in step 1. This gives you the ratio of the elements in the compound.
3. Apply the numbers from the ratio to the formula.

Example

A compound is found to have percentage composition 56.5% potassium, 8.7% carbon and 34.8% oxygen by mass. Calculate its empirical formula.

1. If you had 100 g of the compound you would have 56.5 g of potassium, 8.7 g of carbon and 34.8 g of oxygen. Use the formula, moles = mass $\div$ M_r, to work out how many moles of each element that is.

   K: $\frac{56.5}{39.1} = 1.445$ moles   C: $\frac{8.7}{12} = 0.725$ moles   O: $\frac{34.8}{16} = 2.175$ moles

2. Divide each number of moles by the smallest number (0.725 here).

   K: $\frac{1.445}{0.725} = 2.0$ C: $\frac{0.725}{0.725} = 1.0$ O: $\frac{2.175}{0.725} = 3.0$

   This tells you that the ratio of K : C : O in the molecule is 2 : 1 : 3.

3. So you know the empirical formula's got to be K_2CO_3.

Exam Tip
Make sure you write down all your working for calculation questions. You'll be more likely to spot any mistakes and if you do go wrong you might get some marks for the working.

Sometimes you might only be given the percentage of some of the elements in the compound. Then you'll have to work out the percentages of the others.

Example

An oxide of nitrogen contains 26% by mass of nitrogen. Calculate its empirical formula.

1. The compound only contains nitrogen and oxygen, so if it is 26% N it must be 100 – 26 = 74% O. So if you had 100 g of the compound you would have 26 g of nitrogen and 74 g of oxygen.

   N: $\frac{26}{14}$ = 1.86 moles   O: $\frac{74}{16}$ = 4.63 moles

2. Divide each number of moles by 1.86.

   N: $\frac{1.86}{1.86}$ = 1.0   O: $\frac{4.63}{1.86}$ = 2.5

   This tells you that the ratio of N : O in the molecule is 1 : 2.5.

3. All the numbers in an empirical formula have to be whole numbers, so you need to multiply the ratio by 2 to put it into its simplest whole number form: 2 × (1 : 2.5) = 2 : 5.
   So the empirical formula is N_2O_5.

Practice Questions — Application

Q1 A compound is found to have percentage composition 5.9% hydrogen and 94.1% oxygen by mass. Find its empirical formula.

Q2 A compound is found to have percentage composition 20.2% aluminium and 79.8% chlorine by mass. Find its empirical formula.

Q3 A compound is found to have percentage composition 8.5% carbon, 1.4% hydrogen and 90.1% iodine by mass. Find its empirical formula.

Q4 A compound is found to have percentage composition 50.1% copper, 16.3% phosphorus and 33.6% oxygen by mass. Find its empirical formula.

Q5 A compound containing only vanadium and chlorine is found to be 32.3% vanadium by mass. Find its empirical formula.

Q6 An oxide of chromium contains 31.58% by mass of oxygen. Find its empirical formula.

Tip: You should add up the percentages each time there's a question like this to make sure they add up to 100% and you haven't missed out any elements.

Practice Questions — Fact Recall

Q1 What information does the empirical formula of a compound give you?

Q2 What information does the molecular formula of a compound give you?

Learning Objective:

- Be able to calculate % yields from balanced equations.

Specification Reference 3.1.2

7. Chemical Yield

If you're making a chemical (in a lab or a factory), it helps to know how much of it you can expect to get. In real life you'll never manage to make exactly that much — but percentage yield can give you an idea of how close you got.

Calculating theoretical yield

The **theoretical yield** is the mass of product that should be formed in a chemical reaction. It assumes no chemicals are 'lost' in the process. You can use the masses of reactants and a balanced equation to calculate the theoretical yield for a reaction. It's a bit like calculating reacting masses (see page 38) — here are the steps you have to go through:

1. Work out how many moles of the reactant you have.
2. Use the equation to work out how many moles of product you would expect that much reactant to make.
3. Calculate the mass of that many moles of product — and that's the theoretical yield.

Exam Tip
If you're asked to calculate yields in an exam you should always be given a balanced equation to work from.

Example

1.40 g of iron filings react with ammonia and sulfuric acid to make hydrated ammonium iron(II) sulfate. The balanced equation for the reaction is:

$$Fe_{(s)} + 2NH_{3\,(aq)} + 2H_2SO_{4\,(aq)} + 6H_2O_{(l)} \rightarrow (NH_4)_2Fe(SO_4)_2{\cdot}6H_2O_{(s)} + H_{2\,(g)}$$

Calculate the theoretical yield of this reaction.

1. Work out how many moles of iron you have:
   Molar mass of Fe = 55.8 g mol^{-1}
   Number of moles Fe = mass ÷ molar mass
   = 1.40 ÷ 55.8 = 0.025 moles.
2. Work out how many moles of product you would expect to make:
   From the equation, you know that 1 mole of Fe produces 1 mole of $(NH_4)_2Fe(SO_4)_2{\cdot}6H_2O$ so 0.025 moles of Fe will produce 0.025 moles of $(NH_4)_2Fe(SO_4)_2{\cdot}6H_2O$.
3. Now calculate the mass of that many moles of product:
   Molar mass of $(NH_4)_2Fe(SO_4)_2{\cdot}6H_2O$ = 392 g mol^{-1}
   Theoretical yield = number of moles × molar mass
   = 0.025 × 392 = 9.8 g.

Tip: 'Hydrated' means that the crystals have a bit of water left in them. That's what the dot in $(NH_4)_2Fe(SO_4)_2{\cdot}6H_2O$ means — each molecule of $(NH_4)_2Fe(SO_4)_2$ in the crystal is surrounded by six water molecules.

Calculating percentage yield

For any reaction, the actual mass of product (the actual yield) will always be less than the theoretical yield. There are many reasons for this. For example, sometimes not all the 'starting' chemicals react fully. And some chemicals are always 'lost', e.g. some solution gets left on filter paper, or is lost during transfers between containers. Once you've found the theoretical yield and the actual yield, you can work out the **percentage yield**.

$$\text{Percentage Yield} = \frac{\text{Actual Yield}}{\text{Theoretical Yield}} \times 100$$

Figure 1: *Filtering a solution to collect copper sulfate crystals. When the crystals are removed, traces of copper sulfate will be left behind on the filter paper.*

Examples

In the ammonium iron(II) sulfate example on the previous page, the theoretical yield was 9.8 g. Say you weighed the hydrated ammonium iron(II) sulfate crystals produced and found the actual yield was 5.2 g.

Then you just have to plug the numbers into the formula:

$$\text{Percentage yield} = \frac{\text{actual yield}}{\text{theoretical yield}} \times 100$$

$$= (5.2 \div 9.8) \times 100 = 53\%$$

Here's another example:

In an experiment 5 g of copper was heated in air to produce copper oxide. The theoretical yield of this reaction was 6.26 g. When the copper oxide was weighed it was found to have a mass of 5.23 g.

Calculate the percentage yield of this reaction.

All you need to do here is put the right numbers into the formula:

$$\text{Percentage yield} = \frac{\text{actual yield}}{\text{theoretical yield}} \times 100$$

$$= (5.23 \div 6.26) \times 100 = 83.5\%$$

Exam Tip

This is a percentage yield, so it can never be more than 100%. If you're answer is bigger than 100%, check the working for mistakes.

Practice Questions — Application

Q1 The theoretical yield of a reaction used in an experiment was 3.24 g. The actual yield was 1.76 g. Calculate the percentage yield of the reaction.

Q2 In an experiment sodium metal was reacted with chlorine gas to produce sodium chloride. The theoretical yield of this reaction was 6.1 g. The sodium chloride produced had a mass of 3.7 g. Calculate the percentage yield of this reaction.

Q3 3 g of iron filings are burnt in air to give iron oxide (Fe_2O_3):

$$4Fe_{(s)} + 3O_{2\,(g)} \rightarrow 2Fe_2O_{3\,(s)}$$

a) How many moles of iron are there in 3 g of metal?

b) Calculate the theoretical yield of iron oxide for this reaction.

c) Calculate the percentage yield if 3.6 g of Fe_2O_3 is made.

Q4 Aluminium metal can be extracted from aluminium oxide by electrolysis. The balanced equation for this reaction is:

$$2Al_2O_{3\,(l)} \rightarrow 4Al_{(l)} + 3O_{2\,(g)}$$

How much aluminium would you expect to get from 1000 g of Al_2O_3?

Q5 4.70 g of sodium hydroxide is dissolved in water. This solution is reacted with an excess of sulfuric acid to make sodium sulfate:

$$2NaOH_{(aq)} + H_2SO_{4\,(g)} \rightarrow Na_2SO_{4\,(aq)} + H_2O_{(l)}$$

The sodium sulfate is allowed to crystallise. The dry crystals have a mass of 6.04 g. Calculate the percentage yield of this reaction.

Practice Questions — Fact Recall

Q1 What is meant by the 'theoretical yield' of a reaction?

Q2 Write down the formula for percentage yield.

Learning Objectives:

- Know the formula for calculating % atom economy.
- Be able to calculate % atom economies from balanced equations.

Specification Reference 3.1.2

8. Atom Economy

Atom economy is one way to work out how efficient a reaction is. Efficient reactions are better for the environment and save the chemical industry money.

What is atom economy?

The efficiency of a reaction is often measured by the percentage yield. This tells you how wasteful the process is — it's based on how much of the product is lost because of things like reactions not completing or losses during collection and purification. But percentage yield doesn't measure how wasteful the reaction itself is. A reaction that has a 100% yield could still be very wasteful if a lot of the atoms from the reactants wind up in by-products rather than the desired product. **Atom economy** is a measure of the proportion of reactant atoms that become part of the desired product (rather than by-products) in the balanced chemical equation.

Figure 1: *Tablets of the painkiller ibuprofen. Ibuprofen was originally made using a reaction with a 40% atom economy. Now a new way of making it with a 77% atom economy is used. This produces much less waste.*

Atom economy in industry

Chemical companies try to use reactions that have high atom economy, so they're not producing lots of waste, or spending money making by-products. But reactions with low atom economy may still be used if the waste products can be sold and used for something else (waste products like gases, salts and acids can often be useful reactants for other reactions).

Calculating atom economy

Atom economy is calculated using this formula:

$$\% \text{ atom economy} = \frac{\text{mass of desired product}}{\text{total mass of reactants}} \times 100$$

To calculate the atom economy for a reaction, you just need to add up the molecular masses of the reactants, find the molecular mass of the product you're interested in and put them both into the formula.

Tip: Any reaction where there's only one product will have a 100% atom economy.

Example

Bromomethane is reacted with sodium hydroxide to make methanol:

$$CH_3Br + NaOH \rightarrow CH_3OH + NaBr$$

Calculate the percentage atom economy for this reaction.

First, calculate the total mass of the reactants — add up the relative molecular masses of everything on the left side of the balanced equation:

Total mass of reactants = (12 + (3 × 1) + 79.9) + (23 + 16 + 1) = 134.9

Then find the mass of the desired product — that's the methanol:

Mass of desired product = 12 + (3 × 1) + 16 + 1 = 32

Now you can find the % atom economy:

$$\% \text{ atom economy} = \frac{\text{mass of desired product}}{\text{total mass of reactants}} \times 100$$

$$= \frac{32}{134.9} \times 100 = 23.7\%$$

When you calculate the masses, you should use the number of moles of each compound that is in the balanced equation (e.g. the mass of '$2H_2$' should be 2 × (2 × 1) = 4). Here's a quick example:

Exam Tip
You should always calculate atom economy from a balanced equation. The good news is that if you're asked to do it in the exam, they'll give you the equation.

Example

Ethanol can be produced by fermenting glucose:

$$C_6H_{12}O_6 \rightarrow 2C_2H_5OH + 2CO_2$$

Calculate the percentage atom economy for this reaction.

Calculate the total mass of the reactants (1 mole of glucose):

Total mass of reactants = (6 × 12) + (12 × 1) + (6 × 16) = 180

Then find the mass of the desired product (2 moles of ethanol):

Mass of desired product = 2 × ((12 × 2) + (5 × 1) + 16 + 1) = 92

$$\text{So, \% atom economy} = \frac{\text{mass of desired product}}{\text{total mass of reactants}} \times 100$$

$$= \frac{92}{180} \times 100 = 51.1\%$$

Practice Questions — Application

Q1 Chlorine gas can react with excess methane to make chloromethane:

$$CH_4 + Cl_2 \rightarrow CH_3Cl + HCl$$

a) Find the total molecular mass of the reactants in this reaction.

b) Find the molecular mass of the chloromethane produced.

c) Calculate the percentage atom economy of this reaction.

d) A company wants to use this reaction to make chloromethane, despite its low atom economy. Suggest one way that they could increase their profit and reduce the waste they produce.

Q2 Aluminium chloride can be produced using this reaction:

$$2Al + 3Cl_2 \rightarrow 2AlCl_3$$

Calculate the percentage atom economy of this reaction.

Q3 Pure iron can be produced from iron oxide in the blast furnace:

$$2Fe_2O_3 + 3C \rightarrow 4Fe + 3CO_2$$

Calculate the percentage atom economy of this reaction.

Q4 In industry, ammonia (NH_3) is usually produced using this reaction:

Reaction 1: $N_2 + 3H_2 \rightarrow 2NH_3$

It can also be made using this reaction:

Reaction 2: $2NH_4Cl + Ca(OH)_2 \rightarrow CaCl_2 + 2NH_3 + 2H_2O$

a) Calculate the percentage atom economy of both reactions.

b) Give one reason why reaction 1 is used to produce ammonia industrially rather than reaction 2.

Practice Questions — Fact Recall

Q1 What is meant by the 'atom economy' of a reaction?

Q2 Write down the formula for calculating % atom economy.

Section Summary

Make sure you know...

- What a mole is and how many particles there are in one.
- What Avogadro's constant is.
- How to calculate the molar mass of a compound from its formula.
- How to find the number of moles, mass or molar mass of a substance using the equation 'number of moles = mass of substance ÷ molar mass'.
- How to find the number of moles of a substance in a solution, or its concentration or volume, using the concentration equation.
- How to calculate the volume of a gas or the number of moles it contains at room temperature and pressure.
- What the ideal gas equation is.
- The standard units of all the values in the ideal gas equation.
- How to convert units of temperature, pressure and volume into the correct units for the ideal gas equation.
- How to use the ideal gas equation to calculate the pressure, volume, number of moles or temperature of a gas.
- How to write and balance full and ionic equations for reactions.
- How to calculate the mass of a reactant or a product from a balanced equation.
- How to calculate the volume of gas produced by a reaction.
- The four state symbols used in equations.
- How to perform an accurate titration.
- How to calculate the concentration of an acid or alkali from the results of a titration.
- How to calculate the volume of acid needed to neutralise an alkali (and vice versa).
- What an empirical formula and a molecular formula are.
- How to find the molecular formula of a compound from its empirical formula and molecular mass.
- How to find the empirical formula of a compound from its percentage composition by mass.
- How to calculate the theoretical yield of a reaction.
- How to calculate the percentage yield of a reaction.
- What atom economy is and why it is important in industry.
- How to calculate the atom economy of a reaction.

Exam-style Questions

1 Chlorine gas (Cl_2) is used in water treatment and in the production of plastics. It is usually produced by the electrolysis of sodium chloride solution:

$$2NaCl_{(aq)} + 2H_2O_{(l)} \rightarrow Cl_{2\,(g)} + H_{2\,(g)} + 2NaOH_{(aq)}$$

1 (a) 20.0 g of NaCl was dissolved in an excess of water, and the resulting solution was electrolysed.

1 (a) (i) Calculate the amount, in moles, of NaCl in 20.0 g.

(2 marks)

1 (a) (ii) Calculate the amount, in moles, of Cl_2 gas that would be produced from a 20.0 g sample of NaCl.

(1 mark)

1 (b) In another experiment a different sample of sodium chloride solution was electrolysed to produce 0.65 moles of chlorine gas. Calculate the volume in m^3 that this gas would occupy at 330 K and 98 kPa. (The gas constant, $R = 8.31\ J\ K^{-1}\ mol^{-1}$)

(3 marks)

1 (c) (i) Calculate the percentage atom economy for the formation of Cl_2 gas from the electrolysis of NaCl solution.

(2 marks)

1 (c) (ii) This reaction has a low atom economy. There are other ways of producing chlorine that have a higher atom economy. Given that this is the case, suggest why most chemical companies still use this reaction to produce chlorine.

(1 mark)

2 Octane is a hydrocarbon with the molecular formula C_8H_{18}. It can be used as a fuel in cars, and is a liquid at room temperature.

2 (a) Octane burns completely in air to give water and carbon dioxide. Write a balanced equation for this reaction, including state symbols.

(2 marks)

2 (b) A sample of octane is burnt in air. The amount of carbon dioxide produced occupies a volume of 0.02 m^3 at 308 K and 101 000 Pa.

2 (b) (i) Calculate the number of moles of CO_2 present in 0.02 m^3 of carbon dioxide at this temperature and pressure. (The gas constant, $R = 8.31\ J\ K^{-1}\ mol^{-1}$)

(2 marks)

2 (b) (ii) How many moles of octane were burnt to produce this amount of CO_2?

(1 mark)

2 (c) A different hydrocarbon contains 85.7% carbon by mass. Find the empirical formula of this hydrocarbon.

(3 marks)

3 Phosphoric acid (H_3PO_4) is made by dissolving oxides of phosphorus in water.

3 (a) An oxide of phosphorus contains 43.6% oxygen by mass.

3 (a) (i) Find the empirical formula of this oxide.

(3 marks)

3 (a) (ii) Given that the molecular mass of the oxide is 220, find its molecular formula.

(2 marks)

3 (b) Diammonium phosphate $(NH_4)_2HPO_4$ can be used as a fertiliser.
It can be made from ammonia and phosphoric acid according to this equation:

$$2NH_{3\,(g)} + H_3PO_{4\,(aq)} \rightarrow (NH_4)_2HPO_{4\,(s)}$$

3 (b) (i) Calculate the amount, in moles, of NH_3 in 2.5 g of ammonia gas.

(2 marks)

3 (b) (ii) Calculate the amount, in moles, of $(NH_4)_2HPO_4$ that would be produced from 2.5 g of ammonia gas. (Assume the phosphoric acid was present in excess.)

(1 mark)

3 (b) (iii) Calculate the mass of $(NH_4)_2HPO_4$ that would be produced from 2.5 g of ammonia gas.

(2 marks)

4 A 3.4 g piece of calcium metal was burned in air to make calcium oxide.
Here is the balanced equation for this reaction:

$$2Ca_{(s)} + O_{2\,(g)} \rightarrow 2CaO_{(s)}$$

4 (a) State the atom economy of this reaction.
Explain your answer.

(2 marks)

4 (b) (i) Calculate the amount, in moles, of Ca in 3.4 g of calcium metal.

(2 marks)

4 (b) (ii) Calculate the maximum amount, in moles, of CaO that could be produced by burning this piece of calcium metal.

(1 mark)

4 (b) (iii) Calculate the maximum mass of CaO that could be produced by burning this piece of calcium metal.

(2 marks)

4 (b) (iv) The actual mass of CaO produced was 3.7 g.
Calculate the percentage yield of CaO.

(1 mark)

5 A 20 cm^3 sample of hydrochloric acid was titrated with 0.5 mol dm^{-3} potassium hydroxide in order to determine its concentration.

The acid and the base reacted according to the following equation:

$$HCl_{(aq)} + KOH_{(aq)} \rightarrow KCl_{(aq)} + H_2O_{(l)}$$

5 (a) Calculate the mass of pure solid potassium hydroxide that you would need to dissolve in 150 cm^3 of water to make a 0.5 mol dm^{-3} solution. Give your answer to two significant figures.

(3 marks)

5 (b) The results of the titration experiment are shown in the table below.

Titration	Volume of KOH solution added (cm^3)
1	26.00
2	26.05
3	26.00
4	26.00

Use this data to calculate the concentration of the hydrochloric acid solution that was used in the titration.

(4 marks)

5 (c) Hydrogen chloride gas ($HCl_{(g)}$) is a hydrogen halide. Hydrochloric acid ($HCl_{(aq)}$) can be made by dissolving this gas in water.

A different acid was made by dissolving 3.07 g of a mystery hydrogen halide, HX, in pure water. This produced a 0.20 dm^3 sample of the acid.

This sample of acid was then titrated with KOH and found to have a concentration of 0.12 mol dm^{-3}.

Find the relative atomic mass of the halogen, X, and suggest its identity.

(6 marks)

1. Ionic Bonding

Learning Objectives:

- Understand that ionic bonding involves attraction between oppositely charged ions in a lattice.
- Recognise ionic crystals.
- Know the structure of sodium chloride.
- Be able to relate the physical properties of materials to the type of structure and bonding present.

Specification Reference 3.1.3

When different elements join or bond together, you get a compound. There are two main types of bonding in compounds — ionic and covalent. First up is ionic bonding.

Ions

Ions are formed when electrons are transferred from one atom to another. The simplest ions are single atoms which have either lost or gained 1, 2 or 3 electrons so that they've got a full outer shell.

Examples

The sodium ion

A sodium atom (Na) loses 1 electron to form a sodium ion (Na^+) — see Figure 1.

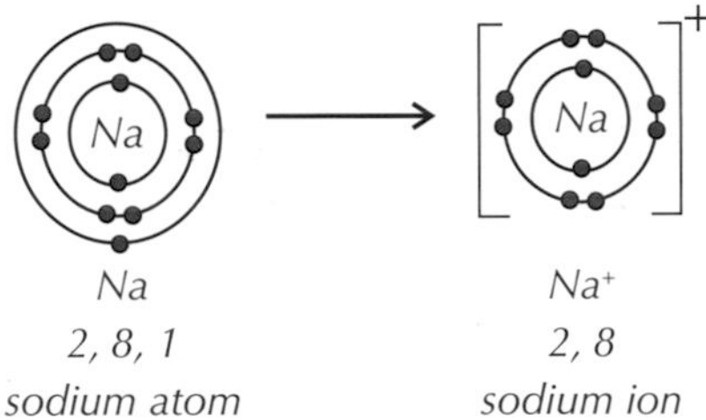

Figure 1: *Formation of a sodium ion.*

This can be shown by the equation: $\mathbf{Na \rightarrow Na^+ + e^-}$.

Tip: The notation '2, 8, 1' shows the electron configuration of an atom or ion. There's more about how to work them out on pages 19-21.

The chloride ion

A chlorine atom (Cl) gains 1 electron to form a chloride ion (Cl^-) — see Figure 2.

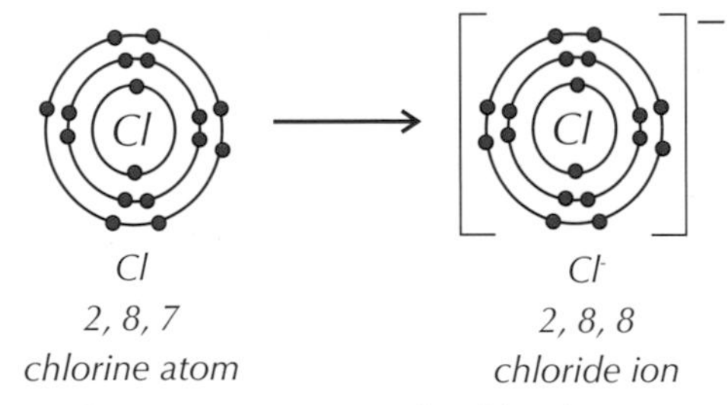

Figure 2: *Formation of a chloride ion.*

This can be shown by the equation: $\mathbf{Cl + e^- \rightarrow Cl^-}$.

Other examples:

A magnesium atom (Mg) loses 2 electrons to form a magnesium ion (Mg^{2+}), shown by the equation: $\mathbf{Mg \rightarrow Mg^{2+} + 2e^-}$.
An oxygen atom (O) gains 2 electrons to form an oxide ion (O^{2-}) shown by the equation: $\mathbf{O + 2e^- \rightarrow O^{2-}}$.

Tip: Equations that show the formation of ions need to be balanced — have a look back at pages 36-37 for how to balance ionic equations.

You don't have to remember what ion each element forms — nope, for many of them you just look at the Periodic Table. Elements in the same group all have the same number of outer electrons. So they have to lose or gain the same number to get the full outer shell that they're aiming for. And this means that they form ions with the same charges. Figure 3 shows the ions formed by the elements in different groups.

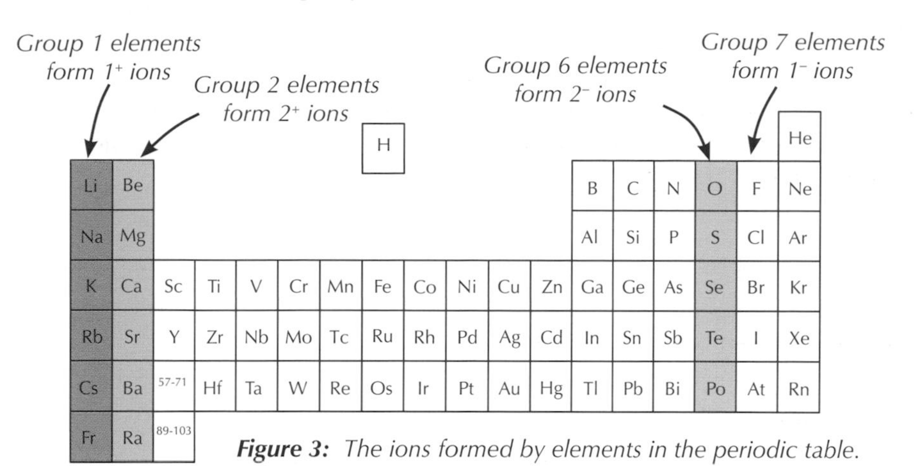

Figure 3: *The ions formed by elements in the periodic table.*

Exam Tip
Make sure you know how to find the charges on different ions from the periodic table — you never know when it'll come in handy in the exam.

Ionic compounds

Electrostatic attraction holds positive and negative ions together — it's very strong. When atoms are held together like this, it's called ionic bonding. When oppositely charged ions form an ionic bond you get an ionic compound. The formula of a compound tells you what ions that compound has in it. The positive charges in the compound balance the negative charges exactly — so the total overall charge is zero. This is a dead handy way of checking the formula. You can use 'dot-and-cross' diagrams to show how ionic bonding works in ionic compounds.

Examples

Sodium chloride

The formula of sodium chloride is NaCl. It just tells you that sodium chloride is made up of Na^+ ions and Cl^- ions (in a 1:1 ratio). In NaCl, the single positive charge on the Na^+ ion balances the single negative charge on the Cl^- ion (see Figure 4).

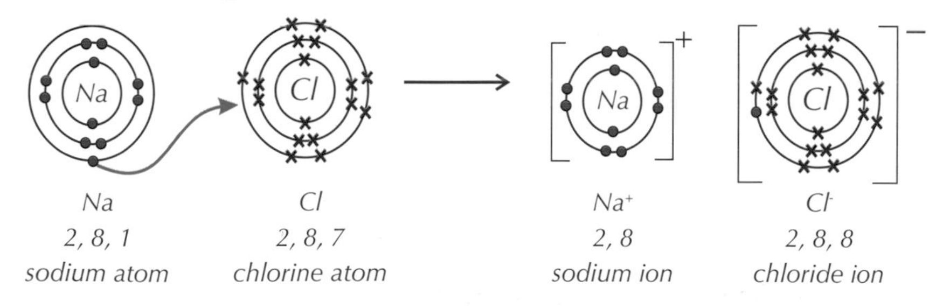

Figure 4: *Formation of sodium chloride from a sodium atom and a chlorine atom.*

Here the dots represent the Na electrons and the crosses represent the Cl electrons. All electrons are really identical, but this is a good way of following their movement.

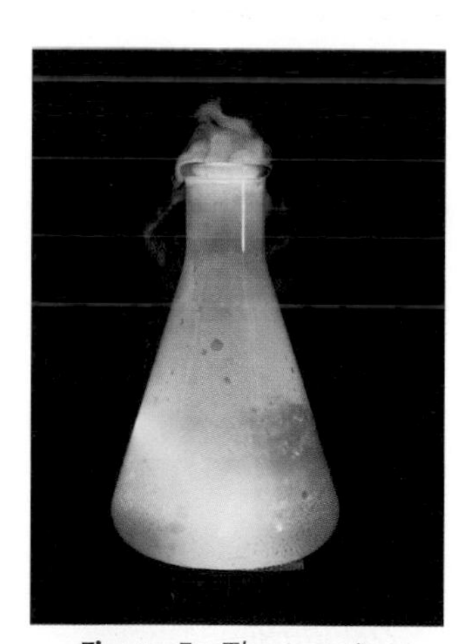

Figure 5: *The reaction between sodium and chlorine to form sodium chloride.*

Figure 7: *Magnesium is burned in oxygen to form magnesium oxide.*

Magnesium oxide

Magnesium oxide, MgO, is another example of an ionic compound. The formation of magnesium oxide involves the transfer of two electrons — see Figure 6. The formula tells you that magnesium oxide is made up of Mg^{2+} ions and O^{2-} ions in a 1:1 ratio.

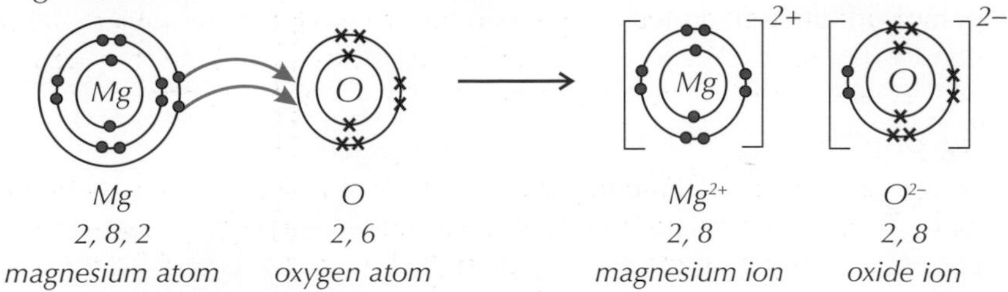

Figure 6: *Formation of magnesium oxide from a magnesium atom and an oxygen atom.*

Magnesium chloride

Magnesium chloride ($MgCl_2$) is different again. In this compound, the 2+ charge on the Mg^{2+} ion balances the two individual charges on the two Cl^- ions — see Figure 9.

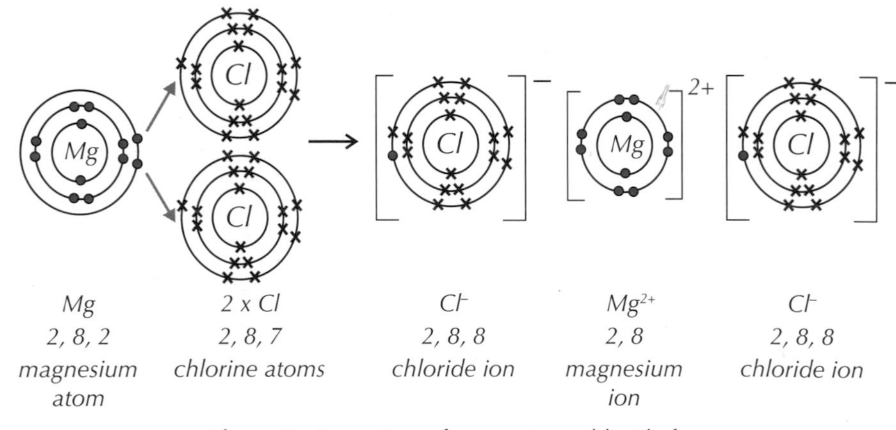

Figure 8: *Magnesium chloride.*

Mg 2, 8, 2 magnesium atom	2 x Cl 2, 8, 7 chlorine atoms	Cl^- 2, 8, 8 chloride ion	Mg^{2+} 2, 8 magnesium ion	Cl^- 2, 8, 8 chloride ion

Figure 9: *Formation of magnesium chloride from a magnesium atom and two chlorine atoms.*

Giant ionic lattices

Ionic crystals are **giant lattices** of ions. A lattice is just a regular structure. The structure's called 'giant' because it's made up of the same basic unit repeated over and over again. In sodium chloride, the Na^+ and Cl^- ions are packed together. The sodium chloride lattice is cube shaped (see Figures 10 and 11).

Figure 10: *Crystals of sodium chloride (table salt).*

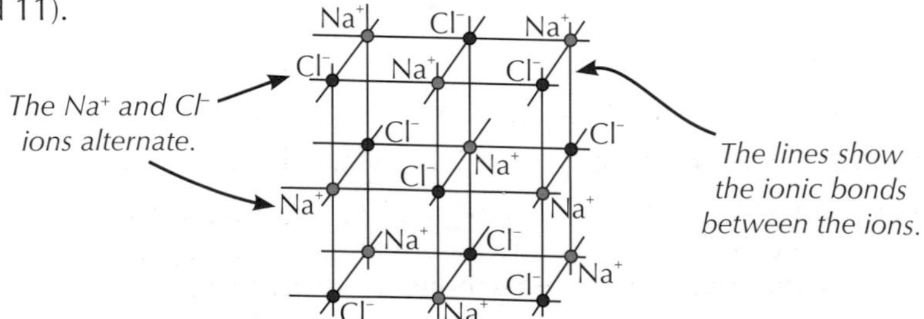

Figure 11: *The structure of sodium chloride.*

Different ionic compounds have different shaped structures, but they're all still giant lattices.

Behaviour of ionic compounds

The structure of ionic compounds decides their physical properties — things like their electrical conductivity, melting point and solubility.

Electrical conductivity

Ionic compounds conduct electricity when they're molten or dissolved — but not when they're solid. The ions in a liquid are free to move (and they carry a charge). In a solid they're fixed in position by the strong ionic bonds.

Melting point

Ionic compounds have high melting points. The giant ionic lattices are held together by strong electrostatic forces. It takes loads of energy to overcome these forces, so melting points are very high (801 °C for sodium chloride).

Solubility

Ionic compounds tend to dissolve in water. Water molecules are polar — part of the molecule has a small negative charge, and the other bits have small positive charges (see p. 70). The water molecules pull the ions away from the lattice and cause it to dissolve.

Exam Tip
Make sure you learn these — you might get asked what properties you'd expect a specific ionic compound to have in the exam. It doesn't matter if you've never heard of the compound before — if you know it's an ionic compound you know it'll have these properties.

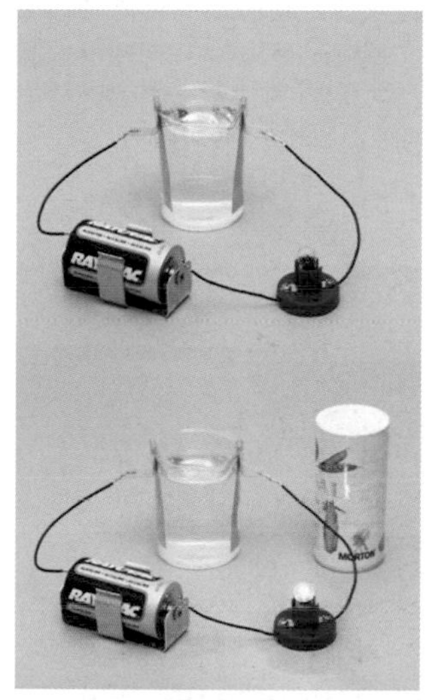

Figure 12: *Water doesn't conduct electricity (see top). When the ionic compound sodium chloride is added to the water (above), it dissolves and the free Na^+ and Cl^- ions allow a current to flow.*

Practice Questions — Application

Q1 Use the periodic table to give the charge on the following ions:
a) Bromide b) Potassium c) Beryllium

Q2 a) Write an equation to show a sulfur atom forming an ion.
b) Draw a 'dot and cross' diagram to show a sulfur atom forming an ion.

Q3 Calcium reacts with iodine to form an ionic compound.
a) What is the charge on a calcium ion?
b) What is the charge on an iodide ion?
c) Give the formula of calcium iodide.

Q4 Fluorine forms ionic bonds with lithium.
a) Give the formula of the compound formed.
b) Describe the formation of an ionic bond between fluorine and lithium atoms.

Practice Questions — Fact Recall

Q1 What effect does electrostatic attraction have on oppositely charged ions?

Q2 Explain what an ionic lattice is.

Q3 Draw the structure of sodium chloride.

Q4 Explain why ionic compounds conduct electricity when molten.

Q5 Magnesium oxide is an ionic compound. Apart from electrical conductivity when molten or dissolved, describe two physical properties you would expect magnesium oxide to have.

Learning Objectives:

- Know that a covalent bond involves a shared pair of electrons.
- Recognise giant covalent (macromolecular) crystals.
- Know the structure of diamond and graphite.
- Be able to relate the physical properties of materials to the type of structure and bonding present.

Specification Reference 3.1.3

2. Covalent Bonding

Ionic bonding done — now it's on to covalent bonding.

Molecules

Molecules are the smallest parts of compounds that can take part in chemical reactions. They're formed when two or more atoms bond together — it doesn't matter if the atoms are the same or different. Chlorine gas (Cl_2), carbon monoxide (CO), water (H_2O) and ethanol (C_2H_5OH) are all molecules. Molecules are held together by strong covalent bonds. Covalent bonds can be single, double or triple bonds.

Single bonds

In covalent bonding, two atoms share electrons, so they've both got full outer shells of electrons. Both the positive nuclei are attracted electrostatically to the shared electrons.

Examples

Two iodine atoms (I) bond covalently to form a molecule of iodine (I_2) — see Figure 1. (These diagrams don't show all the electrons — just the ones in the outer shells.)

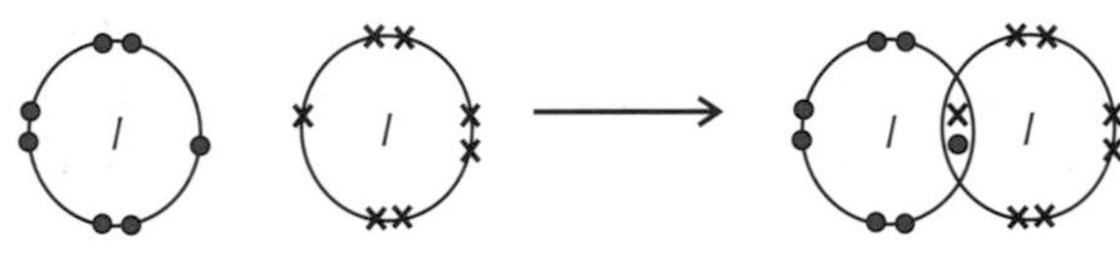

An iodine molecule can also be drawn as:
I—I

Figure 1: Formation of a molecule of iodine.

The diagrams below show other examples of covalent molecules.

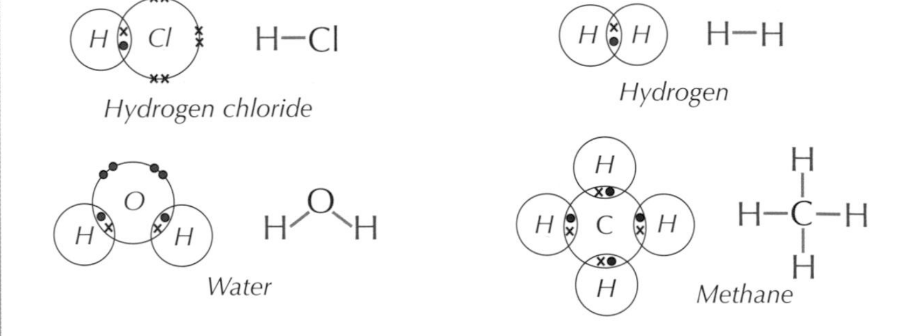

Double and triple bonds

Atoms in covalent molecules don't just form single bonds — double or even triple covalent bonds can form too.

Examples

Double bonds

One carbon atom (C) can bond to two oxygen atoms (O). Each oxygen atom shares two pairs of electrons with the carbon atom. So, each molecule of carbon dioxide (CO_2) contains two double bonds.

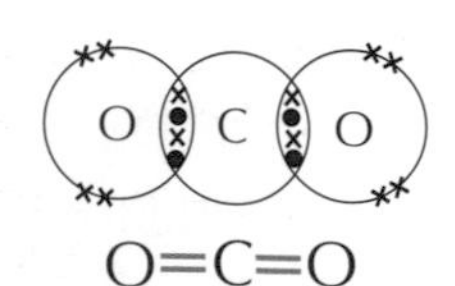

Triple bonds

When a molecule of nitrogen (N_2) forms, the nitrogen atoms share three pairs of electrons. So, each molecule of nitrogen contains one triple bond.

Figure 2: Iodine crystals and vapour in a flask. The crystals are violet-black and give off a violet vapour.

Tip: It's important that you remember that the two shared electrons in a covalent bond come from different atoms. (In some circumstances, it is possible for both electrons in a bond to come from one atom, but that's dative covalent bonding — see pages 63-64).

Behaviour of simple covalent compounds

Simple covalent compounds have strong bonds within molecules but weak forces between the molecules. Their physical properties, such as electrical conductivity, melting point and solubility are determined by the bonding in the compound.

Tip: All the examples on page 60 are simple covalent compounds — strong bonds exist within the molecules, but not between them.

Electrical conductivity

Simple covalent compounds don't conduct electricity because there are no free ions to carry the charge.

Melting point

Simple covalent compounds have low melting points because the weak forces between molecules are easily broken.

Solubility

Some simple covalent compounds dissolve in water depending on how polarised the molecules are (see page 70 for more on polarisation).

Giant covalent structures

Giant covalent structures have a huge network of covalently bonded atoms. (They're sometimes called **macromolecular** structures.) Carbon atoms can form this type of structure because they can each form four strong, covalent bonds. There are two types of giant covalent carbon structure you need to know about, graphite and diamond.

Graphite

The carbon atoms in graphite are arranged in sheets of flat hexagons covalently bonded with three bonds each (see Figure 3). The fourth outer electron of each carbon atom is delocalised. The sheets of hexagons are bonded together by weak van der Waals forces (see pages 71-72).

Tip: 'Delocalised' means an electron isn't attached to a particular atom — it can move around between atoms.

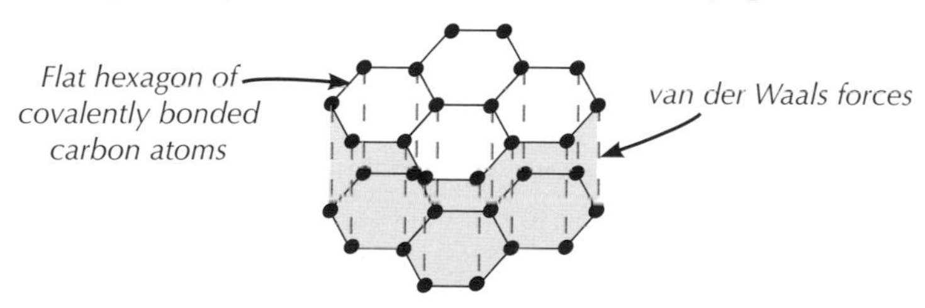

Figure 3: The structure of graphite.

Graphite's structure means it has certain properties:

- The weak bonds between the layers in graphite are easily broken, so the sheets can slide over each other — graphite feels slippery and is used as a dry lubricant and in pencils.
- The 'delocalised' electrons in graphite are free to move along the sheets, so an electric current can flow.
- The layers are quite far apart compared to the length of the covalent bonds, so graphite has a low density and is used to make strong, lightweight sports equipment.
- Because of the strong covalent bonds in the hexagon sheets, graphite has a very high melting point (it sublimes at over 3900 K).
- Graphite is insoluble in any solvent. The covalent bonds in the sheets are too difficult to break.

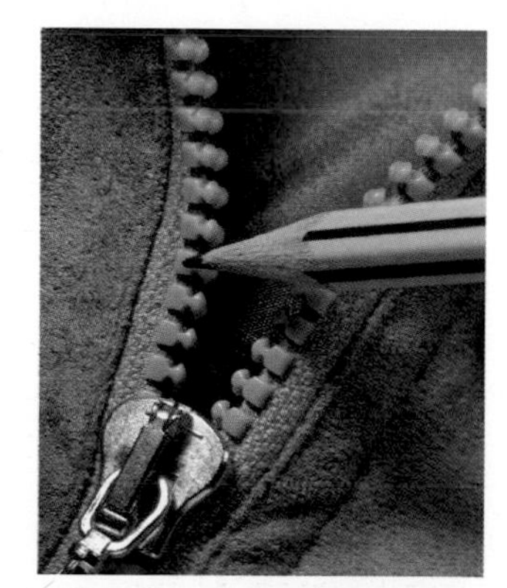

Figure 4: A graphite pencil being used to lubricate a zip fastening.

Diamond

Diamond is also made up of carbon atoms. Each carbon atom is covalently bonded to four other carbon atoms (see Figure 5). The atoms arrange themselves in a tetrahedral shape — its crystal lattice structure.

Tip: Tetrahedral is a molecular shape — see pages 66-69 for more on shapes of molecules.

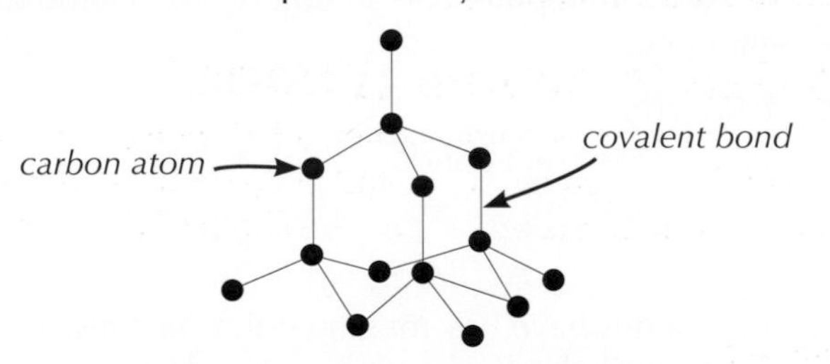

Figure 5: *The structure of diamond.*

Because of its strong covalent bonds:

- Diamond has a very high melting point — it actually sublimes at over 3800 K.
- Diamond is extremely hard — it's used in diamond-tipped drills and saws.
- Vibrations travel easily through the stiff lattice, so it's a good thermal conductor.
- It can't conduct electricity — all the outer electrons are held in localised bonds.
- Like graphite, diamond won't dissolve in any solvent.

Tip: 'Sublimes' means it changes straight from a solid to a gas, skipping out the liquid stage.

Tip: You can 'cut' diamond to form gemstones (see Figure 6). Its structure makes it refract light a lot, which is why it sparkles.

Figure 6: *A cut and polished diamond. Oooh, sparkly.*

Practice Questions — Fact Recall

Q1 How is a covalent bond formed?

Q2 Draw a 'dot-and-cross' diagram to show the bonding in an iodine molecule.

Q3 Explain what a triple covalent bond is.

Q4 Chlorine (Cl_2) is a simple covalent molecule.

a) Explain why chlorine has a very low melting point.

b) Would you expect chlorine to conduct electricity? Explain your answer.

Q5 Explain why graphite is used as a lubricant.

Q6 Describe the structure of diamond.

3. Dative Covalent Bonding

You have to know about a specific example of covalent bonding — catchily titled dative covalent bonding.

Learning Objective:
- Know that co-ordinate bonding is dative covalency.

Specification Reference 3.1.3

What is a dative covalent bond?

In a normal single covalent bond, atoms share a pair of electrons — with one electron coming from each atom. In **dative covalent**, also known as **co-ordinate**, bonding, one of the atoms provides both of the shared electrons.

Example

The ammonium ion

The ammonium ion (NH_4^+) is formed by dative covalent bonding. It forms when the nitrogen atom in an ammonia molecule donates a pair of electrons to a proton (H^+) — see Figure 1.

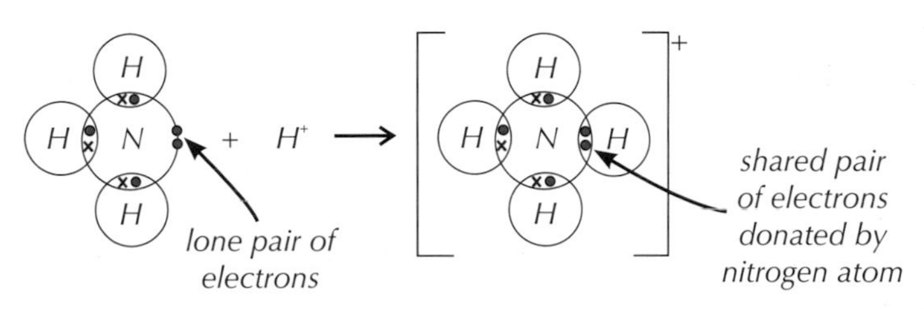

Figure 1: Dative bonding in NH_4^+.

Dative covalent bonding can also be shown in diagrams by an arrow, pointing away from the 'donor' atom (see Figure 2).

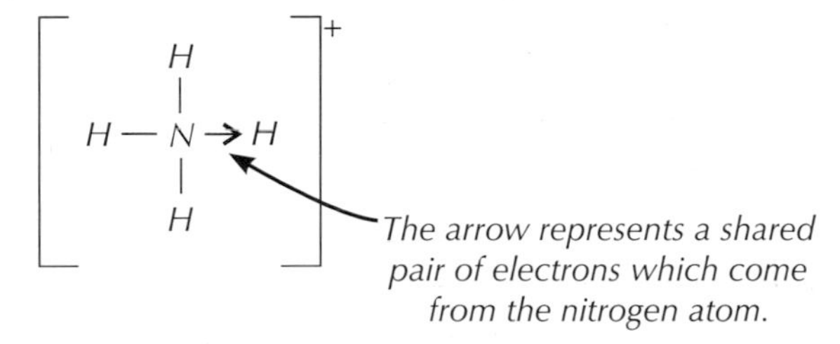

Figure 2: An alternative way of showing dative bonding in NH_4^+.

Tip: Once a dative bond has formed, it's no different to a normal covalent bond.

Identifying a dative covalent bond

In the exam, you might be asked to identify when a molecule has dative bonding. You'll need to say which is the donor atom, so you'll need to work out which atom has a lone pair of electrons. To do this you need to look at the outer electrons of each of the atoms involved in the bonding.

Examples

The hydroxonium ion

For the hydroxonium ion (H_3O^+), start by looking at the reactants — H_2O and H^+. Hydrogen ions have no electrons so can only receive electrons, not donate them. However, a water molecule contains an oxygen atom and two hydrogen atoms. Oxygen has six electrons in its outer shell, which is then filled by sharing one electron from each hydrogen atom. This makes eight electrons in total. Only four of these electrons take part in covalent bonding with H atoms so the oxygen is left with two lone pairs of electrons.

Tip: A lone pair of electrons is a pair of electrons in the outer shell of an atom that isn't involved in bonding with other atoms.

Tip: Make sure you include the charges on any ions when you are working out what happens when a dative bond forms.

So, oxygen donates one lone pair of electrons to the hydrogen ion forming a dative bond (see Figure 3).

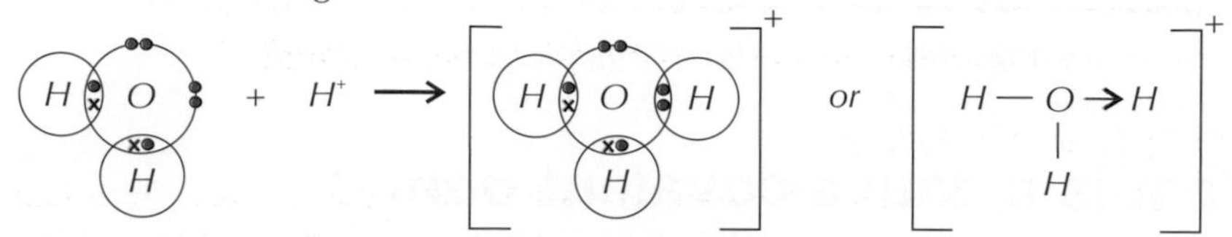

Figure 3: *Dative bonding in H_3O^+.*

Boron trifluoride

Boron trifluoride (BF_3) can react with a fluoride ion (F^-) to form (BF_4^-). Boron has three electrons in its outer shell and the fluorine atoms donate one electron each. This makes six electrons in total. However, as there are three boron-fluorine covalent bonds present, all six electrons are involved in bonding. This means there are no lone pairs to donate.

The fluoride ion has a full outer shell of electrons — i.e. four lone pairs of electrons. So, the fluoride ion donates a pair of electrons to fill the outer shell of the boron atom and to form a dative bond — see Figure 4.

Tip: You can work out the how many electrons are in the outer shell of an atom by using the periodic table. The group number of the element is the same as the number of electrons in its outer shell.

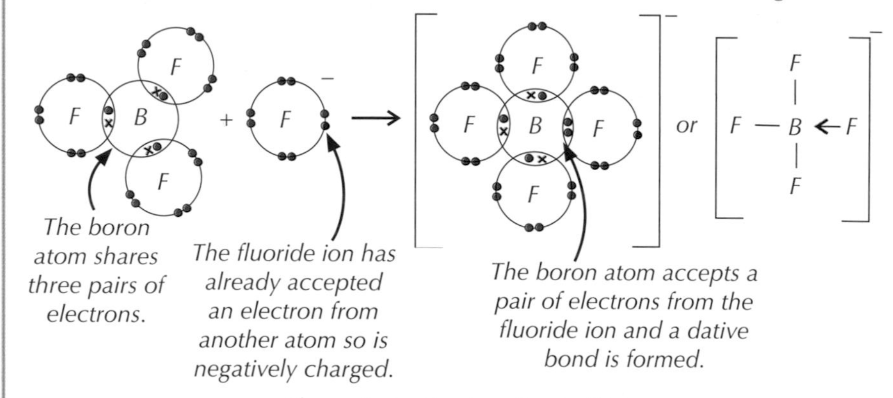

Figure 4: *Dative bonding in BF_4^-.*

Practice Questions — Application

Q1 PH_3 is a covalent compound that reacts with H^+ to form PH_4^+.

a) How many electrons are in the outer shell of a phosphorus atom?

b) How many electrons are in the outer shell of phosphorus in a PH_3 molecule?

c) Name the donor atom in PH_4^+.

d) Draw a diagram to show the formation of PH_4^+.

Q2 BF_3 will form a dative covalent compound with NH_3. Draw a diagram to show the formation of this compound.

Exam Tip
Don't be alarmed if you get asked about a compound you've never heard of in the exam. Just work steadily through the bonding and decide which atom is able to donate a lone pair of electrons to form the dative covalent bond.

Practice Questions — Fact Recall

Q1 What is a dative bond?

Q2 Give another name for dative bonding.

Q3 In a diagram of a molecule with a dative bond, what does the arrow show?

4. Charge Clouds

Electrons are found whizzing around nuclei in charge clouds.

Learning Objectives:

- Understand the concept of bonding and lone (non bonding) pairs of electrons as charge clouds.
- Know that lone pair/lone pair repulsion is greater than lone pair/bonding pair repulsion, which is greater than bonding pair/bonding pair repulsion, and understand the resulting effect on bond angles.

Specification Reference 3.1.3

Charge clouds

Molecules and molecular ions come in loads of different shapes. The shape depends on the number of pairs of electrons in the outer shell of the central atom. Pairs of electrons can be shared in a covalent bond or can be unshared. Shared electrons are called bonding pairs, unshared electrons are called **lone pairs** or non-bonding pairs.

Bonding pairs and lone pairs of electrons exist as charge clouds. A charge cloud is an area where you have a really big chance of finding an electron pair. The electrons don't stay still — they whizz around inside the charge cloud.

Example

In ammonia, the outermost shell of nitrogen has four pairs of electrons. The electrons can be shown by a 'dot-and-cross' diagram or as charge clouds.

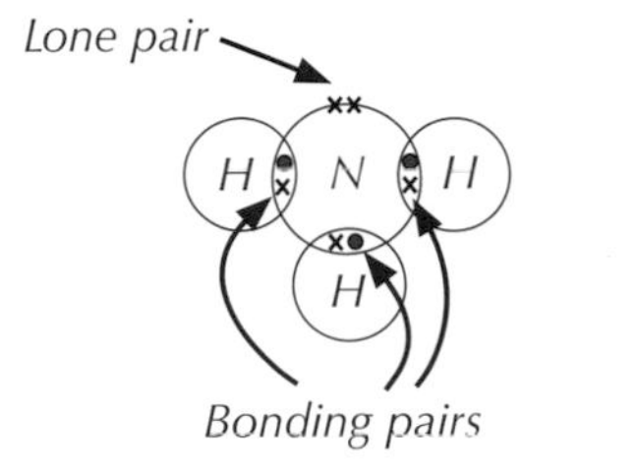

Figure 1: *'Dot-and-cross' diagram.*

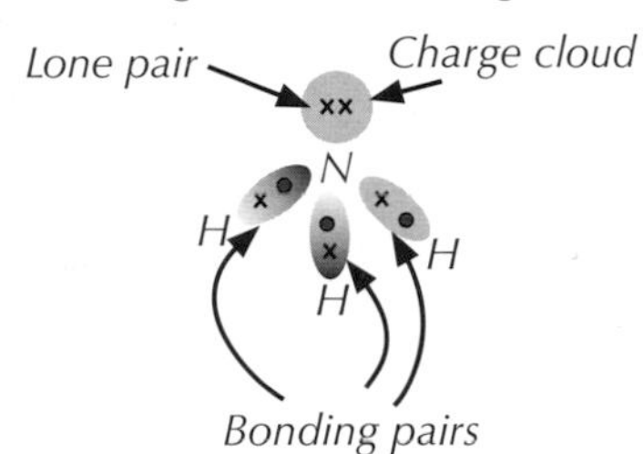

Figure 2: *Diagram showing charge clouds.*

Electron pair repulsion

Electrons are all negatively charged, so it's pretty obvious that the charge clouds will repel each other as much as they can. This sounds straightforward, but the shape of the charge cloud affects how much it repels other charge clouds. Lone-pair charge clouds repel more than bonding-pair charge clouds. So, the greatest angles are between lone pairs of electrons, and bond angles between bonding pairs are often reduced because they are pushed together by lone-pair repulsion. This is known by the long-winded name '**Valence-Shell Electron-Pair Repulsion Theory**'. Figure 3 shows the electron pairs in water.

Tip: It's really important that you know how the shape of the charge cloud affects bond angles — you'll need it for working out the shapes of molecules (see pages 66-69).

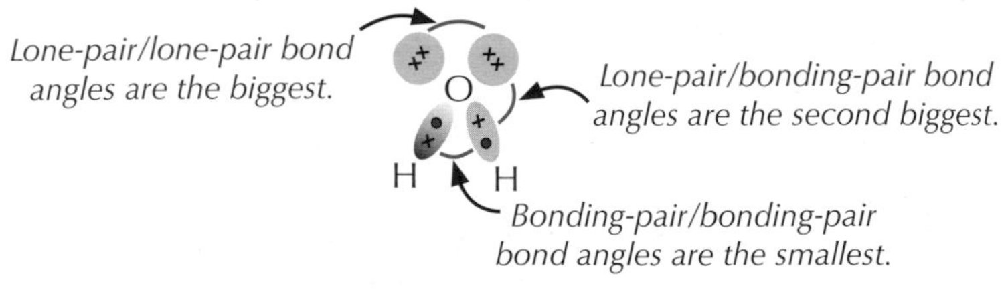

Figure 3: *Bond angles between electron pairs in water.*

Practice Questions — Fact Recall

Q1 What is a lone pair of electrons?

Q2 Briefly describe a charge cloud.

Q3 Describe valence-shell electron-pair repulsion theory.

5. Shapes of Molecules

Learning Objective:

- Be able, in terms of electron pair repulsion, to predict the shapes of, and bond angles in, simple molecules and ions, limited to 2, 3, 4, 5 and 6 co-ordination.

Specification Reference 3.1.3

There's a lot of variation in molecular shape and you need to understand how to work out the shape of any molecule or molecular ion. Don't worry though, the next few pages have lots of advice to help you along.

Drawing shapes of molecules

It can be tricky to draw molecules showing their shapes — but one way to do it is to show which way the bonds are pointing. In a molecule diagram, use wedges to show a bond pointing towards you, and a broken (or dotted) line to show a bond pointing away from you (see Figure 1).

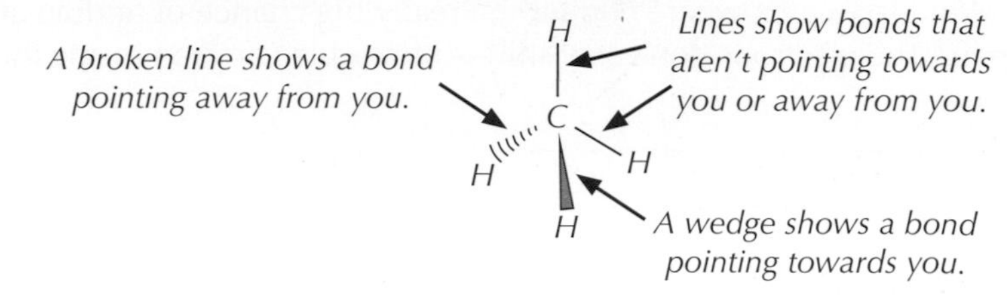

Figure 1: *A molecular diagram showing the shape of methane.*

Tip: It might help you to think of wedges as bonds that stick out of the page, broken lines as bonds that point behind the page and straight lines as bonds that are flat against the page.

Calculating the number of electron pairs

To work out the shape of a molecule or an ion you need to know how many lone pairs and how many bonding pairs of electrons are on the central atom. Follow these steps:

1. Find the central atom — it's the one all the other atoms are bonded to.
2. Work out how many electrons are in the outer shell of the central atom. Use the periodic table to do this.
3. The formula of the molecule or ion will tell you how many atoms are bonded to the central atom so you can work out the number of electrons donated to the central atom by other atoms.
4. Add up the electrons and divide by 2 to find the number of electron pairs. If you're dealing with an ion, you need to take into account its charge, as it will affect the number of electrons involved in the bonding.
5. Compare the number of electron pairs to the number of bonds to find the number of lone pairs and the number of bonding pairs.

Tip: If you're dealing with an ion don't forget to take into account its charge so you know how many electrons it's gained or lost.

Examples

Carbon tetrafluoride, CF_4

1. The central atom in this molecule is carbon.
2. Carbon's in Group 4 — so it has four electrons in its outer shell.
3. There are four covalent bonds bonding the central atom to fluorine atoms, so there are four electrons coming from the fluorine atoms.
4. There are 8 electrons in total, so there are 4 electron pairs.
5. 4 pairs of electrons are involved in bonding the fluorine atoms to the carbon so there must be four bonding pairs of electrons. That accounts for all the electrons — there are no lone pairs (see Figure 2).

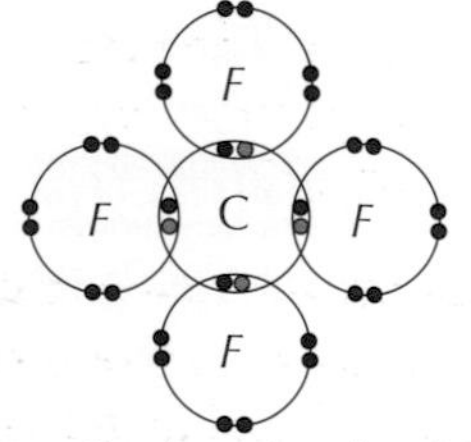

Figure 2: *A molecule of CF_4.*

Tip: Elements that are in Group 7 (e.g. fluorine) can form one covalent bond with another atom to complete their outer shell. See pages 60-62 for more on covalent bonding.

Phosphorus trihydride, PH_3

1. The central atom in this molecule is phosphorus.
2. It's in Group 5 — so it has five electrons in its outer shell.
3. Phosphorus forms three covalent bonds with hydrogen, so there are three electrons coming from the hydrogen atoms.
4. There are 8 electrons in total which means 4 electron pairs.
5. Three electron pairs are involved in bonding with the hydrogen atoms (bonding pairs) and so there's one lone pair of electrons (see Figure 3).

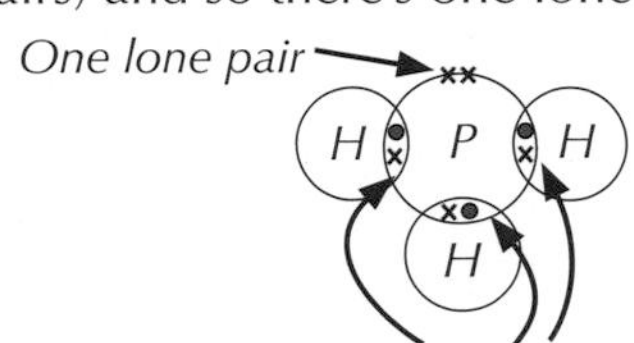

***Figure 3:** Electron pairs in a molecule of PH_3.*

Tip: The number of bonds the central atom forms is also called its co-ordination number.

Tip: A hydrogen atom will form one covalent bond with another atom to complete its outer shell.

Working out the shapes of molecules

Once you know how many electron pairs are on the central atom, you can work out the shape of the molecule.

Central atoms with two electron pairs

Molecules with two electron pairs have a bond angle of 180° and have a **linear** shape. This is because the pairs of bonding electrons want to be as far away from each other as possible.

Example

Beryllium chloride, $BeCl_2$

Beryllium has two bonding pairs of electrons and no lone pairs so the bond angle in $BeCl_2$ is 180° and it has a linear shape.

180°
Cl—Be—Cl

Tip: You need to know how to calculate the number of electron pairs before you try and learn this bit. Make sure you've got the previous page down before you go any further.

Central atoms with three electron pairs

Molecules that have three electron pairs around the central atom don't always have the same shape — the shape depends on the combination of bonding pairs and lone pairs of electrons. If there are three bonding pairs of electrons the repulsion of the charge clouds is the same between each pair and so the bond angles are all 120°. The shape of the molecule is **trigonal planar**.

Example

Boron trifluoride, BF_3

The central boron atom has three bonding pairs of electrons, so the bond angle in BF_3 is 120° and it has a trigonal planar shape.

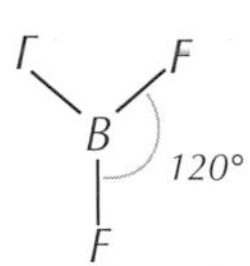

Exam Tip
You'll be expected to know all of the bond angles for the shapes of molecules in your exam — so make sure you learn them.

If there are two bonding pairs of electrons and one lone pair in a molecule you'll get a squished trigonal planar shape which is called non-linear or 'bent' (see next page for more on non-linear molecules). The bond angle will be a bit less than 120°.

Central atoms with four electron pairs

If there are four pairs of bonding electrons and no lone pairs on a central atom, all the bond angles are 109.5° — the charge clouds all repel each other equally. The shape of the molecule is **tetrahedral**.

Exam Tip
You could be asked to name the shape of a molecule so learn the different names — some of the names are quite similar so make sure you spell them correctly.

Example

Ammonium ion, NH_4^+

The nitrogen atom has four bonding pairs of electrons so the shape of NH_4^+ is tetrahedral.

If there are three bonding pairs of electrons and one lone pair, the lone-pair/bonding-pair repulsion will be greater than the bonding-pair/bonding-pair repulsion and so the angles between the atoms will change. There'll be smaller bond angles between the bonding pairs of electrons and larger bond angles between the lone pair and the bonding pairs. The bond angle is 107° and the shape of the molecules is **trigonal pyramidal**.

Tip: Take a look back at the Valence-Shell Electron-Pair Repulsion Theory (page 65) for why more lone pairs means smaller bond angles.

Example

Ammonia, NH_3

The nitrogen has three bonding pairs of electrons and a lone pair so the shape of NH_3 is trigonal pyramidal.

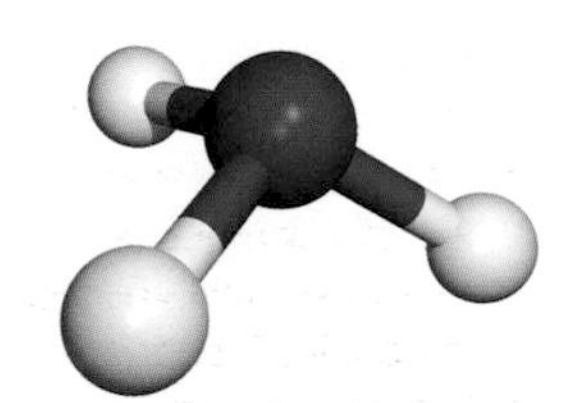

Figure 4: A molecular model of ammonia, showing it to be a trigonal pyramidal shape.

If there are two bonding pairs of electrons and two lone pairs of electrons the lone-pair/lone-pair repulsion will squish the bond angle even further. The bond angle is 104.5° and the shape of the molecules is **non-linear** or **'bent'**.

Example

Water, H_2O

The oxygen atom has two bonding pairs shared with hydrogen atoms and two lone pairs so the shape of H_2O is non-linear (bent).

Central atoms with five or six electron pairs

Some central atoms can use d orbitals and can 'expand the octet' — which means they can have more than eight bonding electrons. A molecule with five bonding pairs will be **trigonal bipyramidal**. Repulsion between the bonding pairs means that three of the atoms will form a trigonal planar shape with bond angles of 120° and the other two atoms will be at 90° to them.

Example

Phosphorus pentachloride, PCl_5

The phosphorus atom has five bonding pairs so it has a trigonal bipyramidal shape.

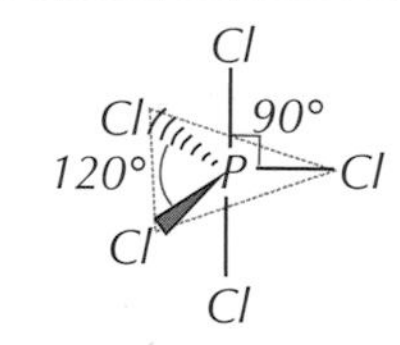

A molecule with six bonding pairs will be **octahedral**. All of the bond angles in the molecule are 90°.

Exam Tip
If you get asked to draw the shape of a specific molecule in the exam, you'll only get the mark if you label the atoms (e.g. as B and F in a BF_4^- molecule) and show the lone pairs.

Example

Sulfur hexafluoride, SF_6

Sulfur has six bonding pairs making its shape **octahedral**.

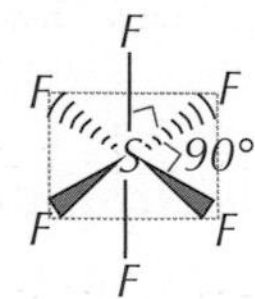

Awkward molecules

There are quite a few special cases where molecules don't follow the rules shown on pages 67-68. If a molecule has two double bonds, you can just treat them the same as single bonds (even though there might be slightly more repulsion between double bonds).

Examples

Carbon dioxide, CO_2

Carbon has four bonding pairs of electrons (found in two carbon-oxygen double bonds). You treat the double bonds like single bonds so CO_2 will have a linear shape.

180°
O=C=O

Sulfur dioxide, SO_2

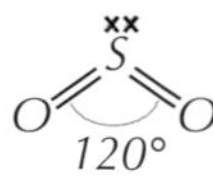

The extra electron density in the double bonds cancels out the extra repulsion from the lone pair, so you get 120° angles.

Sulfur has four bonding pairs of electrons (found in two sulfur-oxygen double bonds) and one lone pair. Double bonds can be taken as one bond so we can say there are two bonds and one lone pair of electrons. So, SO_2 will have a non-linear (bent) shape.

***Figure 5:** A molecular model of carbon dioxide, showing it to be a linear molecule with a bond angle of 180°*

Exam Tip

In the exam you could be asked to draw the shape of a molecule you've never met before. Don't panic, just take it step by step. Work out how many electron pairs the molecule has, then work out how many of those are lone pairs. Decide what the bond angles are in the molecule, then draw the molecule and make sure you label it neatly.

Practice Questions — Application

Q1 a) How many electron pairs are on the central atom of an H_2S molecule?

b) How many lone pairs does a molecule of H_2S have?

c) Draw the shape of an H_2S molecule.

d) Name the shape of an H_2S molecule.

e) Give the bond angle between bonding pairs in H_2S.

Q2 a) How many electron pairs are on the central atom of an H_3O^+ molecule?

b) How many lone pairs does a molecule of H_3O^+ have?

c) Draw and name the shape of H_3O^+.

d) Give the bond angle between bonding pairs in H_3O^+.

Q3 a) Draw and name the shape of a molecule of AsH_3.

b) Give the bonding pair/bonding pair bond angle in AsH_3.

Q4 Draw and name the shape of a molecule of PF_5.

Q5 Draw and name the shape of a molecule of CCl_2F_2.

Practice Questions — Fact Recall

Q1 What is the bond angle between electron pairs in a trigonal planar molecule?

Q2 How many electron pairs are on the central atom in a tetrahedral molecule?

Q3 Name the structure that a molecule will have if it has six bonding pairs on the central atom.

6. Polarisation

Polarisation of bonds occurs because of the nature of different atomic nuclei — some are just more attractive than others.

Learning Objectives:
- Understand that electronegativity is the power of an atom to withdraw electron density from a covalent bond.
- Understand that the electron distribution in a covalent bond may not be symmetrical.
- Know that covalent bonds between different elements will be polar to different extents.

Specification Reference 3.1.3

Electronegativity

The ability to attract the bonding electrons in a covalent bond is called **electronegativity**. Electronegativity is measured on the Pauling Scale. A higher number means an element is better able to attract the bonding electrons. Fluorine is the most electronegative element. Oxygen, nitrogen and chlorine are also very strongly electronegative — see Figure 1.

Element	H	C	N	Cl	O	F
Electronegativity (Pauling Scale)	2.1	2.5	3.0	3.0	3.5	4.0

Figure 1: *The electronegativity of different elements.*

Exam Tip
You don't need to learn the electronegativity values — if you need them you'll be given them in the exam.

Polar and non-polar bonds

The covalent bonds in diatomic gases (e.g. H_2, Cl_2) are non-polar because the atoms have equal electronegativities and so the electrons are equally attracted to both nuclei (see Figure 2). Some elements, like carbon and hydrogen, have pretty similar electronegativities, so bonds between them are essentially non-polar.

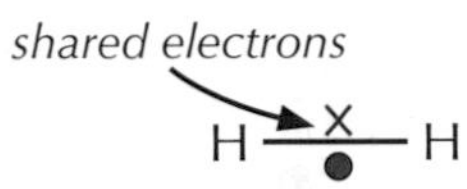

Figure 2: *A non-polar covalent bond in a hydrogen molecule.*

In a covalent bond between two atoms of different electronegativities, the bonding electrons are pulled towards the more electronegative atom. This makes the bond polar (see Figure 3).

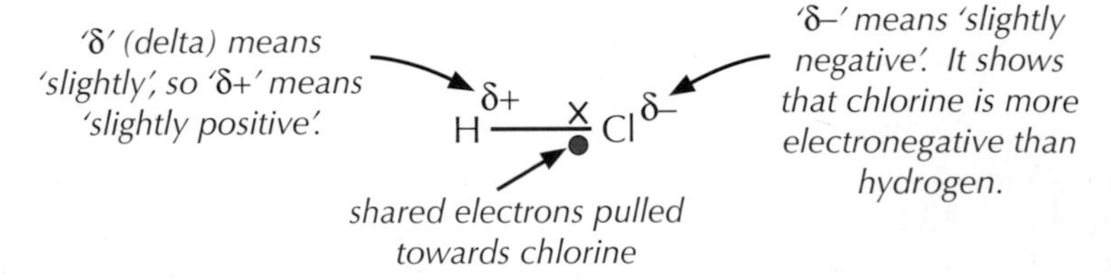

Figure 3: *A polar covalent bond in a hydrogen chloride molecule.*

In a polar bond, the difference in electronegativity between the two atoms causes a **dipole**. A dipole is a difference in charge between the two atoms caused by a shift in electron density in the bond. So what you need to remember is that the greater the difference in electronegativity, the more polar the bond.

Tip: It's really, really important that you get your head around the relationship between electronegativity, polarisation and dipoles. Differences in the electronegativity of atoms cause bonds to become polarised, which results in a dipole — a difference in charge between the two atoms.

Practice Questions — Fact Recall

Q1 Chlorine is more electronegative than hydrogen. Explain what this means.

Q2 Explain why the H — F bond is polarised.

Q3 What is a dipole?

7. Intermolecular Forces

Molecules don't just exist independently — they can interact with each other. And you need to know how they interact.

What are intermolecular forces?

Intermolecular forces are forces between molecules. They're much weaker than covalent, ionic or metallic bonds. There are three types you need to know about: induced dipole-dipole or van der Waals forces (this is the weakest type), permanent dipole-dipole forces and hydrogen bonding (this is the strongest type).

Learning Objectives:
- Understand qualitatively how molecules may interact by permanent dipole–dipole, induced dipole–dipole (van der Waals') forces and hydrogen bonding.
- Know the structures of iodine and ice.
- Understand the importance of hydrogen bonding in determining the boiling points of compounds and the structures of some solids (e.g. ice).

Specification Reference 3.1.3

Van der Waals forces

Van der Waals forces cause all atoms and molecules to be attracted to each other. Electrons in charge clouds are always moving really quickly. At any particular moment, the electrons in an atom are likely to be more to one side than the other. At this moment, the atom would have a temporary dipole. This dipole can cause another temporary dipole in the opposite direction on a neighbouring atom (see Figure 1). The two dipoles are then attracted to each other. The second dipole can cause yet another dipole in a third atom. It's kind of like a domino rally. Because the electrons are constantly moving, the dipoles are being created and destroyed all the time. Even though the dipoles keep changing, the overall effect is for the atoms to be attracted to each other.

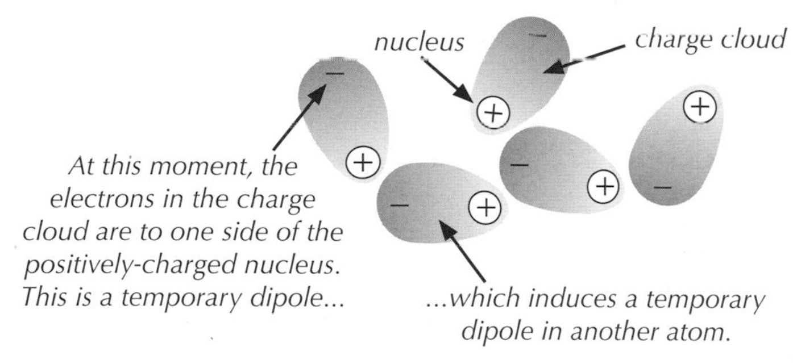

Figure 1: *Temporary dipoles in a liquid resulting in van der Waals forces.*

Tip: Temporary dipoles are also called induced dipoles.

Example

Van der Waals forces are responsible for holding iodine molecules together in a lattice. Iodine atoms are held together in pairs by strong covalent bonds to form molecules of I_2 (see Figure 2). But the molecules are then held together in a molecular lattice arrangement by weak van der Waals attractions (see Figure 3).

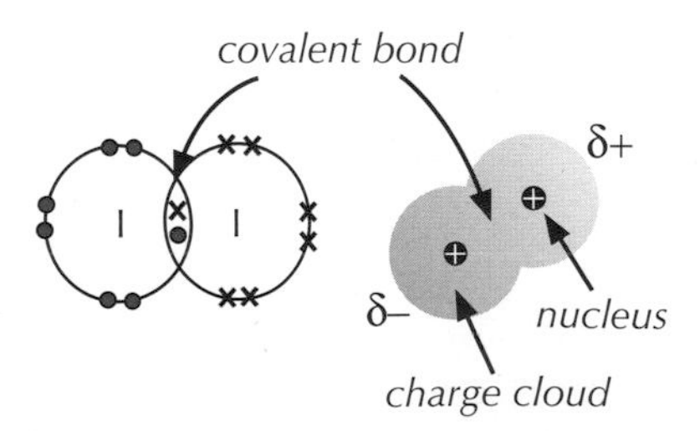

Figure 2: *A dot and cross diagram and a charge cloud diagram showing a molecule of iodine.*

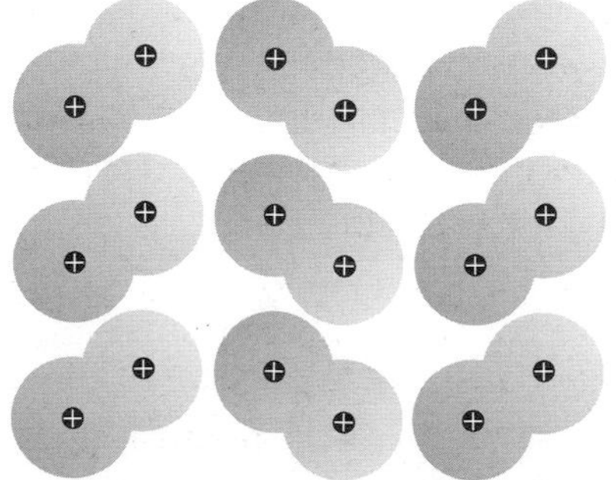

Figure 3: *Lattice of iodine molecules held together by van der Waals forces.*

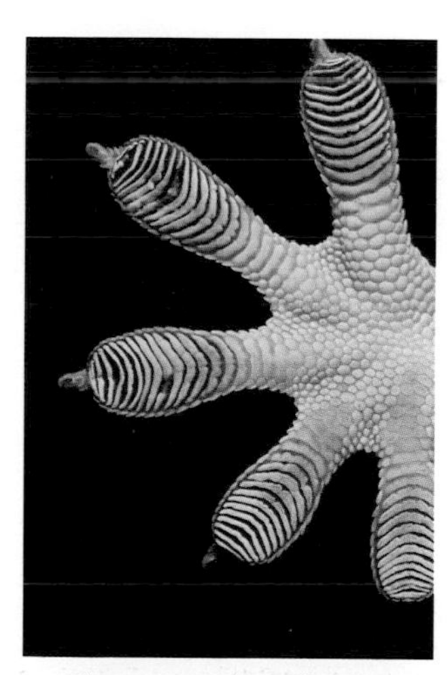

Figure 4: *The adhesive ability of a gecko's foot is thought to be due to van der Waals forces.*

Tip: Remember — there are van der Waals forces between the molecules in every chemical.

Not all van der Waals forces are the same strength — larger molecules have larger electron clouds, meaning stronger van der Waals forces. Molecules with greater surface areas also have stronger van der Waals forces because they have a more exposed electron cloud.

When you boil a liquid, you need to overcome the intermolecular forces, so that the particles can escape from the liquid surface. It stands to reason that you need more energy to overcome stronger intermolecular forces, so liquids with stronger van der Waals forces will have higher boiling points. Van der Waals forces affect other physical properties, such as melting point and viscosity too.

Figure 5: Johannes Diderik van der Waals (1837-1923), a Dutch physicist who was the first to understand the importance of the intermolecular forces that are now named after him.

Example

As you go down the group of noble gases, the number of electrons increases. So the van der Waals forces increase, and so do the boiling points (see Figure 6).

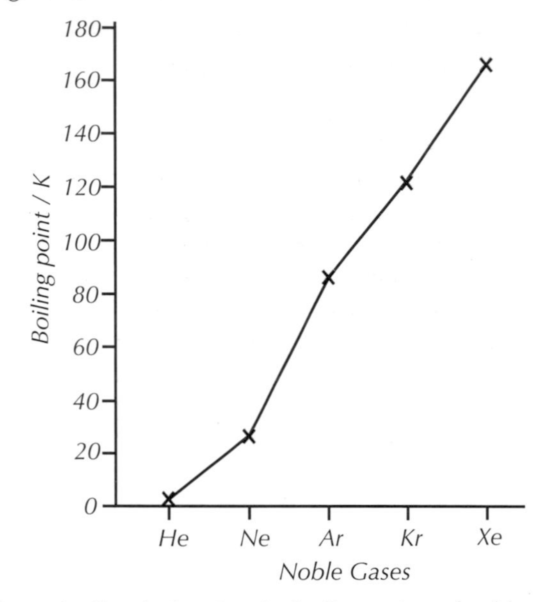

Figure 6: *Graph showing the boiling points of noble gases.*

Permanent dipole-dipole forces

The δ+ and δ– charges on polar molecules cause weak electrostatic forces of attraction between molecules. These are called permanent dipole-dipole forces.

Example

Hydrogen chloride gas has polar molecules due to the difference in electronegativity of hydrogen and chlorine.

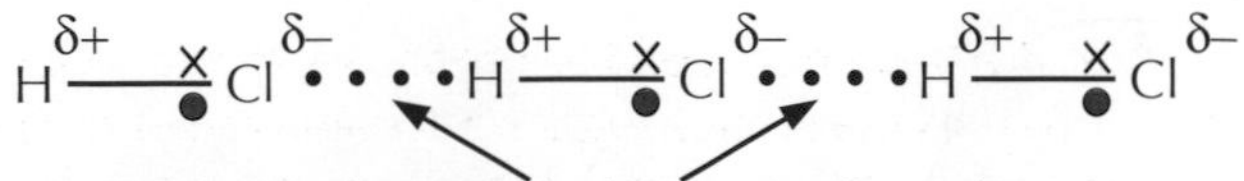

The molecules have weak electrostatic forces between them because of the shift in electron density.

Figure 7: *Permanent dipole-dipole forces in hydrogen chloride gas.*

Exam Tip
When you're drawing dipoles in the exam, make sure you include the δ+ and δ– symbols to show the charges.

If you put an electrostatically charged rod next to a jet of a polar liquid, like water, the liquid will move towards the rod. It's because polar liquids contain molecules with permanent dipoles. It doesn't matter if the rod is positively or negatively charged. The polar molecules in the liquid can turn around so the oppositely charged end is attracted towards the rod (see Figures 8 and 9).

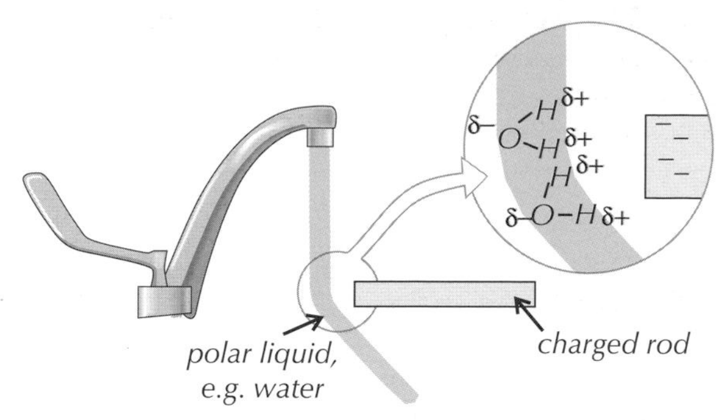

Figure 8: Dipoles in a stream of water cause it to move towards a charged glass rod.

Figure 9: A charged glass rod bends water.

Tip: Charge density is just a measure of how much positive or negative charge there is in a certain volume.

Hydrogen bonding

Hydrogen bonding is the strongest intermolecular force. It only happens when hydrogen is covalently bonded to fluorine, nitrogen or oxygen. Fluorine, nitrogen and oxygen are very electronegative, so they draw the bonding electrons away from the hydrogen atom. The bond is so polarised, and hydrogen has such a high charge density because it's so small, that the hydrogen atoms form weak bonds with lone pairs of electrons on the fluorine, nitrogen or oxygen atoms of other molecules. Molecules which have hydrogen bonding are usually organic, containing -OH or -NH groups.

Examples

Water and ammonia both have hydrogen bonding (see Figures 10 and 11).

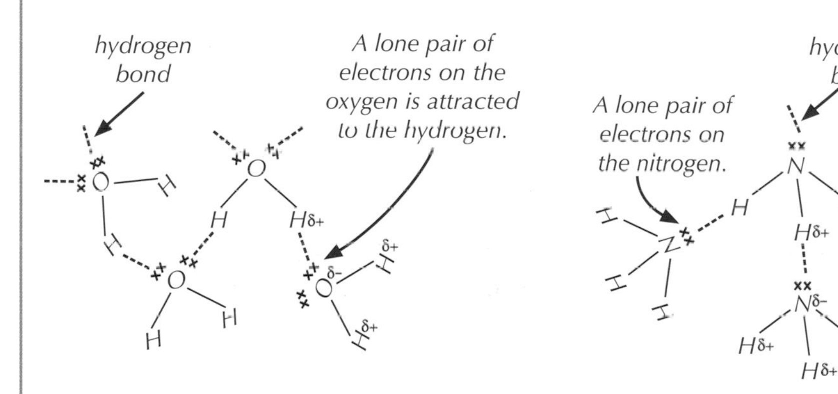

Figure 10: Hydrogen bonding in water.

Figure 11: Hydrogen bonding in ammonia.

Hydrogen bonding has a huge effect on the properties of substances. Substances with hydrogen bonds have higher boiling and melting points than other similar molecules because of the extra energy needed to break the hydrogen bonds. This is the case with water, and also hydrogen fluoride, which has a much higher boiling point than the other hydrogen halides — see Figure 12.

Exam Tip

Hydrogen bonding is a special case scenario — it only happen in specific molecules. In the exam, you could be asked to compare intermolecular forces in different substances, so you'll need to know the different intermolecular forces and their relative strengths. Don't forget that not every molecule with hydrogen in it makes hydrogen bonds.

Exam Tip

If you're asked to draw a diagram to show hydrogen bonding you'll need to include the lone pairs of electrons on the electronegative atom (O, N or F). You may also have to show the partial charges — the δ+ goes on the H atom and the δ– goes on the electronegative atom.

Exam Tip
You don't need to learn the actual boiling points of the substances in Figure 12, but you should be able to explain the trend.

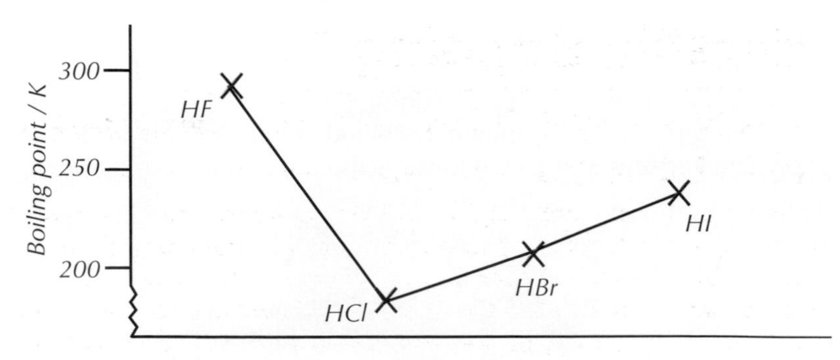

Figure 12: *Graph showing the boiling points of hydrogen halides.*

Ice has more hydrogen bonds than liquid water, and hydrogen bonds are relatively long. So the H_2O molecules in ice are further apart on average, making ice less dense than liquid water.

Exam Tip
It's pretty common to be asked to identify and compare the intermolecular forces in different substances in the exam. You'll also need to know the effects that the intermolecular forces have on the properties of the substances, so make sure you know all this stuff inside out.

Practice Questions — Application

Q1 What intermolecular force(s) exist(s) in H_2?

Q2 The table below shows the electronegativity values of some elements

Element	H	C	Cl	O	F
Electronegativity (Pauling Scale)	2.1	2.5	3.0	3.5	4.0

a) Use the table above to explain why there are hydrogen bonds between H_2O molecules but not between HCl molecules.

b) Identify one other element from the table that would form hydrogen bonds when covalently bonded to hydrogen.

c) What is the strongest type of intermolecular force between molecules of HCl?

d) Name one other element from the table that would not form hydrogen bonds when covalently bonded to hydrogen.

Q3 Hydrogen has an electronegativity value of 2.1 on the Pauling scale, nitrogen has a value of 3.0 and phosphorous has a value of 2.2.

a) The boiling point of NH_3 is –33 °C and the boiling point of PH_3 is –88 °C. Explain why the boiling point of PH_3 is lower.

b) Arsenic (As) has an electronegativity value of 2.18. Would you expect the boiling point of AsH_3 to be higher or lower than that of NH_3?

Practice Questions — Fact Recall

Q1 What is the weakest type of intermolecular force?

Q2 Describe the bonding within and between iodine molecules.

Q3 What are permanent dipole-dipole forces?

Q4 a) What is the strongest intermolecular force in ammonia?

b) Draw a diagram to show this intermolecular force between two ammonia molecules.

Q5 Name the strongest intermolecular force in water.

Q6 Explain why ice is less dense that liquid water.

8. Metallic Bonding

You'll be familiar with metallic bonding from GCSE, but there's more to know...

Learning Objectives:

- Understand that metallic bonding involves a lattice of positive ions surrounded by delocalised electrons.
- Recognise metallic crystals.
- Know the structure of magnesium.
- Be able to relate the physical properties of materials to the type of structure and bonding present.

Specification Reference 3.1.3

Metallic bonding

Metal elements exist as **giant metallic lattice structures**. The outermost shell of electrons of a metal atom is delocalised — the electrons are free to move about the metal. This leaves a positive metal ion, e.g. Na^+, Mg^{2+}, Al^{3+}. The positive metal ions are attracted to the delocalised negative electrons. They form a lattice of closely packed positive ions in a sea of delocalised electrons — this is metallic bonding (see Figure 1).

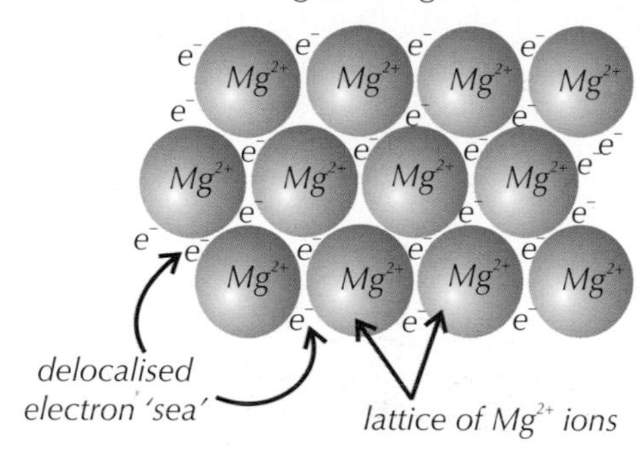

Figure 1: *Metallic bonding in magnesium.*

Metallic bonding explains the properties of metals — for example, their melting point, their ability to be shaped, their conductivity and their solubility.

Melting point

The number of delocalised electrons per atom affects the melting point. The more there are, the stronger the bonding will be and the higher the melting point. Mg^{2+} has two delocalised electrons per atom, so it's got a higher melting point than Na^+, which only has one. The size of the metal ion and the lattice structure also affect the melting point.

Ability to be shaped

As there are no bonds holding specific ions together, the metal ions can slide over each other when the structure is pulled, so metals are malleable (can be shaped, see Figure 2) and ductile (can be drawn into a wire).

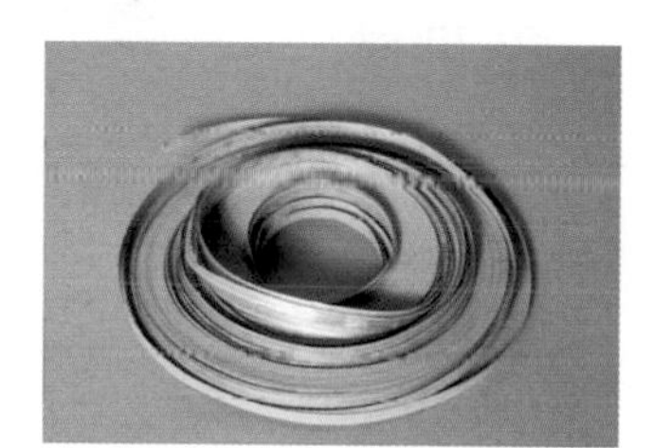

Figure 2: *Magnesium shaped into a ribbon.*

Conductivity

The delocalised electrons can pass kinetic energy to each other, making metals good thermal conductors. Metals are good electrical conductors because the delocalised electrons can carry a current.

Solubility

Metals are insoluble, except in liquid metals, because of the strength of the metallic bonds.

Practice Questions — Fact Recall

Q1 Describe the structure of magnesium.

Q2 What type of bonding can be found in magnesium?

Q3 Explain the following:

a) Copper can be drawn into wires.

b) Copper is a good thermal conductor.

Learning Objectives:

- Be able to explain the energy changes associated with changes of state.
- Be able to relate the physical properties of materials to the type of structure and bonding present.

Specification Reference 3.1.3

Figure 2: Bromine liquid changing state to become a gas and diffusing to fill the container.

Tip: This is true for most covalent substances — for example, when you boil water, you don't get hydrogen and oxygen, because the covalent bonds holding the water molecule together don't break. The exception is giant molecular substances, like diamond. In these substances covalent bonds have to break to allow a change in state.

Tip: Take a look at pages 71-72 for more on van der Waals forces.

9. Properties of Structures

You've covered loads of different types of bonds and intermolecular forces. Here's the last few bits on how these bonds and forces affect the properties of materials, and a quick look at particle arrangement in solids, liquids and gases.

Solids, liquids and gases

A typical solid has its particles very close together. This gives it a high density and makes it incompressible. The particles vibrate about a fixed point and can't move about freely. A typical liquid has a similar density to a solid and is virtually incompressible. The particles move about freely and randomly within the liquid, allowing it to flow. In gases, the particles have loads more energy and are much further apart. So the density is generally pretty low and it's very compressible. The particles move about freely, with not a lot of attraction between them, so they'll quickly diffuse to fill a container (see Figures 1 and 2).

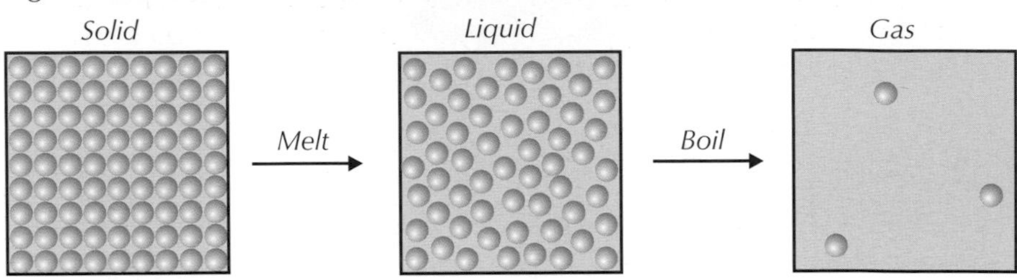

Figure 1: The arrangement of particles in solids, liquids and gases.

Covalent compounds

Covalent bonds don't break during melting and boiling — this is something that confuses loads of people, but prepare to be enlightened. To melt or boil a simple covalent compound you only have to overcome the van der Waals forces or hydrogen bonds that hold the molecules together. You don't need to break the much stronger covalent bonds that hold the atoms together in the molecules. That's why simple covalent compounds have relatively low melting and boiling points.

Example

Chlorine, Cl_2, has stronger covalent bonds than bromine, Br_2. But under normal conditions, chlorine is a gas and bromine a liquid. Bromine has the higher boiling point because its molecules have more electrons, giving stronger van der Waals forces. So more energy is needed to break the forces and turn it from a liquid into a gas.

The covalent bond is unbroken when there's a change in state.

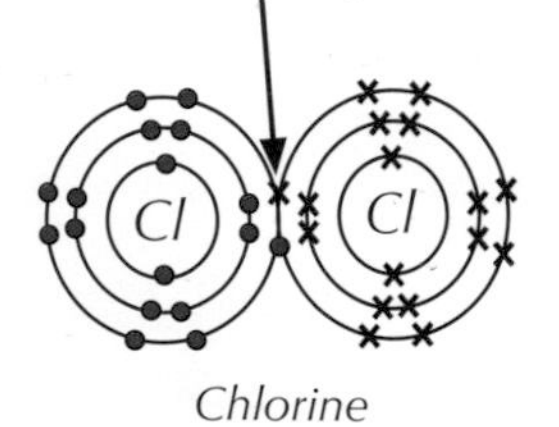

Chlorine

Bromine is below chlorine in the periodic table so it has more electrons and stronger van der Waals forces between molecules.

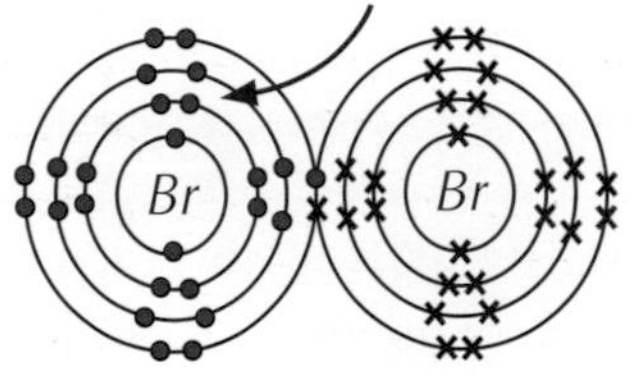

Bromine

Figure 3: Atomic diagrams showing the number of electrons and the bonding in chlorine and bromine molecules.

Bonding models

Scientists develop models based on experimental evidence — they're an attempt to explain observations. Bonding models explain how substances behave. E.g. the physical properties of ionic compounds provide evidence that supports the theory of ionic bonding. They have high melting points — this tells you that the atoms are held together by a strong attraction. Positive and negative ions are strongly attracted, so the model fits the evidence. They are often soluble in water but not in non-polar solvents — this tells you that the particles are charged. The ions are pulled apart by polar molecules like water, but not by non-polar molecules. Again, the model of ionic structures fits this evidence.

HOW SCIENCE WORKS

However, like pretty much all models, bonding models aren't totally accurate. Dot-and-cross models of ionic and covalent bonding are great for explaining what's happening nice and clearly. But like most things in life, it's not really quite as simple as that. One important reason is that most bonds aren't purely ionic or purely covalent but somewhere in between. This is down to bond polarisation (see page 70). Most compounds end up with a mixture of ionic and covalent properties.

Tip: The bonding models in this section became accepted by scientists as results from scientific experiments supported the models — there was evidence that the models were correct. This is part of How Science Works — have a look at pages 1-3 for more on how theories and models are developed.

Tip: Take a look back at polarisation (page 70) for more on polar and non-polar bonds.

Practice Questions — Application

Q1 Iodine has a higher boiling point than bromine. Explain why.

Q2 Look at the information in the table below.

Compound	Structure	Melting point / °C
Decane, $C_{10}H_{22}$	Simple covalent	–27.9
Diamond	Giant covalent	3550
Graphite	Giant covalent	3642
Methane, CH_4	Simple covalent	–161

a) Explain why the melting point of decane is higher than the melting point of methane.

b) The melting point of silicon dioxide is 1610 °C. Suggest what type of structure silicon dioxide has and explain why it has a high melting point.

Practice Questions — Fact Recall

Q1 Describe what happens to the particles in a substance when a solid changes to a liquid.

Q2 Describe the movement of particles in a gas.

Q3 Explain why simple covalent compounds have lower melting points than giant molecular structures.

Q4 Why do most compounds end up with a mixture of ionic and covalent properties?

10. The Periodic Table

Learning Objective:

- Be able to classify an element as s, p or d block according to its position in the periodic table.

Specification Reference 3.1.4

Figure 1: *Dmitri Mendeleev (1834-1907) was a Russian chemist who developed the periodic table.*

Exam Tip
You'll be given a periodic table in your exam, so you'll always have a copy to refer to to answer exam questions. It's a good idea to be familiar with how it works before you go into the exam though.

You'll remember from GCSE that the periodic table isn't just arranged how it is by chance. There are well-thought-out reasons behind it, and you can find out lots of stuff from it, not least about the numbers of electron shells and electrons each element has. Read on....

How is the periodic table arranged?

Dmitri Mendeleev developed the modern periodic table in the 1800s. Although, there have been changes since then, the basic idea is still the same. The periodic table is arranged into periods (rows) and groups (columns), by atomic (proton) number.

Period	Group 1	Group 2											Group 3	Group 4	Group 5	Group 6	Group 7	Group 0
								1 H Hydrogen 1										4 He 2
2	7 Li 3	9 Be 4											11 B 5	12 C 6	14 N 7	16 O 8	19 F 9	20 Ne 10
3	23 Na 11	24 Mg 12											27 Al 13	28 Si 14	31 P 15	32 S 16	35.5 Cl 17	40 Ar 18
4	39 K 19	40 Ca 20	45 Sc 21	48 Ti 22	51 V 23	52 Cr 24	55 Mn 25	56 Fe 26	59 Co 27	59 Ni 28	64 Cu 29	65 Zn 30	70 Ga 31	73 Ge 32	75 As 33	79 Se 34	80 Br 35	84 Kr 36
5	86 Rb 37	88 Sr 38	89 Y 39	91 Zr 40	93 Nb 41	96 Mo 42	99 Tc 43	101 Ru 44	103 Rh 45	106 Pd 46	108 Ag 47	112 Cd 48	115 In 49	119 Sn 50	122 Sb 51	128 Te 52	127 I 53	131 Xe 54
6	133 Cs 55	137 Ba 56	57-71 Lanthanides	179 Hf 72	181 Ta 73	184 W 74	186 Re 75	190 Os 76	192 Ir 77	195 Pt 78	197 Au 79	201 Hg 80	204 Tl 81	207 Pb 82	209 Bi 83	210 Po 84	210 At 85	222 Rn 86
7	223 Fr 87	226 Ra 88	89-103 Actinides															

Figure 2: *The periodic table.*

The period and group of an element gives you information about the number of electrons and electron shells that that element has.

Elements and periods

All the elements within a period have the same number of electron shells (if you don't worry about s and p sub-shells).

Example

The elements in Period 2 have 2 electron shells — see Figure 3.

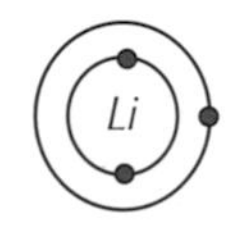

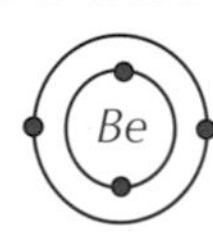

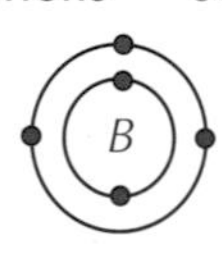

Figure 3: *Atoms of the first three elements in Period 2.*

Elements and groups

All the elements within a group have the same number of electrons in their outer shell — so they have similar properties (see Figure 4). The group number tells you the number of electrons in the outer shell.

Figure 4: *The Group 1 elements potassium, sodium and lithium all react strongly with water.*

Examples

Group 1 elements have 1 electron in their outer shell (see Figure 5), Group 4 elements have 4 electrons and so on.

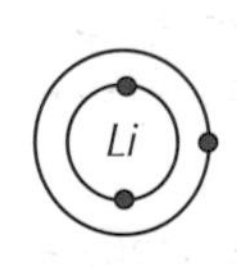

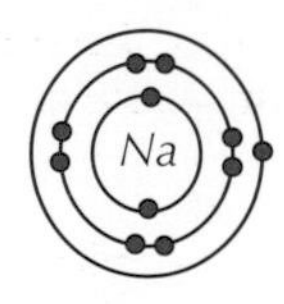

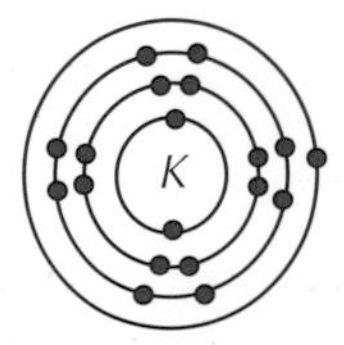

Figure 5: *Atoms of elements in Group 1.*

Electron configurations

The periodic table can be split into an s block, d block and p block (see Figure 6). Doing this shows you which sub-shells all the electrons go into.

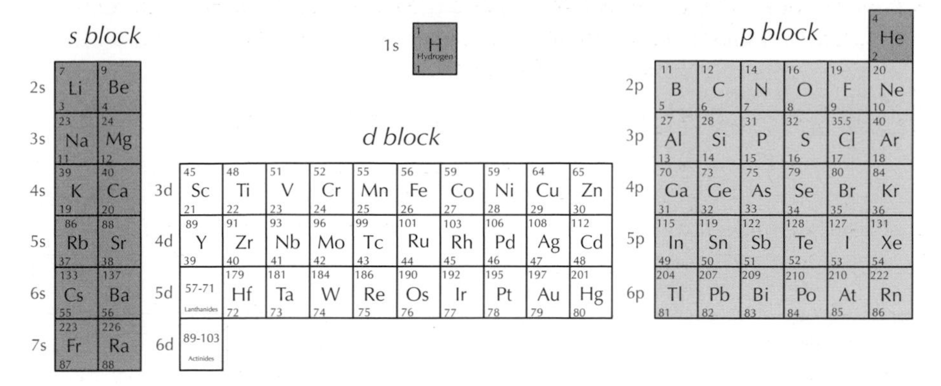

Figure 6: The periodic table showing the s block, p block and d block.

Exam Tip
You won't get a periodic table split up like this in the exam so you need to remember what the different blocks are.

s-block elements

The s-block elements have an outer shell electron configuration of s^1 or s^2.

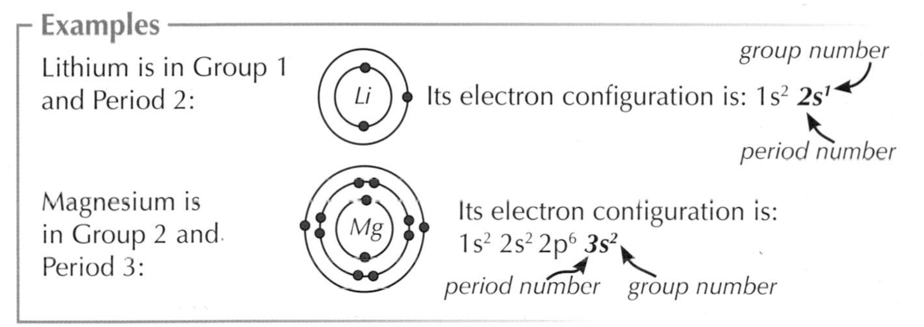

Examples

Lithium is in Group 1 and Period 2: Its electron configuration is: $1s^2$ $\mathbf{2s^1}$ (group number; period number)

Magnesium is in Group 2 and Period 3: Its electron configuration is: $1s^2\ 2s^2\ 2p^6$ $\mathbf{3s^2}$ (period number; group number)

Tip: If you can't remember what sub-shells are, don't know what the electron configuration of an element shows, or can't quite get your head around what all this $1s^2\ 2s^2\ 2p^6$ business is, then have a look back at pages 18 and 19 — it's all explained in more detail there.

p-block elements

The p-block elements have an outer shell configuration of s^2p^1 to s^2p^6.

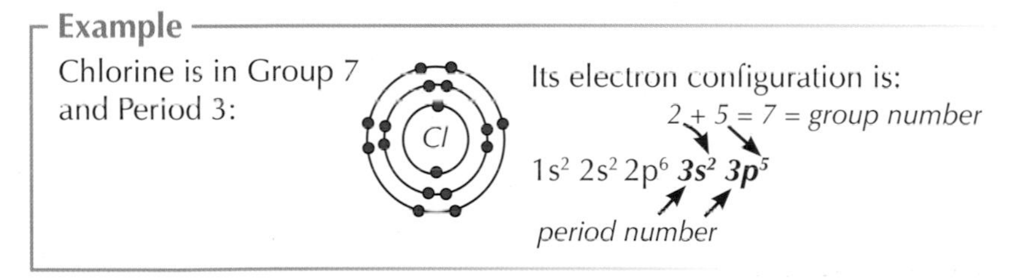

Example

Chlorine is in Group 7 and Period 3: Its electron configuration is:

$2 + 5 = 7$ = group number

$1s^2\ 2s^2\ 2p^6$ $\mathbf{3s^2\ 3p^5}$

period number

d-block elements

The d-block elements have electron configurations in which d sub-shells are being filled. They're a bit trickier — you don't always write the sub-shells in the order they're filled.

Example

The electron configuration of cobalt is: $1s^2\ 2s^2\ 2p^6\ 3s^2\ 3p^6$ $\mathbf{3d^7}$ $4s^2$

Even though the 3rd sub-shell fills last in cobalt, it's not written at the end of the line.

Tip: Watch out for the fact that 3d is on the same row as 4s and 4p in the periodic table. Remember that the 4s sub-shell is of lower energy than the 3d sub-shell so it fills first. Sneaky.

When you've got the periodic table labelled with the shells and sub-shells, it's pretty easy to read off the electron structure of any element by starting at the top and working your way across and down until you get to your element.

Tip: It doesn't really matter how you work out the electron configurations of elements, whether you use the rules on pages 19 and 20 or whether you read them off the periodic table like on this page. The important thing is that you get them right — so find a method you're happy with and stick with it.

Example

To work out the electron structure of phosphorus (P), you can use the periodic table to see that it's in Group 5 and Period 3. Starting with Period 1, the electron configuration of a full shell is $1s^2$. For Period 2 it's $2s^2\,2p^6$. However, phosphorus' outer shell is only partially filled — it's got 5 outer electrons in the configuration $3s^2\,3p^3$.

So: Period 1 — $1s^2$

Period 2 — $2s^2\,2p^6$

Period 3 — $3s^2\,3p^3$

The full electron structure of phosphorus is: $1s^2\,2s^2\,2p^6\,3s^2\,3p^3$.

Practice Questions — Application

Q1 Give the number of electron shells that atoms of the following elements have:

a) Sulfur, S
b) Beryllium, Be
c) Bromine, Br
d) Neon, Ne
e) Rubidium, Rb

Q2 How many electrons are in the outer shell of atoms of the following elements?

a) Selenium, Se
b) Potassium, K
c) Fluorine, F
d) Aluminium, Al
e) Strontium, Sr

Tip: Don't forget that for d-block elements, the sub-shells aren't written in the order that they're filled.

Q3 Work out the electron configurations of the following elements:

a) Sodium, Na
b) Calcium, Ca
c) Chlorine, Cl
d) Arsenic, As
e) Vanadium, V
f) Scandium, Sc

Practice Questions — Fact Recall

Q1 How is the periodic table arranged?

Q2 Look at the diagram below.

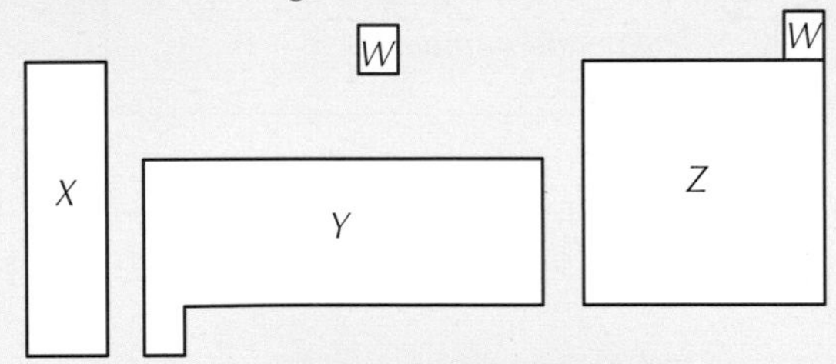

a) Which letter(s) (W, X, Y or Z) represent(s) the p block of the periodic table?

b) Which letter(s) (W, X, Y or Z) represent(s) the d block of the periodic table?

c) Which letter(s) (W, X, Y or Z) represent(s) the s block of the periodic table?

11. Periodicity

Periodicity is an important idea in chemistry. It's all to do with the trends in physical and chemical properties of elements across the periodic table — things like atomic radius, melting point, boiling point, and ionisation energy.

Learning Objectives:

- Be able to describe the trends in atomic radius, first ionisation energy, melting and boiling points of the elements Na – Ar.
- Understand the reasons for the trends in these properties.

Specification Reference 3.1.4

Atomic radius

Atomic radius decreases across a period (see Figure 1). As the number of protons increases, the positive charge of the nucleus increases. This means electrons are pulled closer to the nucleus, making the atomic radius smaller (see Figure 2). The extra electrons that the elements gain across a period are added to the outer energy level so they don't really provide any extra shielding effect (shielding works with inner shells mainly).

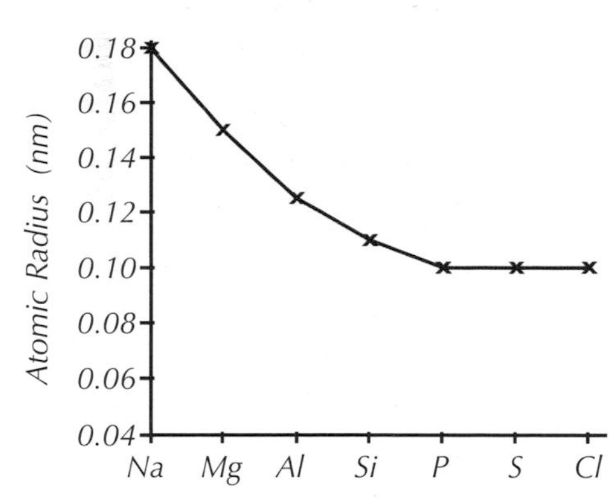

Figure 1: *The atomic radii of the first seven Period 3 elements.*

Exam Tip
There's no need to memorise the graphs on this page, but you do need to know their shapes and be able to explain them.

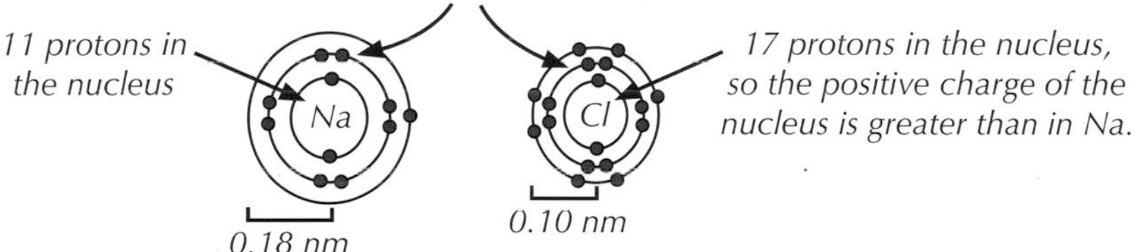

Figure 2: *The atomic radii of sodium and chlorine.*

Tip: Shielding is when the inner electrons effectively 'screen' the outer electrons from the pull of the nucleus. Look back at page 22 for more on shielding.

Melting and boiling points

If you look at how the melting and boiling points change across Period 3, the trend isn't immediately obvious. The melting and boiling points generally increase from sodium to silicon, but then decrease from silicon to argon (see Figure 3).

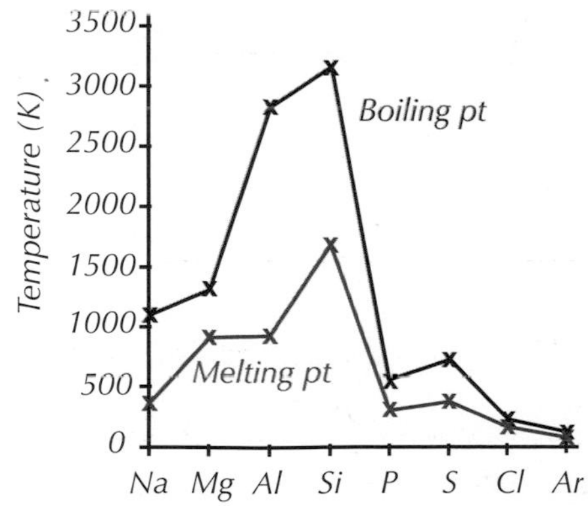

Figure 3: *Melting and boiling points of Period 3 elements.*

Once you start looking at the bond strengths and structures of the Period 3 elements, the reasons for the trend become clear.

Figure 4: *Chlorine (top) has lower melting and boiling points than silicon (bottom), so is a gas at r.t.p., whilst silicon is a solid.*

Figure 5: Magnesium (top) and aluminium (bottom).

Sodium, magnesium and aluminium

Sodium, magnesium and aluminium are metals. Their melting and boiling points increase across the period because the metal-metal bonds get stronger. The bonds get stronger because the metal ions have an increasing number of delocalised electrons and a decreasing radius. This leads to a higher charge density, which attracts the ions together more strongly (see Figure 6).

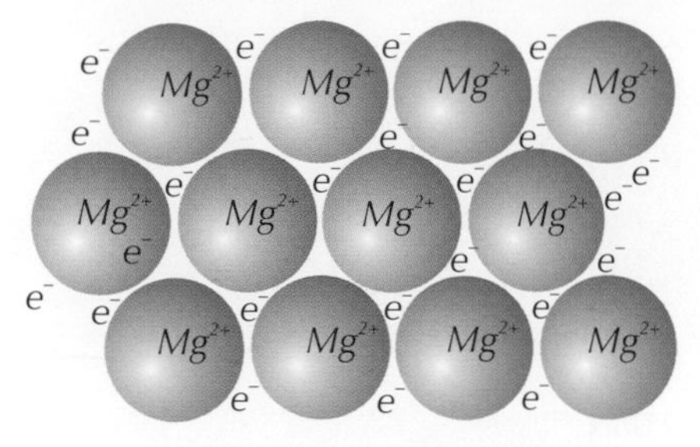

The magnesium ions have a larger radius and a charge of 2+ so there are two delocalised electrons for each ion...

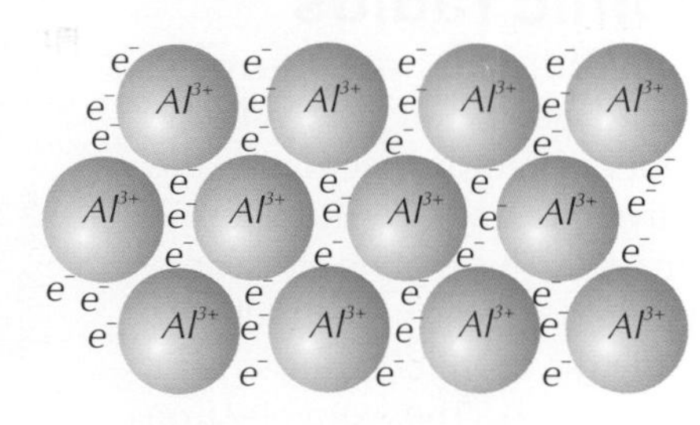

...whereas the aluminium ions have a smaller radius and a charge of 3+ so there are three delocalised electrons for each ion.

Figure 6: *The structures of magnesium and aluminium.*

Tip: The structure of silicon should look familiar — it's similar to diamond (page 62). There's a good reason — carbon and silicon are both in Group 4, so have the same number of electrons in their outer shell.

Silicon

Silicon is **macromolecular**, with a tetrahedral structure — strong covalent bonds link all its atoms together (see Figure 7). A lot of energy is needed to break these bonds, so silicon has high melting and boiling points.

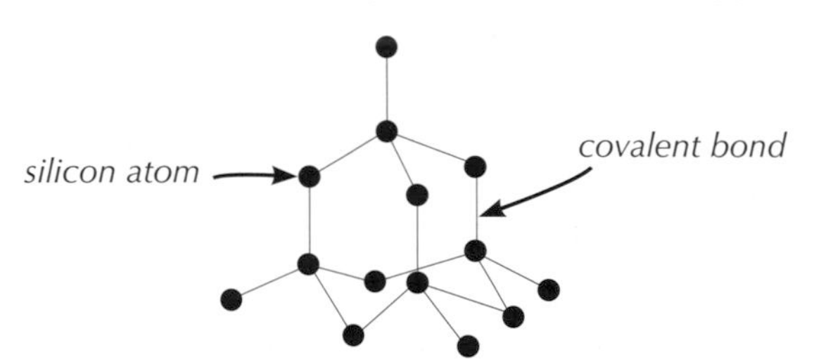

Figure 7: *The structure of silicon.*

Figure 8: *Sulfur (yellow powder) and phosphorus (stored under water) are solids at room temperature, whereas chlorine is a gas (see Figure 4).*

Phosphorus, sulfur, chlorine and argon

Phosphorus (P_4), sulfur (S_8) and chlorine (Cl_2) are all molecular substances. Their melting and boiling points depend upon the strength of the van der Waals forces (see pages 71-72) between their molecules. Van der Waals forces are weak and easily overcome so these elements have low melting and boiling points. More atoms in a molecule mean stronger van der Waals forces. Sulfur is the biggest molecule (S_8 — see Figure 9), so it's got higher melting and boiling points than phosphorus or chlorine. Argon has very low melting and boiling points because it exists as individual atoms (they're monatomic) resulting in very weak van der Waals forces.

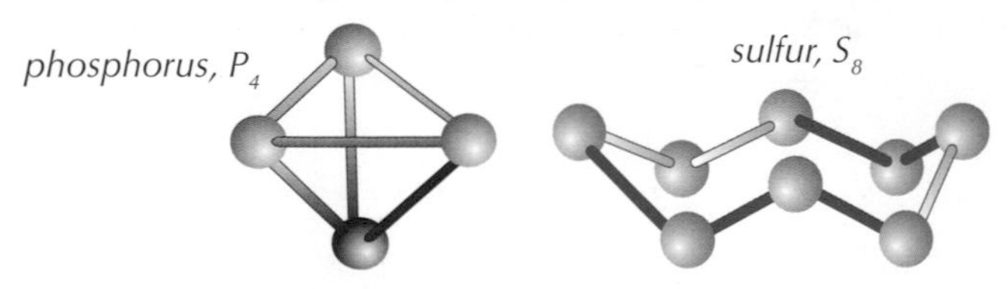

Figure 9: *The structures of phosphorus and sulfur.*

First ionisation energy

The first ionisation energy is the energy needed to remove 1 electron from each atom in 1 mole of gaseous atoms to form 1 mole of gaseous 1+ ions. There's a general increase in the first ionisation energy as you go across Period 3 (see Figure 10). This is because of the increasing attraction between the outer shell electrons and the nucleus, due to the number of protons increasing.

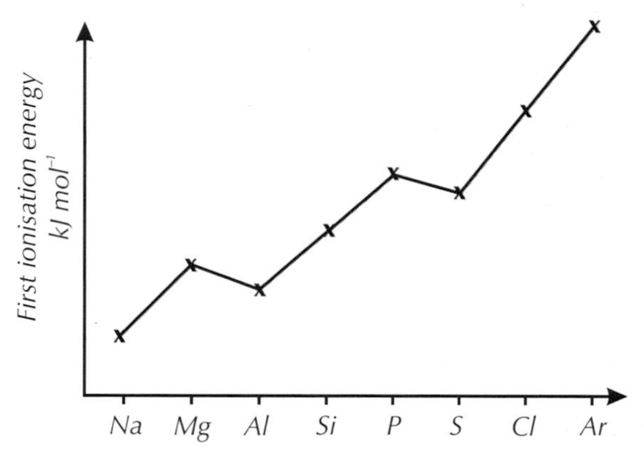

***Figure 10**: First ionisation energies of Period 3.*

Tip: There are a few blips in the trend for first ionisation energy — check back to page 23 for more details.

Practice Questions — Application

Q1 a) Explain why the atomic radius of aluminium is larger than the atomic radius of sulfur.

b) Name a Period 3 element with a larger atomic radius than aluminium.

Q2 Explain why the boiling point of aluminium is higher than the boiling point of sulfur.

Q3 The melting point of silicon is 1414 °C and the melting point of phosphorus is 44 °C.

a) Explain why the melting point of phosphorus is lower than the melting point of silicon.

b) Name a Period 3 element with a lower melting point than phosphorus.

Exam Tip
If you're asked about a specific trend, it might help you to roughly sketch out the shape of the relevant graph. That way you'll easily be able to see how the values for the elements compare to each other.

Practice Questions — Fact Recall

Q1 Describe the trend in atomic radius across Period 3 of the periodic table.

Q2 Describe the trend in melting and boiling points across Period 3 of the periodic table.

Q3 Describe the general trend in first ionisation energy across Period 3 of the periodic table.

Section Summary

Make sure you know...

- That ions form when electrons are transferred from one atom to another.
- That electrostatic attraction holds ions together and that this is called ionic bonding.
- That ions form crystals that are giant ionic lattices.
- The structure of sodium chloride.
- How the structure of ionic compounds decides their physical properties — their electrical conductivity, melting point and solubility.
- That covalent bonds form when atoms share pairs of electrons.
- How single, double and triple covalent bonds form between atoms.
- How the structure of covalent compounds decides their physical properties — their electrical conductivity, melting point and solubility.
- What a giant covalent (macromolecular) structure is.
- The structures of graphite and diamond and how the structures determine their properties.
- That dative (or co-ordinate) bonds form when an atom donates both the shared electrons in a bond.
- How to identify the donor atom in a dative covalent bond by working out which atom has an available lone pair.
- What a charge cloud is.
- That Valence-Shell Electron-Pair Repulsion Theory states that lone-pair/lone-pair bond angles are the biggest, lone-pair/bonding-pair bond angles are the second biggest and bonding-pair/bonding-pair bond angles are the smallest.
- How to predict the shapes of 2, 3, 4, 5 and 6 co-ordinate molecules, including their bond angles and shape names.
- That electronegativity is the ability to attract the bonding electrons in a covalent bond.
- How differences in electronegativities between bonding atoms causes polarisation.
- The difference between polar and non-polar bonds.
- The relative strengths of permanent dipole-dipole forces, van der Waals forces and hydrogen bonds.
- What permanent dipole-dipole forces and van der Waals forces are, and what causes them.
- How hydrogen bonds form and their effect on the properties of compounds.
- What metallic bonding is and how to recognise giant metallic lattice structures.
- How the structure of metals decides their physical properties — their conductivity, melting point, ability to be shaped and solubility.
- The arrangement and movement of particles in solids, liquids and gases.
- How the periodic table is arranged and the significance of its rows and columns.
- What the s-block, d-block and p-block of the periodic table are.
- How to work out electron configurations from the periodic table.
- What periodicity is.
- The trends in atomic radius, melting point, boiling point and first ionisation energy across Period 3.
- The reasons for the trends in atomic radius, melting point, boiling point and first ionisation energy across Period 3.

Exam-style Questions

1 Germanium is in the same group of the periodic table as carbon.

1 (a) Germanium reacts with hydrogen to form the compound germane, GeH_4.

1 (a) (i) The electron configuration of hydrogen $1s^1$. Give the electron configuration of germanium.

(1 mark)

1 (a) (ii) Name the type of bonding between germanium and hydrogen in germane, and describe how the bonds are formed.

(2 marks)

1 (a) (iii) Draw the shape of a molecule of GeH_4 and name the shape.

(2 marks)

1 (a) (iv) Give the bond angle in a GeH_4 molecule.

(1 mark)

1 (a) (v) State whether or not you would expect germane to conduct electricity. Explain your answer.

(2 marks)

1 (b) Germanium can combine with chlorine to form germanium dichloride, ($GeCl_2$).

1 (b) (i) Draw the shape of a molecule of $GeCl_2$ and name the shape.

(2 marks)

1 (b) (ii) Suggest a value for the bond angle in $GeCl_2$ and explain your answer.

(2 marks)

2 Sodium chloride (NaCl) is an ionic compound formed from sodium metal and chlorine gas (Cl_2).

2 (a) (i) Describe the structure of sodium.

(2 marks)

2 (a) (ii) Name the type of bonding found in sodium.

(1 mark)

2 (a) (iii) Explain how this bonding structure allows sodium to be easily shaped.

(1 mark)

2 (b) Explain why the atomic radius of chlorine is smaller than the atomic radius of sodium.

(3 marks)

2 (c) State what is meant by the term ionic bond.

(1 mark)

2 (d) Write an equation to show the formation of 1 mole of NaCl from sodium and chlorine.

(1 mark)

2 (e) Describe the structure of sodium chloride.

(2 marks)

3 The Group 5 elements include nitrogen, phosphorus, arsenic and antimony. They can form covalent bonds with hydrogen.

3 (a) Which block of the periodic table are the Group 5 elements found in?

(1 mark)

3 (b) The graph below shows the boiling points of some Group 5 hydrides.

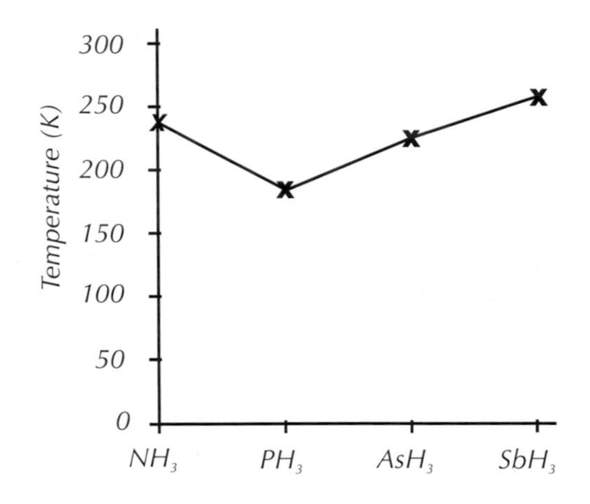

3 (b) (i) Explain the trend in boiling points shown by the graph for PH_3, AsH_3 and SbH_3.

(3 marks)

3 (b) (ii) Suggest what the trend in melting point would be for PH_3, AsH_3 and SbH_3.

(1 mark)

3 (c) Name the strongest type of intermolecular force found in NH_3.

(1 mark)

3 (d) (i) NH_3 reacts with H^+ to form an NH_4^+ ion. Name the type of bond that forms in this reaction and explain how it is formed.

(3 marks)

3 (d) (ii) Explain why the bond angle in NH_3 is smaller than in NH_4^+.

(3 marks)

4 The table below shows the electronegativities of some elements.

Element	C	H	Cl	O	F
Electronegativity (Pauling Scale)	2.5	2.1	3.0	3.5	4.0

4 (a) Define the term electronegativity.

Explain how electronegativity can give rise to permanent dipole-dipole forces.

(5 marks)

4 (b) Use the information in the table to name the strongest intermolecular forces in HCl, CH_4 and HF.

Draw a diagram to show the strongest intermolecular forces between HF molecules. Include partial charges and all lone pairs.

Explain why the only forces between Cl_2 molecules are van der Waals forces

(7 marks)

5 Carbon can form lots of different structures and can combine with other elements to form lots of different compounds.

5 (a) Graphite and diamond contain only carbon atoms.

5 (a) (i) Both substances have the same type of structure. Name this structure.

(1 mark)

5 (a) (ii) Describe the structures and bonding of graphite and diamond

(5 marks)

5 (a) (iii) Explain why graphite can conduct electricity but diamond cannot.

(2 marks)

5 (b) State the type of intermolecular forces found between molecules of methane, CH_4.

Compare the strength of the intermolecular forces between molecules of CH_4 to the intermolecular forces between molecules of C_3H_8.

Explain why the boiling point of diamond is much higher than the boiling point of methane.

(5 marks)

Organic Chemistry

Organic chemistry is the study of carbon-containing compounds. In this section you'll cover the basics of organic chemistry — things like nomenclature (naming), formulas and isomers. You'll also see some real life applications of organic molecules — bet you can't wait.

The basics

There are a few basic concepts in organic chemistry which you need to understand to really get on with this section.

Nomenclature

There are thousands, if not millions, of known organic compounds and it would be pretty silly if we didn't have an easy way to describe them. That's where nomenclature comes in. Don't be put off by the long name, all it means is naming molecules using specific rules. These rules (known as the IUPAC system for naming organic compounds) allow scientists to discuss organic chemistry safe in the knowledge that they're all talking about the same molecules. It means that some molecules end up with really long and complicated looking names (e.g. 1,2-dichloro-3-methylbutane) but once you know the rules it's easy to work out what they all mean. There's loads more about nomenclature on pages 95-99.

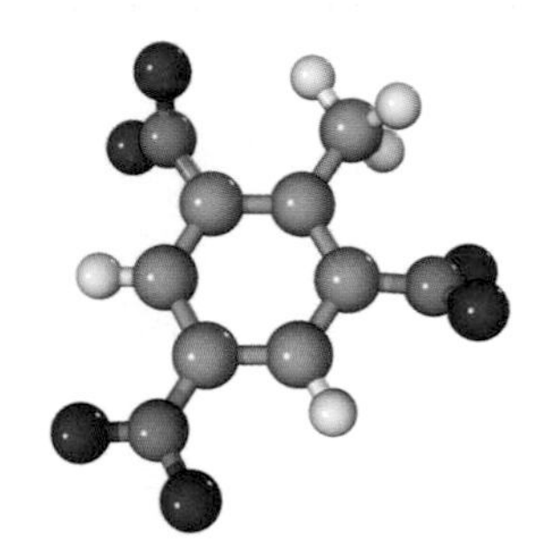

Figure 1: *A molecular model of a TNT molecule. Each grey sphere represents a carbon atom, each white sphere represents a hydrogen atom, the purple ones represent nitrogen atoms and the red ones oxygen atoms.*

Formulas

Picturing molecules can be pretty difficult when you can't see them all around you. We can use the elemental symbols from the periodic table to help visualise molecules. For example, a molecule of methane is one carbon atom attached to four hydrogen atoms. You could show this by giving its molecular formula, CH_4, or you could draw its displayed formula like this:

```
    H
    |
H — C — H
    |
    H
```

There's more on formulas on page 89. This isn't exactly what methane looks like, but visualising it like this lets us compare it to other molecules and means we can predict its properties and how it might react with other molecules. Molecular models can also be used to represent molecules (see Figure 1).

Tip: That stuff about carbon atoms making four bonds, hydrogen making one bond and oxygen making two is right <u>most</u> of the time, but isn't always the case. The good news is that you don't need to worry about that right now.

Functional groups

A functional group is the reactive part of the molecule — it's where all the interesting stuff happens. They're usually pretty easy to spot because they're the bits which aren't just hydrogen and carbon atoms (e.g. bromine atoms, oxygen atoms, etc.). You'll come across a few different functional groups in AS chemistry — here are a few examples...

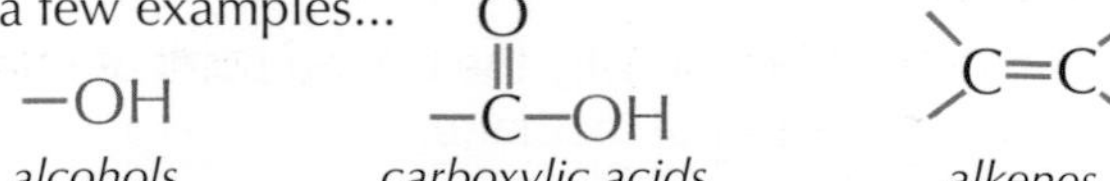

Functional groups of... *alcohols* *carboxylic acids* *alkenes*

For now, remember that carbon atoms have four bonds, hydrogen atoms have one bond and oxygen atoms have two bonds joining them to other atoms.

So there you go. That's pretty much all you need to know to get started. You'd better get on — first up is formulas...

1. Formulas

Organic compounds can be represented in lots of different ways, using different types of formulas. You need to be familiar with what these formulas show and how to switch between them.

Learning Objective:

- Know and understand the terms: molecular formula, functional group, displayed formula, empirical formula, homologous series and structural formula.

Specification Reference 3.1.5

Types of formulas

Molecular formulas

A molecular formula is the actual number of atoms of each element in a molecule.

Examples

Ethane has the molecular formula C_2H_6 — it's made up of 2 carbon atoms and 6 hydrogen atoms.

Pentene has the molecular formula C_5H_{10} — it's made up of 5 carbon atoms and 10 hydrogen atoms.

1,4-dibromobutane has the molecular formula $C_4H_8Br_2$ — it's made up of 4 carbon atoms, 8 hydrogen atoms and 2 bromine atoms.

1,3-dichloropropane has the molecular formula $C_3H_6Cl_2$ — it's made up of 3 carbon atoms, 6 hydrogen atoms and 2 chlorine atoms.

Tip: A functional group is a reactive part of a molecule — it gives it most of its chemical properties. For example, in an alcohol it's –OH. A molecule's formula shows you all the functional groups found in the molecule.

Structural formulas

A structural formula shows the atoms carbon by carbon, with the attached hydrogens and functional groups.

Examples

Ethane has the structural formula CH_3CH_3.

Pentene has the structural formula $CH_3CH_2CH_2CHCH_2$.

1,4-dibromobutane has the structural formula $BrCH_2CH_2CH_2CH_2Br$.

1,3-dichloropropane has the structural formula $ClCH_2CH_2CH_2Cl$.

Displayed formulas

A displayed formula shows how all the atoms are arranged, and all the bonds between them.

Examples

Displayed formula of ethane:

```
    H  H
    |  |
 H—C—C—H
    |  |
    H  H
```

Displayed formula of pentene:

```
    H  H  H  H
    |  |  |  |     H
 H—C—C—C—C=C<
    |  |  |        H
    H  H  H
```

Displayed formula of 1,4-dibromobutane:

```
     H  H  H  H
     |  |  |  |
 Br—C—C—C—C—Br
     |  |  |  |
     H  H  H  H
```

Displayed formula of 1,3-dichloropropane:

```
     H  H  Cl
     |  |  |
 Cl—C—C—C—H
     |  |  |
     H  H  H
```

Tip: Drawing a displayed formula from a structural formula is dead easy — just draw it out exactly as it's written:

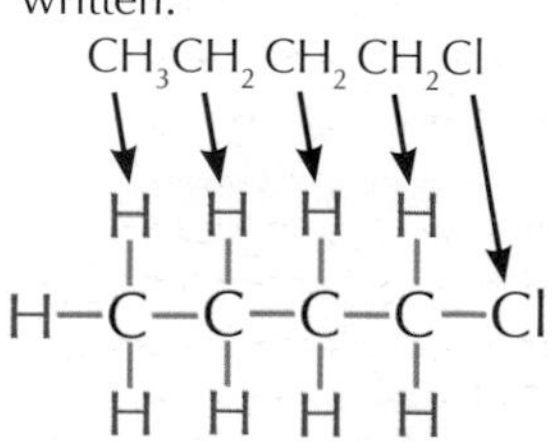

Empirical formulas

An empirical formula is the simplest ratio of whole number atoms of each element in a compound. To find the empirical formula you have to divide the molecular formula by the smallest number of atoms for a given element in the molecule. For example, if the molecular formula is $C_2H_4Cl_2$, the smallest number of atoms is 2 (for both C and Cl). So you divide the molecular formula by 2 and get the empirical formula CH_2Cl. Sometimes the empirical formula will be the same as the molecular formula. This happens when you can't divide the molecular formula by the smallest number of atoms and still end up with whole numbers of atoms.

Tip: If there's just one atom of something in a formula then you know you've got an empirical formula — it can't be simplified any further.

$C_4H_{10}O$ is an empirical formula — there's only 1 oxygen atom.

Examples

Name	Molecular Formula	Divide by...	Empirical Formula
Ethane	C_2H_6	2	CH_3
Pentene	C_5H_{10}	5	CH_2
1,4-dibromobutane	$C_4H_8Cl_2$	2	C_2H_4Cl
1,3-dichloropropane	$C_3H_6Cl_2$		$C_3H_6Cl_2$
1,2,3-trichloroheptane	$C_7H_{13}Cl_3$		$C_7H_{13}Cl_3$

In the last two examples in the table, the molecular formula is same as the empirical formula — you can't divide by the smallest number of atoms for a given element and still get whole numbers.

Exam Tip

You need to make sure you know which type of formula is which. You won't get any marks for writing a structural formula when the examiner wants a molecular one.

General formulas and homologous series

A general formula is an algebraic formula that can describe any member of a family of compounds. A **homologous series** is a bunch of organic compounds which have the same general formula and similar chemical properties. Each member differs by $-CH_2-$.

Examples

Alkanes are made up of carbon and hydrogen atoms. There are always twice as many hydrogen atoms as carbon atoms, plus two more. So the general formula for alkanes is C_nH_{2n+2}. You can use this formula to work out how many hydrogen atoms there are in any alkane if you know the number of carbon atoms. For example...

If an alkane has 1 carbon atom, $n = 1$.
This means the alkane will have $(2 \times 1) + 2 = 4$ hydrogen atoms.

If an alkane has 5 carbon atoms, $n = 5$.
This means the alkane will have $(2 \times 5) + 2 = 12$ hydrogen atoms.

If an alkane has 15 carbon atoms, $n = 15$.
This means the alkane will have $(2 \times 15) + 2 = 32$ hydrogen atoms.

Practice Questions — Application

Q1 2-bromopropane has the structural formula $CH_3CHBrCH_3$. Draw the displayed formula of 2-bromopropane.

Q2 Here is the structure of 3-ethyl-2-methylpentane.

```
    H  H  H  CH3 H
    |  |  |  |   |
 H—C—C—C—C—C—H
    |  |  |  |   |
    H  H  CH2 H  H
          |
          CH3
```

Write down the molecular formula for 3-ethyl-2-methylpentane.

Q3 Write down the empirical formula of the following compounds:

a) C_2H_4

b) $C_8H_{14}Br_2$

c) $C_9H_{17}Cl_3$

Q4 Alkenes have the general formula C_nH_{2n}.

a) Butene is an alkene with 4 carbon atoms. Write the molecular formula of butene.

b) Heptene is an alkene with 7 carbon atoms. How many hydrogen atoms does it contain?

Q5 1,2-dibromopropane has the structural formula $CH_3CHBrCH_2Br$.

a) Write down the molecular formula of 1,2-dibromopropane.

b) Draw the displayed formula of 1,2-dibromopropane.

c) Write the empirical formula of 1,2-dibromopropane.

Q6 Here is the displayed formula of pent-1-ene.

```
    H  H  H  H
    |  |  |  |     H
 H—C—C—C—C=C<
    |  |  |        H
    H  H  H
```

a) Write down the molecular formula of pent-1-ene.

b) Write down the structural formula of pent-1-ene.

c) What is the empirical formula of pent-1-ene?

Tip: It doesn't matter whether you show atoms bonding above, below or to the side of a carbon atom, they all mean the same thing — it's which atoms they're bonding to that's the important thing.

Exam Tip

It's really important to double check your answers for questions like these. It's so easy to miscount and you need to make sure you collect all the easy marks in the exam.

Practice Questions — Fact Recall

Q1 What is a molecular formula?

Q2 What does a displayed formula show?

Q3 How do you work out the empirical formula of a compound?

Q4 What is a homologous series?

2. Isomers

You can put the same atoms together in different ways to make completely different molecules. Two molecules that have the same molecular formula but are put together in a different way are isomers of each other.

Learning Objectives:

- Know and understand the meaning of the term structural isomerism.
- Be able to draw the structures of chain, position and functional group isomers.

Specification Reference 3.1.5

Structural isomers

In structural isomers the atoms are connected in different ways. But they still have the same molecular formula. There are three types of structural isomers — chain isomers, position isomers and functional group isomers.

1. Chain isomers

Chain isomers have different arrangements of the carbon skeleton. Some are straight chains and others are branched in different ways.

Examples

There are different chain isomers of C_4H_{10}. The diagrams below show the straight chain isomer butane and a branched chain isomer methylpropane.

```
    H  H  H  H            H CH3 H
    |  |  |  |            |  |  |
 H--C--C--C--C--H      H--C--C--C--H
    |  |  |  |            |  |  |
    H  H  H  H            H  H  H
```

Here the longest carbon chain is 4 carbon atoms.

butane

methylpropane

Here the longest carbon chain is 3 carbon atoms.

Exam Tip
You don't always have to draw all of the bonds when you're drawing a molecule — writing CH_3 next to a bond is just as good as drawing out the carbon atom, three bonds and three hydrogen atoms. But if you're asked for a displayed formula you must draw out all of the bonds to get the marks.

There are different chain isomers of $C_4H_8O_2$. The diagrams below show the straight chain isomer butanoic acid and a branched chain isomer methylpropanoic acid.

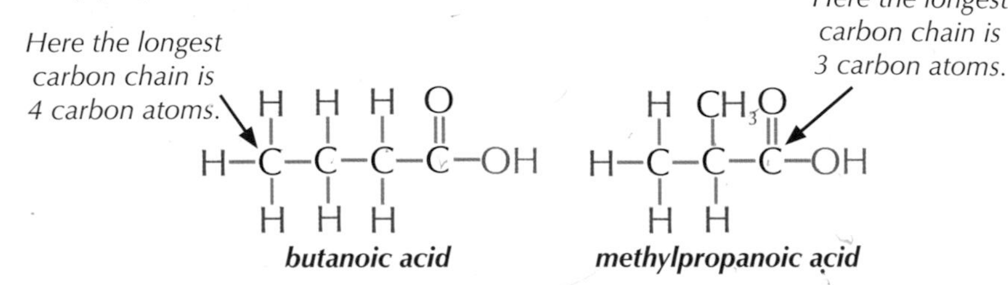

Tip: Number the carbon atoms — it makes it easier to see what the longest carbon chain is and where side chains and atoms are attached:

```
    H  H  H  H
    |4 |3 |2 |1
 H--C--C--C--C--Cl
    |  |  |  |
    H  H  H  H

    H  H  Cl H
    |4 |3 |2 |1
 H--C--C--C--C--H
    |  |  |  |
    H  H  H  H
```

2. Positional isomers

Positional isomers have the same skeleton and the same atoms or groups of atoms attached. The difference is that the atom or group of atoms is attached to a different carbon atom.

Example

There are two position isomers of C_4H_9Cl. The chlorine atom is attached to different carbon atoms in each isomer.

```
    H  H  H  H
    |  |  |  |
 H--C--C--C--C--Cl
    |  |  |  |
    H  H  H  H
```

The Cl is attached to the first carbon atom.

1-chlorobutane

The Cl is attached to the second carbon atom.

2-chlorobutane

Tip: If the chlorine atom was attached to the second carbon atom from the left, it would still be the same molecule — just drawn the other way round. It would still be 2-chlorobutane.

3. Functional group isomers

Functional group isomers have the same atoms arranged into different functional groups.

Example

The formulas below show two functional group isomers of C_6H_{12}.

The functional group is the C=C — it's an alkene.

hex-1-ene

This molecule is an alkane.

cyclohexane

Identifying isomers

Atoms can rotate as much as they like around single C–C bonds. Remember this when you work out structural isomers — sometimes what looks like an isomer, isn't.

Exam Tip
To avoid mistakes when you're identifying isomers in an exam, draw the molecule so the longest carbon chain goes left to right across the page. This will make it easier to see the isomers.

Example

There are only two positional isomers of C_3H_7Br — 1-bromopropane and 2-bromopropane.

1-bromopropane

The Br is always on the first carbon atom.

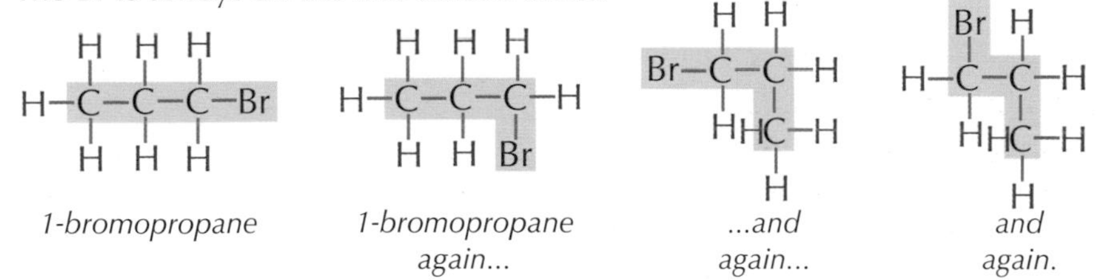

1-bromopropane *1-bromopropane again...* *...and again...* *and again.*

All these molecules are the same, they're just drawn differently.

2-bromopropane

The Br is always on the second carbon atom.

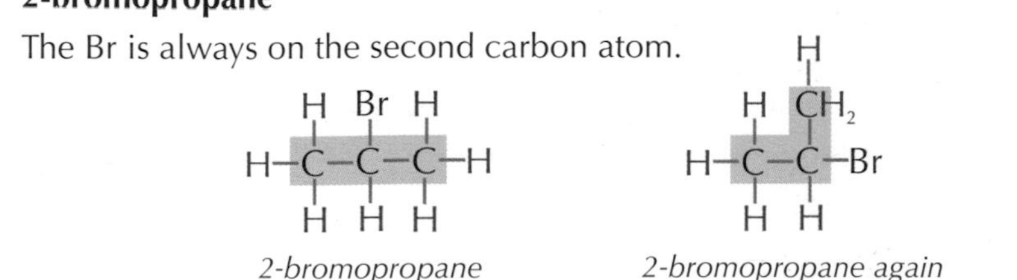

2-bromopropane *2-bromopropane again*

Tip: In propane, the Br can only really go on the first or second carbon atom. If it was on the "third" it would be the same as being on the first again because you start counting from whichever end the Br is on.

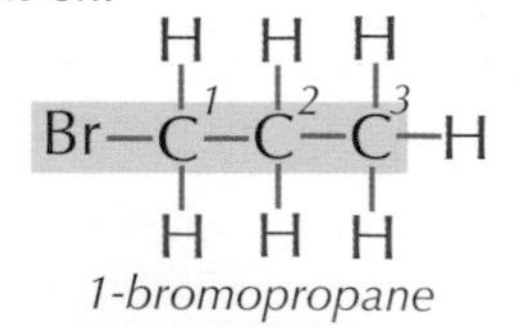

1-bromopropane

Practice Questions — Application

Q1 Here is an isomer of chloro-2-methylpropane.

```
       CH3
        |
  H3C - C - CH3
        |
        Cl
```

Draw the other positional isomer of chloro-2-methylpropane.

Q2 Draw all the chain isomers of C_5H_{12}.

Q3 Here is the displayed formula of propanal.

```
    H   H   O
    |   |   ||
H - C - C - C - H
    |   |
    H   H
```

Propanal has the functional group $\overset{O}{\overset{\|}{C}}-H$.
Draw an isomer of propanal with the functional group $\overset{O}{\overset{\|}{C}}$.

Q4 Here is the displayed formula of 1-chlorohexane.

```
    H   H   H   H   H   H
    |   |   |   |   |   |
H - C - C - C - C - C - C - Cl
    |   |   |   |   |   |
    H   H   H   H   H   H
```

a) Which of the molecules (A–D) are isomers of 1-chlorohexane?

A

```
    H   Cl  H   H
    |   |   |   |
H - C - C - C - C - H
    |   |   |   |
    H   H  CH2  H
            |
           CH3
```

B

```
    H   Cl CH3  H
    |   |   |   |
H - C - C - C - C - H
    |   |   |   |
    H   H  CH3  H
```

C

```
    H   H   H   H
    |   |   |   |
H - C - C - C - C - H
    |   |   |   |
    H   H  CH2  H
            |
           CH3
```

D

```
    H   H   Cl  H   H
    |   |   |   |   |
H - C - C - C - C - C - H
    |   |   |   |   |
    H   H   H   H   H
```

b) State the type of isomerism shown in part a).

Practice Questions — Fact Recall

Q1 What is a chain isomer?

Q2 What is a positional isomer?

Q3 What is a functional group isomer?

3. Alkanes and Nomenclature

Alkanes are molecules with hydrogen atoms, carbon atoms and single bonds. Nomenclature is just a fancy word for naming organic compounds.

Learning Objectives:

- Know that alkanes are saturated hydrocarbons.
- Be able to name simple alkanes, limited to chains with up to 6 carbon atoms.

Specification References 3.1.5, 3.1.6

Structure of alkanes

Alkanes have the general formula C_nH_{2n+2}. They've only got carbon and hydrogen atoms, so they're **hydrocarbons**. Every carbon atom in an alkane has four single bonds with other atoms. It's impossible for carbon to make more than four bonds, so alkanes are saturated.
Here are a few examples of alkanes —

```
   H           H H            H H H
   |           | |            | | |
 H-C-H       H-C-C-H        H-C-C-C-H
   |           | |            | | |
   H           H H            H H H
```

methane *ethane* *propane*

You get **cycloalkanes** too. They have a ring of carbon atoms with two hydrogens attached to each carbon. Cycloalkanes have two fewer hydrogens than other alkanes (assuming they have only one ring) so cycloalkanes have a different general formula from that of normal alkanes (C_nH_{2n}), but they are still saturated.

cyclohexane, C_6H_{12}

Naming alkanes

The IUPAC system for naming organic compounds is the agreed international language of chemistry. Years ago, organic compounds were given whatever names people fancied, such as acetic acid and ethylene. But these names caused confusion between different countries.

The IUPAC system means scientific ideas can be communicated across the globe more effectively. So it's easier for scientists to get on with testing each other's work, and either confirm or dispute new theories.

You need to be able to name straight chain and branched alkanes using the IUPAC system for naming organic compounds.

Straight chain alkanes

There are two parts to the name of a straight chain alkane. The first part — the stem, states how many carbon atoms there are in the molecule (see Figure 1).

Number of Carbon Atoms	Stem
1	*meth-*
2	*eth-*
3	*prop-*
4	*but-*
5	*pent-*
6	*hex-*

Figure 1: *Stems for naming organic compounds.*

Tip: These stems come up again and again in chemistry so it's really important that you know all of them.

The second part is always "-ane". It's the "-ane" bit that lets people know it's an alkane.

Example

```
    H  H  H  H  H
    |  |  |  |  |
H — C — C — C — C — C — H
    |  |  |  |  |
    H  H  H  H  H
```

pentane

There are 5 carbon atoms so the stem is 'pent-' — the alkane is called pentane.

Branched alkanes

Branched alkanes have side chains. These are the carbon atoms that aren't part of the longest continuous chain. To name branched alkanes you first need to count how many carbon atoms are in the longest chain and work out the stem (just like you would for a straight chain alkane). Once you've done that you can name the side chains. The side chains are named according to how many carbon atoms they have (see Figure 2) and which carbon atom they are attached to. If there's more than one side chain in a molecule, you place them in alphabetical order. So but- groups come before eth- groups which come before meth- groups.

Number of Carbon Atoms	Side Chain Prefix
1	*methyl-*
2	*ethyl-*
3	*propyl-*
4	*butyl-*
5	*pentyl-*
6	*hexyl-*

Figure 2: *Names of carbon side chains.*

Tip: Always number the longest continuous carbon chain so that the name contains the lowest numbers possible. For example, you could number this chain:

```
     H   H   H   H
     |1  |2  |3  |4
H — C — C — C — C — H
     |   |   |   |
     H   H  CH3  H
```

which would make it 3-methylbutane. But you should actually number it in the opposite direction to get 2-methylbutane.

```
     H   H   H   H
     |4  |3  |2  |1
H — C — C — C — C — H
     |   |   |   |
     H   H  CH3  H
```

Examples

```
     H  CH3 H
     |1  |2  |3
H — C — C — C — H
     |   |   |
     H   H   H
```

2-methylpropane

The longest continuous carbon chain is 3 carbon atoms, so the stem is propane.

There's one side chain, which has one carbon atom so it's a methyl group.

It's joined to the main carbon chain at the 2nd carbon atom, so it's a 2-methyl group.

The alkane is called 2-methylpropane.

The longest continuous carbon chain is 5 carbon atoms, so the stem is pentane.

There are two side chains.

One side chain is a methyl group joined to the 2nd carbon atom: 2-methyl-.

The other is an ethyl group (2 carbons) joined to the 3rd carbon atom: 3-ethyl-.

Side chains go in alphabetical order, so the alkane is 3-ethyl-2-methylpentane.

```
     H   H   H  CH3  H
     |5  |4  |3  |2  |1
H — C — C — C — C — C — H
     |   |   |   |   |
     H   H  CH2  H   H
             |
            CH3
```

3-ethyl-2-methylpentane

If there are two or more side chains of the same type then you add a prefix of di- for two, tri- for three etc.. (You can ignore these prefixes when you're putting the other prefixes in alphabetical order.)

Example

The longest carbon chain is 5 atoms long, so the stem is pentane.

There's an ethyl group on the 3rd carbon atom: 3-ethyl-.

There are methyl groups on the 2nd and the 4th carbon atoms: 2,4-dimethyl-.

The alkane is called 3-ethyl-2,4-dimethylpentane.

```
  H CH3H CH3H
  |5 |4 |3 |2 |1
H-C--C--C--C--C-H
  |  |  |  |  |
  H  H CH2 H  H
        |
       CH3
```

3-ethyl-2,4-dimethylpentane

Tip: Be careful, the longest carbon chain may not be in a straight line:

```
  H  Cl H  H
  |1 |2 |3 |
H-C--C--C--C-H
  |  | 4|  |
  H  H CH2 H
        |
      5CH3
```

Practice Questions — Application

Q1 Name the alkane shown below.

```
  H  H  H  H
  |  |  |  |
H-C--C--C--C-H
  |  |  |  |
  H  H  H  H
```

Q2 Name the following branched alkanes:

a)

```
  H  H  H  H
  |  |  |  |
H-C--C--C--C-H
  |  |  |  |
  H  H CH2 H
        |
       CH3
```

b)

```
       CH3
        |
  H  H CH2 H
  |  |  |  |
H-C--C--C--C-H
  |  |  |  |
  H  H CH2 H
        |
       CH3
```

c)

```
       CH3
        |
  H  H CH2 H
  |  |  |  |
H-C--C--C--C-CH3
  |  |  |  |
  H  H CH2 H
        |
     H3C-CH2
```

d)

```
       CH3
        |
  H CH3CH2 H
  |  |  |  |
H-C--C--C--C-CH3
  |  |  |  |
  H  H CH2 H
        |
     H3C-CH2
```

Tip: When you're naming molecules <u>commas</u> are put between <u>numbers</u> (for example 2,2) and <u>dashes</u> are put between <u>numbers and letters</u> (for example 2-methyl).

Practice Questions — Fact Recall

Q1 Give the general formula for an alkane.

Q2 Describe a cycloalkane.

Q3 What is the stem for a carbon chain containing six carbon atoms?

Q4 What is the name for a carbon side chain containing two carbon atoms?

Q5 If there are two methyl- side chains what prefix should you add to methyl- when naming the molecule?

Learning Objective:

- Be able to name haloalkanes and alkenes, limited to chains with up to 6 carbon atoms.

Specification Reference 3.1.5

4. More Nomenclature

You can name haloalkanes and alkenes using similar rules to those used for naming alkanes.

Naming haloalkanes

Haloalkanes are just alkanes where one or more hydrogens have been swapped for a halogen. You name them in exactly the same way that alkanes are named (see page 95) but you have to add in a prefix before the name of the alkane (see Figure 1). The prefixes are always placed in alphabetical order.

Halogen	Prefix
Fluorine	*fluoro-*
Chlorine	*chloro-*
Bromine	*bromo-*
Iodine	*iodo-*

Figure 1: *Prefixes for naming haloalkanes.*

Examples

The longest carbon chain is 1 carbon atom, so the stem is methane.

There's one chlorine atom attached to the carbon chain so it has a chloro- prefix: chloromethane.

chloromethane

The longest carbon chain is 2 carbon atoms, so the stem is ethane.

There's one bromine atom attached to the second carbon atom so it has a bromo- prefix.

There are two chlorine atoms attached to the first carbon so it also has the prefix dichloro-.

So the molecule is 2-bromo-1,1-dichloroethane.

2-bromo-1,1-dichloroethane

Tip: The carbon atoms in this molecule are numbered so that the lowest possible numbers are in the name... 2-bromo-1,1-dichloroethane has smaller numbers than 1-bromo-2,2-dichloroethane.

Naming alkenes

Alkenes have at least one double bond between carbon atoms in their carbon chain. They're named in the same way as alkanes but the -ane ending is changed to an -ene ending. For alkenes with more than three carbons, you need to say which carbon the double bond starts from.

Example

The longest chain is 5 carbons, so the stem of the name is pent-.

The functional group is C=C, so it's pentene.

Number the carbons from right to left (so the double bond starts on the lowest possible number). The first carbon in the double bond is carbon 2.

So this molecule is pent-2-ene.

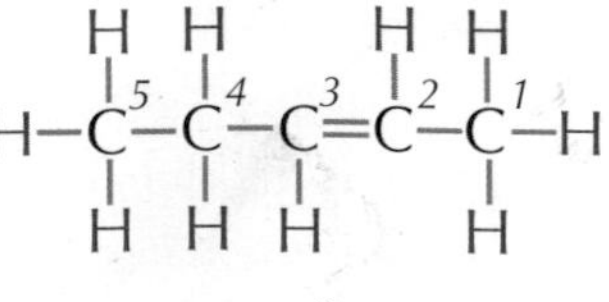

pent-2-ene

Tip: When you're naming alkenes the stem is based on the longest continuous carbon chain <u>containing a double bond</u> — even if there is a carbon chain that is longer.

If the alkene has two double bonds the suffix becomes diene. The stem of the name usually gets an extra 'a' too (e.g. buta-, penta- not but-, pent-) when there's more than one double bond. And you might see the numbers written first.

Example

```
         H
         |
H\              /H
   C=C—C=C
H/    |        \H
      H
```

This molecule can be named as buta-1,3-diene or 1,3-butadiene.

Tip: If there is more than one double bond in a molecule the stem is based on the longest continuous carbon chain that contains the most double bonds — even if there are longer carbon chains.

Practice Questions — Application

Q1 Name the haloalkanes shown below.

a)

```
     H  H  H  H
     |  |  |  |
Br—C—C—C—C—Br
     |  |  |  |
     H  H  H  H
```

b)

```
     H  H  Cl
     |  |  |
Cl—C—C—C—H
     |  |  |
     H  H  H
```

c)

```
     CH3
     |
  C—C—CH3
 H3  |
     Cl
```

d)

```
    H  H  H
    |  |  |
H—C—C—C—H
    |  |  |
    H  I  H
```

Q2 Name the alkenes shown below.

a)

```
    H  H  H  H  H
    |  |  |  |  |      /H
H—C—C—C—C—C=C
    |  |  |  |         \H
    H  H  H  H
```

b)

```
    H  H     H  H
    |  |     |  |      /H
H—C—C—C=C—C=C
    |  |  |            \H
    H  H  H
```

c)

```
    H  H  H  Cl H
    |  |  |  |  |      /H
H—C—C—C—C—C=C
    |  |  |  |         \H
    H  H  Cl H
```

Practice Questions — Fact Recall

Q1 What is a haloalkane?

Q2 What is the prefix used when there is an iodine in an alkane?

Q3 What is an alkene?

Q4 If an alkene contains two double bonds what is the suffix to the stem?

Learning Objectives:

- Know that petroleum is a mixture consisting mainly of alkane hydrocarbons.
- Understand that different fractions of petroleum can be drawn off at different levels in a fractionating column because of the temperature gradient.
- Understand that cracking involves the breaking of C–C bonds in alkanes.
- Understand the economic reasons for the cracking of alkanes.
- Be able to describe the conditions and products of thermal cracking.
- Be able to describe the conditions and products of catalytic cracking.

Specification Reference 3.1.6

5. Petroleum

Petroleum is just a poncy word for crude oil — the black, yukky stuff they get out of the ground with huge oil wells. It's mostly alkanes. They range from smallish alkanes, like pentane, to massive alkanes with more than 50 carbons.

Fractional distillation

Crude oil isn't very useful as it is, but you can separate it into more useful bits (or fractions) by fractional distillation. Here's how fractional distillation works — don't try this at home.

- First, the crude oil is vaporised at about 350 °C.
- The vaporised crude oil goes into the bottom of the fractionating column and rises up through the trays.
- The largest hydrocarbons don't vaporise at all, because their boiling points are too high — they just run to the bottom and form a gooey residue.
- As the crude oil vapour goes up the fractionating column, it gets cooler creating a temperature gradient.
- Because boiling points of alkanes increase as the molecules get bigger, each fraction condenses at a different temperature. The fractions are drawn off at different levels in the column.
- The hydrocarbons with the lowest boiling points don't condense. They're drawn off as gases at the top of the column.

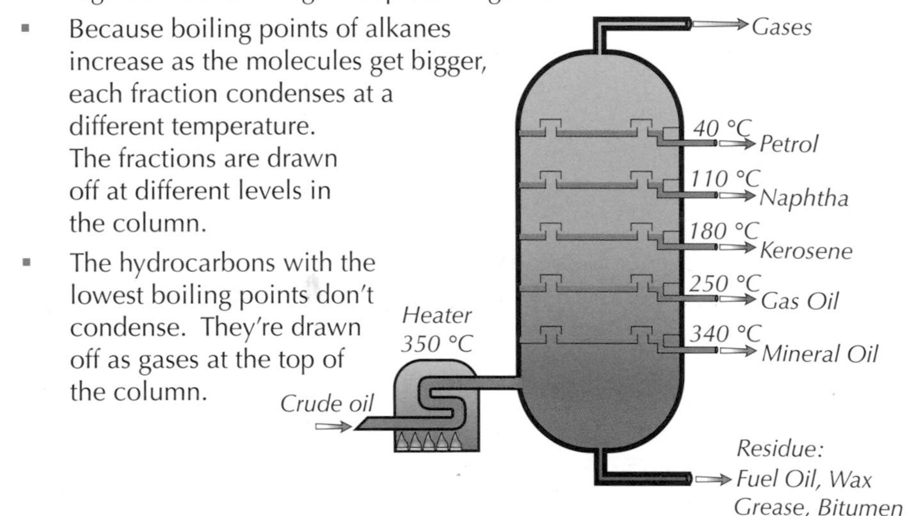

Figure 1: *A fractionating column.*

Figure 2: *Laboratory fractional distillation apparatus.*

Uses of crude oil fractions

Fraction	Carbon Chain	Uses
Gases	C_1 - C_4	Liquefied Petroleum Gas (LPG), camping gas
Petrol (gasoline)	C_5 - C_{12}	petrol
Naptha	C_7 - C_{14}	processed to make petrochemicals
Kerosene (paraffin)	C_{11} - C_{15}	jet fuel, petrochemicals, central heating fuel
Gas Oil (diesel)	C_{15} - C_{19}	diesel fuel, central heating fuel
Mineral Oil (lubricating)	C_{20} - C_{30}	lubricating oil
Fuel Oil	C_{30} - C_{40}	ships, power stations,
Wax, grease	C_{40} - C_{50}	candles, lubrication
Bitumen	C_{50+}	roofing, road surfacing

Cracking hydrocarbons

People want loads of the light fractions, like petrol and naphtha. They don't want so much of the heavier stuff like bitumen though. Stuff that's in high demand is much more valuable than the stuff that isn't. To meet this demand, the less popular heavier fractions are cracked. Cracking is breaking long-chain alkanes into smaller hydrocarbons (which can include alkenes). It involves breaking the C–C bonds.

Example

Decane could be cracked into smaller hydrocarbons like this:

decane → *ethene* + *octane*

But, because the bond breaking in cracking is random, this isn't the only way that decane could be cracked — it could be cracked to produce different short chain hydrocarbons. For example...

decane → *ethane* + *pent-2-ene* + *propene*

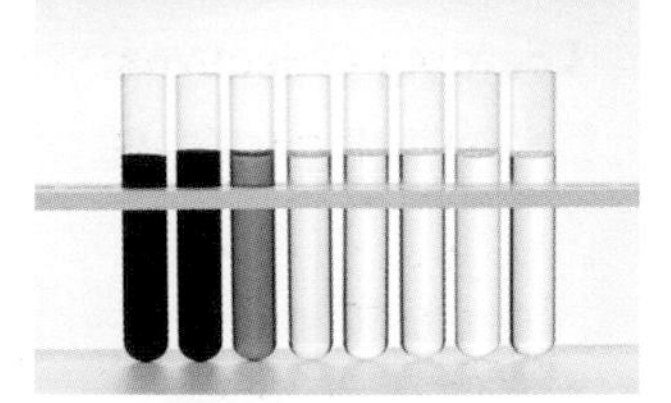

Figure 3: *Fractions produced from fractional distillation of crude oil. The fractions are arranged in order of boiling point, with higher boiling points towards the left.*

Exam Tip

In the exam you might have to write equations for cracking. The marks are pretty simple to pick up, as long as you check that you have the same number of carbons and hydrogens on each side of the equation.

Types of cracking

There are two types of cracking you need to know about — thermal cracking and catalytic cracking.

Thermal cracking

It takes place at high temperature (up to 1000 °C) and high pressure (up to 70 atm). It produces a lot of alkenes. These alkenes are used to make heaps of valuable products, like polymers. A good example is poly(ethene), which is made from ethene (have a squiz at pages 182-183 for more on polymers).

Catalytic cracking

This makes mostly motor fuels and aromatic hydrocarbons. It uses something called a zeolite catalyst (hydrated aluminosilicate), at a slight pressure and high temperature (about 450 °C). Using a catalyst cuts costs, because the reaction can be done at a lower temperature and pressure. The catalyst also speeds up the rate of reaction.

Tip: Aromatic compounds contain benzene rings. Benzene rings look like this:

benzene

Practice Questions — Fact Recall

Q1 What is petroleum?

Q2 Fractional distillation separates hydrocarbons. What property are they separated by?

Q3 What is cracking?

Q4 Why do we crack heavier petroleum fractions?

Q5 Why does using a catalyst for catalytic cracking cut costs?

6. Alkanes as Fuels

Learning Objectives:

- Know that alkanes are used as fuels.
- Understand that the combustion of alkanes can be complete or incomplete.
- Know that the internal combustion engine produces a number of pollutants and that these pollutants can be removed using catalytic converters.
- Know that combustion of hydrocarbons containing sulfur leads to sulfur dioxide that causes air pollution.
- Understand how sulfur dioxide can be removed from flue gases using calcium oxide.
- Know that the combustion of fossil fuels (including alkanes) results in the release of carbon dioxide into the atmosphere.
- Know that carbon dioxide, methane and water vapour are referred to as greenhouse gases and that these gases may contribute to global warming.

Specification Reference 3.1.6

Alkanes make great fuels — burning just a small amount of methane releases a humongous amount of energy. Alkanes are found in fossil fuels such as coal, oil and natural gas. Unfortunately, burning them can release pollutants.

Combustion

Complete combustion

If you burn (oxidise) alkanes with plenty of oxygen, you get carbon dioxide and water — it's a combustion reaction.

Example

If you burn a molecule of propane in plenty of oxygen, you get three molecules of carbon dioxide and four water molecules.
The equation for this is shown below.

$$C_3H_{8(g)} + 5O_{2(g)} \rightarrow 3CO_{2(g)} + 4H_2O_{(g)}$$

Incomplete combustion

If there's not enough oxygen, hydrocarbons combust incompletely, and you get particulate carbon (soot) and carbon monoxide gas as well as carbon dioxide.

Example

If you burn propane in a limited supply of oxygen you'll produce carbon monoxide and carbon as well as carbon dioxide and water.

$$C_3H_{8(g)} + 3\frac{1}{2}O_{2(g)} \rightarrow CO_{2(g)} + 4H_2O_{(g)} + CO_{(g)} + C_{(s)}$$

This is bad news because carbon monoxide gas is poisonous. Carbon monoxide molecules bind to the same sites on haemoglobin molecules in red blood cells as oxygen molecules. So oxygen can't be carried around the body.

Luckily, carbon monoxide can be removed from exhaust gases by catalytic converters on cars.

Tip: Not all incomplete combustion reactions will produce carbon dioxide, carbon monoxide, particulate carbon and water. Some, for example, will only produce water and carbon monoxide. Just make sure your equation balances and you should be fine.

Pollution from burning fuels

Unburnt hydrocarbons and oxides of nitrogen

Nitrogen oxides are a series of toxic and poisonous molecules which have the general formula NO_x. Nitrogen oxide is produced when the high pressure and temperature in a car engine cause the nitrogen and oxygen atoms in the air to react together. Nitrogen oxide can react further to produce nitrogen dioxide — the equations for these reactions are shown below.

$$N_{2(g)} + O_{2(g)} \rightarrow 2NO_{(g)}$$

$$2NO_{(g)} + O_{2(g)} \rightarrow 2NO_{2(g)}$$

Engines don't burn all the fuel molecules. Some of these come out as unburnt hydrocarbons. These hydrocarbons react with nitrogen oxides in the presence of sunlight to form ground-level ozone (O_3), which is a major component of smog. Ground-level ozone irritates people's eyes, aggravates respiratory problems and even causes lung damage (ozone isn't nice stuff, unless it is high up in the atmosphere as part of the ozone layer).

The three main pollutants from vehicle exhausts are nitrogen oxides, unburned hydrocarbons and carbon monoxide. Catalytic converters on cars remove these pollutants from the exhaust by the following reactions:

$$C_3H_{8(g)} + 5O_{2(g)} \rightarrow 3CO_{2(g)} + 4H_2O_{(g)}$$

This equation is just an equation for the complete combustion of a hydrocarbon.

$$2NO_{(g)} \rightarrow N_{2(g)} + O_{2(g)}$$

$$2NO_{(g)} + 2CO_{(g)} \rightarrow N_{2(g)} + 2CO_{2(g)}$$

Catalytic converters contain transition metal catalysts such as rhodium, palladium, platinum or iridium which help to convert the pollutants into less harmful chemicals.

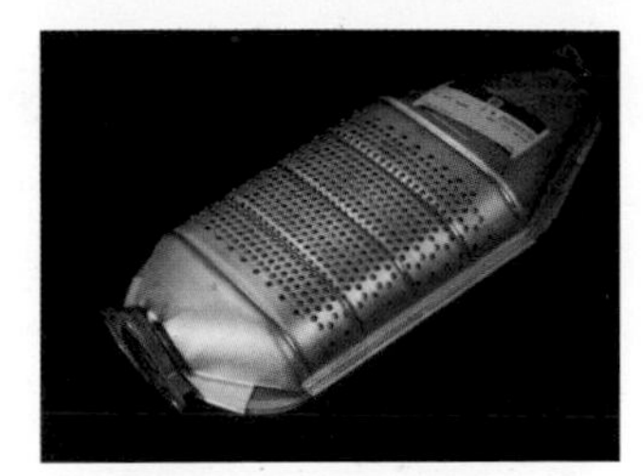

Figure 1: *A catalytic converter.*

Tip: Catalytic converters are designed to have very large surface areas to make sure that the harmful pollutants have the best chance of being turned into less harmful chemicals.

Sulfur dioxide

Acid rain is caused by burning fossil fuels that contain sulfur. The sulfur burns to produce sulfur dioxide gas which then enters the atmosphere, dissolves in the moisture, and is converted into sulfuric acid. The same process occurs when nitrogen dioxide escapes into the atmosphere — nitric acid is produced. Acid rain destroys trees and vegetation, as well as corroding buildings and statues and killing fish in lakes. Luckily, sulfur dioxide (an acidic gas) can be removed from power station flue gases using calcium oxide (a basic oxide):

$$CaO_{(s)} + SO_{2(g)} \rightarrow CaSO_{3(s)}$$

This reaction is called flue-gas desulfurisation.

Figure 2: *Trees killed by acid rain, Czech Republic.*

Global warming

The vast majority of scientists believe that global warming is caused by increased levels of carbon dioxide in the atmosphere due to burning fossil fuels (coal, oil and natural gas). Not everyone agrees with this theory, but here's what is true:

- Greenhouse gases stop some of the heat from the Sun from escaping back into space.
- This is the greenhouse effect — it's what keeps the Earth warm enough for us to live here (see page 104).
- Carbon dioxide is a greenhouse gas.
- Burning fossil fuels produces carbon dioxide.
- The level of carbon dioxide in the atmosphere has increased in the last 50 years or so.
- The average temperature of the Earth has increased dramatically over the same period.
- This is global warming, and it's a big headache for the whole planet.

Tip: See pages 1-3 for more on how theories are formed.

Most scientists have looked at all the evidence and agree that the rise in carbon dioxide levels is down to human activity, including burning fossil fuels. They also agree that the extra CO_2 is enhancing the greenhouse effect, and that this is the cause of global warming. There are still a few scientists who think that there are other explanations, either for the rise in CO_2 levels, or for the cause of global warming. That's part of science — it can take a long time for everyone to accept a theory (and you never know when some new evidence might turn up to prove everyone wrong).

HOW SCIENCE WORKS

Greenhouse gases

Some of the electromagnetic radiation from the Sun reaches the Earth and is absorbed. The Earth then re-emits it as infrared radiation (heat). Various gases in the troposphere (the lowest layer of the atmosphere) absorb some of this infrared radiation... and re-emit it in all directions — including back towards Earth, keeping us warm (see Figure 3). This is called the 'greenhouse effect' (even though a real greenhouse doesn't actually work like this, annoyingly).

Tip: Don't get confused — the greenhouse effect isn't a bad thing. In fact, without it the Earth would be too cold for us to live on. The problem comes when the greenhouse effect is enhanced by adding more greenhouse gases to the atmosphere. This causes global warming, which is where all the problems come in.

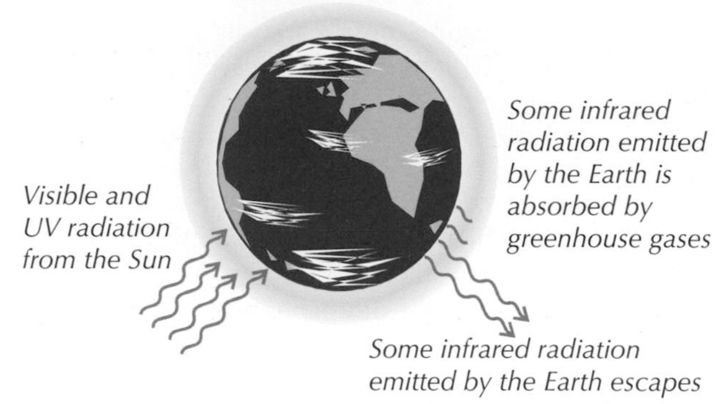

Figure 3: *The greenhouse effect.*

Figure 4: *Methane is released from cows...*

Figure 5: *...and from paddy fields (fields where rice is grown).*

The three main greenhouse gases are water vapour, carbon dioxide and methane. Human activities have caused a rise in greenhouse gas concentrations, which enhances the greenhouse effect. So now too much heat is being trapped and the Earth is getting warmer — this is global warming. Items about global warming on TV and in newspapers usually focus on cutting the levels of carbon dioxide, but the other greenhouse gases are important, too. When alkanes in fossil fuels are burned they also produce water vapour. People tend not to worry so much about water vapour in the atmosphere. There's always been lots of it, and unlike carbon dioxide, the levels have stayed pretty constant — and some of it gets removed every time it rains. The other important greenhouse gas is methane. Methane's produced by rubbish rotting in landfill sites. Methane levels have also risen as we've had to grow more food for our rising population. Cows are responsible for large amounts of methane. From both ends.

Exam Tip
You could be asked to write equations for the complete or incomplete combustion of other alkanes. Make sure you get lots of practice writing out different equations.

Practice Questions — Application

Q1 Write the equation for the complete combustion of pentane (C_5H_{12}).

Q2 Write the equation for the incomplete combustion of pentane (C_5H_{12}) to produce carbon monoxide and water only.

Practice Questions — Fact Recall

Q1 Give the general formula for nitrogen oxides.

Q2 Write an equation to show how nitrogen oxide can be removed from car exhausts by a catalytic converter.

Q3 Explain how acid rain is caused by burning fossil fuels containing sulfur.

Q4 Name three greenhouse gases.

Q5 Briefly describe the greenhouse effect.

Section Summary

Make sure you know...

- What empirical formulas, molecular formulas, structural formulas, displayed formulas, homologous series and functional groups are. You also need to be able to use all the different types of formulas.
- What structural isomerism is.
- How to draw the structures of chain, positional and functional group isomers.
- What alkanes are.
- How to name straight chain and branched alkanes with up to 6 carbon atoms in the stem.
- What haloalkanes and alkenes are.
- How to name haloalkanes and alkenes with up to 6 carbon atoms in the stem.
- What petroleum is.
- How petroleum can be separated by fractional distillation.
- What cracking is and why it is useful.
- The conditions needed for thermal cracking and catalytic cracking and what the products are.
- That alkanes are used as fuels.
- What complete combustion and incomplete combustion are.
- How to write equations for the incomplete and complete combustion of alkanes.
- What pollutants are produced by internal combustion engines and how they are removed.
- How air pollution is created.
- How sulfur dioxide can be removed from flue gases.
- That the combustion of fossil fuels releases carbon dioxide into the atmosphere.
- That carbon dioxide, methane and water vapour are all greenhouse gases.
- That greenhouse gases may contribute to global warming.

Exam-style Questions

1 Heptane is an alkane which is found in crude oil.

1 (a) Give the general formula for an alkane.

(1 mark)

1 (b) Below is the displayed formula for heptane.

```
    H   H   H   H   H   H   H
    |   |   |   |   |   |   |
H — C — C — C — C — C — C — C — H
    |   |   |   |   |   |   |
    H   H   H   H   H   H   H
```

Draw a chain isomer of heptane.

(1 mark)

1 (c) Crude oil can be burnt to generate energy.

1 (c) (i) Write an equation for the incomplete combustion of heptane.

(2 marks)

1 (c) (ii) Explain why the incomplete combustion of heptane can be dangerous.

(3 marks)

1 (d) Heptane can be cracked to form smaller chain hydrocarbons.

1 (d) (i) Explain why it is necessary to crack heptane into smaller chain hydrocarbons.

(1 mark)

1 (d) (ii) Write an equation for the cracking of heptane into smaller chain hydrocarbons.

(1 mark)

1 (d) (iii) In industry, a catalyst can be used to crack heptane.
Explain why a catalyst is used.

(2 marks)

1 (e) Lots of other alkanes can be found in crude oil.
Name the following alkanes.

1 (e) (i)

```
    H   H   H   H   H
    |   |   |   |   |
H — C — C — C — C — C — H
    |   |   |   |   |
    H   H   H   H   H
```

(1 mark)

1 (e) (ii)

```
    H  CH3   H   H
    |   |    |   |
H — C — C  — C — C — H
    |   |    |   |
    H   H   CH3  H
```

(1 mark)

2 The molecule below shows the displayed formula of molecule **A**.

```
    H  H  H  Cl H
    |  |  |  |  |
H—C—C—C—C—C=C<H
    |  |  |  |      H
    H  H  Cl H
```

2 (a) (i) Name molecule **A**.

(1 mark)

2 (a) (ii) Write down the molecular formula of molecule **A**.

(1 mark)

2 (a) (iii) Give the empirical formula of molecule **A**.

(1 mark)

2 (b) (i) The diagram below shows a structural isomer of molecule **A** — molecule **B**.

```
       Cl    Cl
       |     /
    H—C——C—H
     /       \
H—C          C—H
H/  \        /  \H
     C——C—H
  H/ |     \
     H      H
```

Identify what type of structural isomer molecule **B** is.

(1 mark)

2 (b) (ii) Draw a positional isomer of molecule **B**.

(1 mark)

2 (c) The diagram below shows another isomer of molecule **A** — molecule **C**.

```
    H  H  H  Cl H
    |  |  |  |  |
H—C—C—C—C—C=C<H
    |  |  |  |      H
    H  Cl H  H
```

2 (c) (i) Identify what type of structural isomer molecule **C** is.

(1 mark)

2 (c) (ii) Name molecule **C**.

(1 mark)

3 The diagram below shows a molecule of methane.

$$\begin{array}{c} H \\ | \\ H-C-H \\ | \\ H \end{array}$$

3 (a) Methane belongs to the alkane homologous series.

3 (a) (i) Define the term homologous series.

(3 marks)

3 (a) (ii) The molecule below is also from the alkane homologous series.
Give the name of the molecule and its molecular formula.

$$\begin{array}{ccccccc} & H & & H & & H & \\ & | & & | & & | & \\ H- & C & - & C & - & C & -H \\ & | & & | & & | & \\ & H & & H & & H & \end{array}$$

(1 mark)

3 (b) Fractional distillation can be used to produce methane.

3 (b) (i) Explain how the temperature gradient in fractional distillation allows crude oil to be separated.

(3 marks)

3 (b) (ii) Give one use for the gas fraction obtained by fractional distillation.

(1 mark)

3 (c) Methane can also be produced by cracking.

3 (c) (i) Name two different types of cracking.

(1 mark)

3 (c) (ii) State the conditions needed for each type of cracking,
and the products they are used to make.

(4 marks)

3 (d) Methane is a greenhouse gas.

3 (d) (i) Describe why the methane concentration in the upper atmosphere is increasing.

(3 marks)

3 (d) (ii) Explain how this could lead to global warming.

(3 marks)

1. Enthalpy

When chemical reactions happen, there'll be a change in energy. The souped-up chemistry term for this is enthalpy change.

Learning Objectives:
- Understand that enthalpy change (ΔH) is the heat energy change measured under conditions of constant pressure.
- Know that standard enthalpy changes refer to standard conditions, i.e. 100 kPa and a stated temperature (e.g. ΔH_{298}).
- Know that reactions can be endothermic or exothermic.

Specification Reference 3.2.1

Enthalpy notation

Enthalpy change, ΔH (delta H), is the heat energy transferred in a reaction at constant pressure. The units of ΔH are kJ mol^{-1}. You write ΔH° to show that the reactants and products were in their standard states and that the measurements were made under **standard conditions**. Standard conditions are 100 kPa (about 1 atm) pressure and a stated temperature (e.g. ΔH°_{298}). In this book, all the enthalpy changes are measured at 298 K (25 °C). Sometimes the notation will also include a letter to signify whether the enthalpy change is for a reaction (r), combustion (c), or the formation of a new compound (f). See page 112 for more on this notation.

Exothermic reactions

Exothermic reactions give out energy to their surroundings. The products of the reaction end up with less energy than the reactants. This means that the enthalpy change for the reaction, ΔH, will be negative..

Examples

Oxidation is exothermic. Here are two examples:

The combustion of a fuel like methane:

$$CH_{4(g)} + 2O_{2(g)} \rightarrow CO_{2(g)} + 2H_2O_{(l)} \qquad \Delta H^\circ_{c,298} = -890 \text{ kJ mol}^{-1}$$

ΔH is negative so the reaction is **exothermic**.

The oxidation of carbohydrates, like glucose, in respiration is exothermic.

Tip: $\Delta H^\circ_{c,298}$ is the notation for the enthalpy change of a combustion under standard conditions (a pressure of 100 kPa with all substances in their standard states) and at a temperature of 298 K.

Endothermic reactions

Endothermic reactions take in energy from their surroundings. This means that the products of the reaction have more energy than the reactants, so the enthalpy change for the reaction, ΔH, is positive.

Examples

The thermal decomposition of calcium carbonate is endothermic.

$$CaCO_{3(s)} \rightarrow CaO_{(s)} + CO_{2(g)} \qquad \Delta H^\circ_{r,298} = +178 \text{ kJ mol}^{-1}$$

ΔH is positive so the reaction is **endothermic**.

The main reactions of photosynthesis are also endothermic — sunlight supplies the energy.

Figure 1: Photosynthesis in plants is endothermic.

Practice Questions — Fact Recall

Q1 Give the notation for an enthalpy change under standard conditions, at a temperature of 298 K.

Q2 Describe the difference between exothermic and endothermic reactions.

Learning Objectives:

- Be able to determine mean bond enthalpies from given data.
- Be able to use mean bond enthalpies to calculate a value of ΔH for simple reactions.
- Be able to recall the definition of standard enthalpies of combustion (ΔH_c) and formation (ΔH_f).

Specification Reference 3.2.1

2. Bond Enthalpies

Reactions involve breaking and making bonds. The enthalpy change for a reaction depends on which bonds are broken and which are made.

What are bond enthalpies?

Atoms in molecules are held together by strong bonds. It takes energy to break apart the bonds, and energy is given out when new bonds form. The energy needed to break a bond between two atoms is the same amount of energy that is given out when that bond is formed. These 'bond enthalpies' have specific values that differ depending on the atoms (or molecules) attached to either side of the bond.

Breaking and making bonds

When reactions happen, reactant bonds are broken and product bonds are formed. You need energy to break bonds, so bond breaking is endothermic (ΔH is positive). Stronger bonds take more energy to break. Energy is released when bonds are formed, so this is exothermic (ΔH is negative). Stronger bonds release more energy when they form. The enthalpy change for a reaction is the overall effect of these two changes. If you need more energy to break bonds than is released when bonds are made, ΔH is positive. If it's less, ΔH is negative.

Example

Nitrogen reacts with hydrogen to form ammonia (NH_3) in this reaction:

$$N_2 + 3H_2 \rightarrow 2NH_3$$

The energy needed to break all the bonds in N_2 and H_2 = 2253 kJ mol^{-1}.

The energy released when forming the bonds in NH_3 = 2346 kJ mol^{-1}.

The amount of energy released is bigger than the amount needed, so the reaction is exothermic, and ΔH is negative. (See p. 111 for full calculation.)

Tip: You can look up the mean (average) bond enthalpies for different bonds in a data book, or calculate the mean bond enthalpies from given data. In an exam you'll be given any bond enthalpies you need.

Mean bond enthalpies

We tend to use **mean bond enthalpies** in calculations because the energy required to break an individual bond can change depending on where it is.

Example

Water (H_2O) has got two O–H bonds (see Figure 1). You'd think it'd take the same amount of energy to break them both, but it doesn't.

The first bond, H–$OH_{(g)}$: E(H–OH) = +492 kJ mol^{-1}

The second bond, H–$O_{(g)}$: E(H–O) = +428 kJ mol^{-1}

(OH^- is a bit easier to break apart because of the extra electron repulsion.)

So, the mean bond enthalpy for O–H bonds in water is:

$$\frac{492 + 428}{2} = +460 \text{ kJ mol}^{-1}.$$

The data book says the bond enthalpy for O–H is +463 kJ mol^{-1}. It's a bit different than the one calculated above because it's the average for a much bigger range of molecules, not just water. For example, it includes the O-H bonds in alcohols and carboxylic acids too.

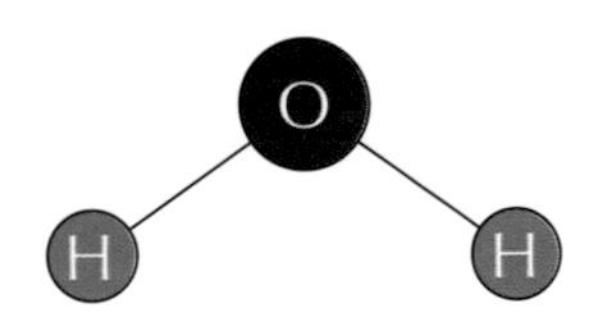

Figure 1: The bonds in a water molecule.

Breaking bonds is always an endothermic process, so mean bond enthalpies are always positive.

Calculating enthalpy changes

In any chemical reaction, energy is absorbed to break bonds and given out during bond formation. The difference between the energy absorbed and released is the overall enthalpy change of reaction:

Enthalpy change of reaction = Total energy absorbed – Total energy released

- To calculate the overall enthalpy change for a reaction, first calculate the total energy needed to break the bonds in the reactants. You'll usually be given the average bond enthalpies for each type of bond, so just multiply each value by the number of each bond present. This total will be the total energy absorbed in the reaction.
- To find the total energy released by the reaction, calculate the total energy needed to form all the new bonds in the products. Use the average bond enthalpies to do this.
- The overall enthalpy change for the reaction can then be found by subtracting the total energy released from the total energy absorbed.

Tip: Draw sketches to show the bonds present in the reactants and products to make sure you include them all in your calculations.

Bond	Bond Enthalpy (Mean value except where stated)
N≡N	945 kJ mol^{-1}
H–H	436 kJ mol^{-1}
N–H	391 kJ mol^{-1}
O=O	498 kJ mol^{-1}
O–H (water)	460 kJ mol^{-1}

Figure 2: Table of bond enthalpies.

Examples

Calculate the overall enthalpy change for the following reaction:

$$N_2 + 3H_2 \rightarrow 2NH_3$$

Use the bond enthalpy values shown in Figure 2.

You might find it helpful to draw a sketch of the molecules in the reaction:

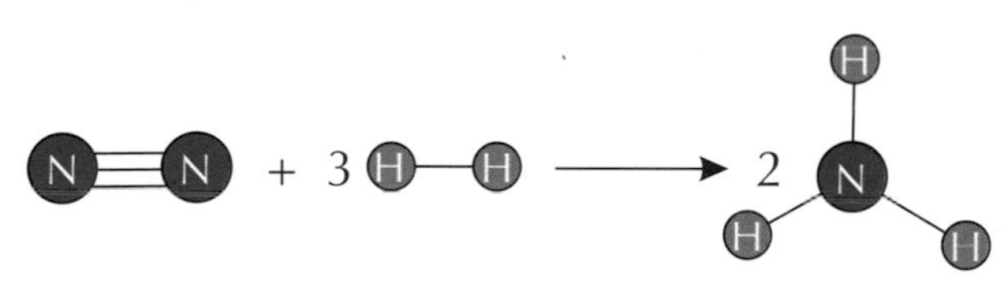

Bonds broken: 1 × N≡N bond broken = 1 × 945 = 945 kJ mol^{-1}
3 × H–H bonds broken = 3 × 436 = 1308 kJ mol^{-1}
Total Energy Absorbed = 945 + 1308 = 2253 kJ mol^{-1}

Bonds formed: 6 × N–H bonds formed = 6 × 391 = 2346 kJ mol^{-1}
Total Energy Released = 2346 kJ mol^{-1}

Now you just subtract 'total energy released' from 'total energy absorbed':

Enthalpy change of reaction = 2253 – 2346 = –93 kJ mol^{-1}.

Calculate the overall enthalpy change for the following reaction:

$$H_{2(g)} + \frac{1}{2}O_{2(g)} \rightarrow H_2O_{(g)}$$

The molecules present are shown below:

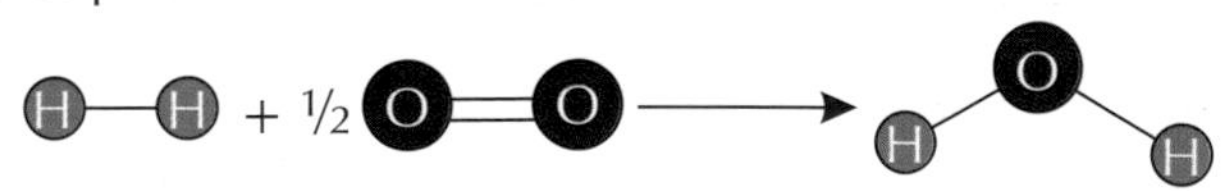

Bonds broken: 1 × H–H bond broken = 1 × 436 = 436 kJ mol^{-1}
½ × O=O bonds broken = ½ × 498 = 249 kJ mol^{-1}
Total Energy Absorbed = 436 + 249 = 685 kJ mol^{-1}

Bonds formed: 2 × O–H bonds formed = 2 × 460 = 920 kJ mol^{-1}
Total Energy Released = 920 kJ mol^{-1}

Enthalpy change of reaction = 685 – 920 = –235 kJ mol^{-1}.

Tip: If you can't remember which value to subtract from which, just take the smaller number from the bigger one then add the sign at the end — positive if 'bonds broken' was the bigger number (endothermic), negative if 'bonds formed' was bigger (exothermic).

Exam Tip
There's quite a bit of maths in this section but you need to learn all these definitions too — you can be asked to write them down in an exam, and it's often the thing that people forget or get wrong.

The different types of ΔH

Standard enthalpy change of reaction

Standard enthalpy change of reaction, ΔH_r°, is the enthalpy change when a reaction occurs in the molar quantities shown in the chemical equation, under standard conditions with all reactants and products in their standard states.

Standard enthalpy change of formation

Standard enthalpy change of formation, ΔH_f°, is the enthalpy change when 1 mole of a compound is formed from its elements in their standard states under standard conditions, e.g $2C_{(s)} + 3H_{2(g)} + \frac{1}{2}O_{2(g)} \rightarrow C_2H_5OH_{(l)}$

Standard enthalpy change of combustion

Standard enthalpy change of combustion, ΔH_c°, is the enthalpy change when 1 mole of a substance is completely burned in oxygen under standard conditions with all reactants and products in their standard states.

Tip: You can ignore any bonds that don't actually change during the reaction. Just work out which bonds actually break and which new bonds form.

Bond	Bond Enthalpy (Mean value except where stated)
C–H	413 kJ mol⁻¹
C=C	612 kJ mol⁻¹
C–C	347 kJ mol⁻¹
C–O	358 kJ mol⁻¹
C–Cl	346 kJ mol⁻¹
C=O (in CO_2)	805 kJ mol⁻¹
C–N	286 kJ mol⁻¹
H–Cl	432 kJ mol⁻¹
Cl–Cl	243.4 kJ mol⁻¹

Figure 3: Table of bond enthalpies.

Practice Questions — Application

Q1 Use the mean bond enthalpies shown in Figures 2 and 3 to calculate the enthalpy changes for the following reactions:

a) $H_2C{=}CH_2$ + H–H → $H_3C{-}CH_3$

b) $H_3C{-}OH$ + H–Cl → $H_3C{-}Cl$ + H–O–H

c) $C_3H_8 + 5O_2 \rightarrow 3CO_2 + 4H_2O$

d) $C_2H_5Cl + NH_3 \rightarrow C_2H_5NH_2 + HCl$

Q2 Calculate the enthalpy change for the complete combustion of ethene (C_2H_4) using the bond enthalpies given in Figures 2 and 3. (The products of complete combustion are CO_2 and H_2O.)

Q3 Calculate the enthalpy change for the formation of hydrogen chloride ($HCl_{(g)}$) from hydrogen ($H_{2(g)}$) and chlorine ($Cl_{2(g)}$) using the bond enthalpies given in Figures 2 and 3.

Q4 The enthalpy change for the following reaction is –181 kJ mol⁻¹:

$$2NO_{(g)} \rightarrow N_{2(g)} + O_{2(g)}$$

Use this value for ΔH_r, along with the data in Figure 2, to estimate a value for the mean bond enthalpy for the bond between nitrogen and oxygen in NO.

Practice Questions — Fact Recall

Q1 What notation is used for the standard enthalpy change of:

a) formation?

b) combustion?

Q2 Define the 'standard enthalpy change of a reaction', and write down the notation used.

3. Measuring Enthalpy Changes

A lot of the data we have on enthalpy changes has come from someone, somewhere, measuring the enthalpy change of a reaction in a lab.

Learning Objective:

- Be able to calculate the enthalpy change from the heat change in a reaction using the equation $q = mc\Delta T$.

Specification Reference 3.2.1

Measuring enthalpy changes in the lab

To measure the enthalpy change for a reaction, you only need to know two things — the number of moles of the stuff that's reacting, and the change in temperature. How you go about doing the experiment depends on what type of reaction it is. Some reactions will quite happily take place in a container and you can just stick a thermometer in to find out the temperature change. It's best to use a polystyrene beaker, so that you don't lose or gain much heat through the sides (see Figure 1).

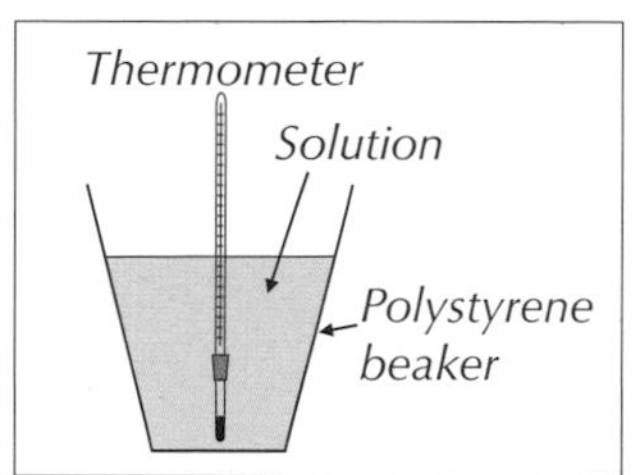

Figure 1: *Simple equipment used to measure the enthalpy change of reaction.*

Combustion reactions are trickier because the reactant is burned in air. A copper calorimeter containing a known mass of water is often used (see Figure 2). You burn a known mass of the reactant and record the temperature change of the water.

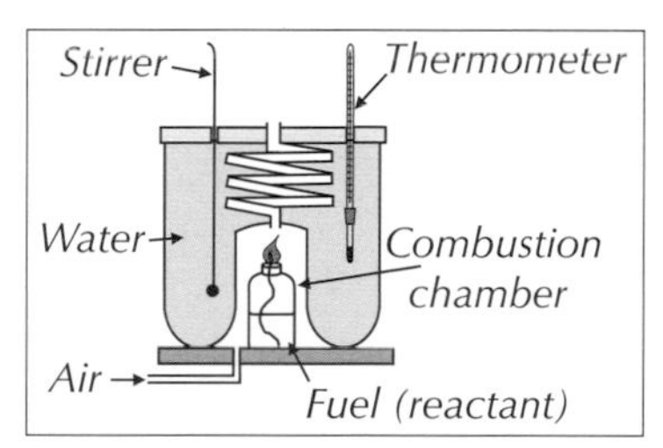

Figure 2: *A copper calorimeter used to measure the enthalpy change of combustion.*

A 'bomb' calorimeter, like the one shown in Figure 3, is a much more accurate piece of equipment, but works on the same principle.

Figure 3: *A bomb calorimeter.*

Using the equation $q = mc\Delta T$

The equation for enthalpy change is:

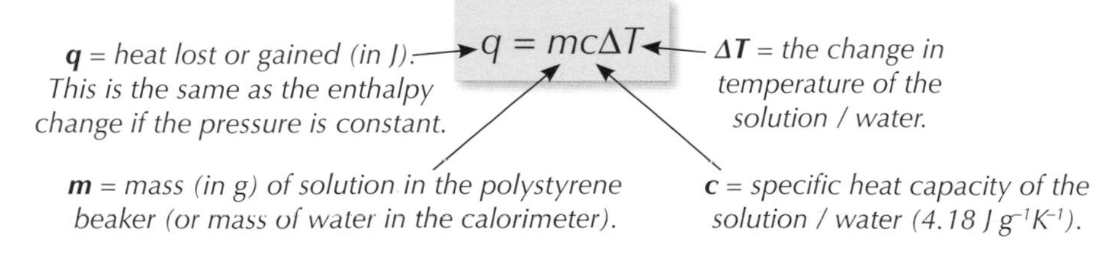

Tip: ΔH° is the standard enthalpy change of a reaction carried out at 100 kPa with all reactants and products in their standard states (see page 109). If the experiment was carried out under different conditions, this method wouldn't give you the value for ΔH°.

Calculating the standard enthalpy change of combustion

To calculate the standard enthalpy change of combustion, ΔH_c°, using data from a laboratory experiment, follow these steps:

Figure 4: A combustion reaction — glucose burning.

Tip: M_r is the relative molecular mass — and it's exactly the same as the molar mass (M). See page 11 for more about this.

Exam Tip
You'll often be asked to suggest why a measured enthalpy change value is different to one in a data book. It's usually to do with heat losses to the surroundings, but it can also be due to things like incomplete combustion.

Step 1: Calculate the amount of heat lost or gained during the combustion using $q = mc\Delta T$ and your measured or given values of m and ΔT. You'll then need to change the units of q from joules to kilojoules.

Step 2: Calculate the number of moles of fuel that caused this enthalpy change, from the mass that reacted. Use the equation:

$$n = \frac{\text{mass}}{M}$$

n is the number of moles of fuel burned.
M is the fuel's molar mass (see page 29).

Step 3: Calculate the standard enthalpy change of combustion, ΔH_c° (in kJ mol^{-1}), using the actual heat change for the reaction, q (in kJ), and the number of moles of fuel that burned, n. Use the equation:

$$\Delta H_c^\circ = \frac{q}{n}$$

Example

Calculating the standard enthalpy change of combustion:

In a laboratory experiment, 1.16 g of an organic liquid fuel was completely burned in oxygen. The heat formed during this combustion raised the temperature of 100 g of water from 295.3 K to 357.8 K. Calculate the standard enthalpy of combustion, ΔH_c°, of the fuel. Its M_r is 58.

Step 1: Calculate the amount of heat given out by the fuel using $q = mc\Delta T$. Remember that m is the mass of water, not the mass of fuel.

$q = mc\Delta T$

$q = 100 \times 4.18 \times (357.8 - 295.3) = 26\,125$ J

Change the amount of heat from J to kJ: $q = 26.125$ kJ.

Step 2: Find out how many moles of fuel produced this heat:

$$n = \frac{\text{mass}}{M} = \frac{1.16\text{ g}}{58\text{ g mol}^{-1}} = 0.02 \text{ moles of fuel.}$$

Step 3: The standard enthalpy of combustion involves 1 mole of fuel.

$$\text{So } \Delta H_c^\circ = \frac{q}{n} = \frac{-26.125\text{ kJ}}{0.02\text{ mol}} \approx -1306\text{ kJ mol}^{-1}.$$

(Note: q is negative because combustion is an exothermic reaction.)

The actual ΔH_c° of this compound is -1615 kJ mol^{-1} — loads of heat has been lost and not measured. E.g. it's likely a fair bit would escape through the copper calorimeter and also the fuel might not combust completely.

Calculating the standard enthalpy change of reaction

The standard enthalpy change of a reaction, ΔH_r°, is calculated in a slightly different way. Instead of calculating the enthalpy change per mole of substance reacted, you need to find the enthalpy change for the number of moles shown in the balanced chemical equation. Step 1 is exactly the same as step 1 for calculating the standard enthalpy change of combustion. It's steps 2 and 3 that are a bit different...

Step 2: Calculate the number of moles of one of the reactants that caused this enthalpy change, from the mass of it that reacted. Use the equation $n = \text{mass} \div M$ again.

Step 3: Calculate the standard enthalpy change of reaction, ΔH_r° (in kJ mol^{-1}) using the actual heat change for the reaction, q (in kJ), and the number of moles that reacted, n, using the equation:

$$\Delta H_r^\circ = \frac{q}{n} \text{ (× number of moles reacting in balanced chemical equation)}$$

Example

Calculating the standard enthalpy change of reaction:

30 g of ammonium chloride ($NH_4Cl_{(s)}$) is dissolved in water in a polystyrene beaker. The temperature of the contents of the beaker decreases from 298 K to 296 K. The total mass of the solution is 980 g. Calculate the standard molar enthalpy change for the reaction.

The balanced reaction is: $NH_4Cl_{(s)} \rightarrow NH_4^+{}_{(aq)} + Cl^-{}_{(aq)}$

The molar mass, M, of $NH_4Cl = 14 + (4 \times 1) + 35.5 = 53.5 \text{ g mol}^{-1}$.

Step 1: $q = mc\Delta T = 980 \times 4.18 \times (298 - 296) = 8192.8 \text{ J} = 8.1928 \text{ kJ}$

Step 2: $n = \dfrac{30 \text{ g}}{53.5 \text{ g mol}^{-1}} = 0.5607$ moles of NH_4Cl.

Step 3: The balanced reaction involves one mole of NH_4Cl so:

$$\Delta H_r^{\circ} = \frac{q}{n} = \frac{8.1928 \text{ kJ}}{0.5607 \text{ mol}} \approx +14.6 \text{ kJ mol}^{-1}.$$

Tip: When finding the standard enthalpy change of a reaction, always write out a balanced equation for the reaction so you can see the correct molar quantities.

Practice Questions — Application

Q1 0.05 mol of a compound dissolves in water, causing the temperature of the solution to increase from 298 K to 301 K. The total mass of the solution is 220 g. Calculate the enthalpy change for the reaction in kJ mol^{-1}. Assume $c = 4.18 \text{ J g}^{-1} \text{ K}^{-1}$.

Q2 A calorimeter, containing 200 g of water ($c = 4.18 \text{ J g}^{-1} \text{ K}^{-1}$), was used to measure the enthalpy change of combustion of pentane ($C_5H_{12(l)}$, $M_r = 72$). 0.5 g of pentane was burnt, which increased the temperature of the water by 29 K.

a) Calculate the enthalpy change of combustion of pentane. Give your answer in kJ mol^{-1}.

b) Suggest reasons why this value may be different to the standard enthalpy change of combustion of pentane given in a data book.

Q3 The standard enthalpy of combustion of octane ($C_8H_{18(l)}$, $M_r = 114$) is −5512 kJ mol^{-1}. Some octane was burnt in a calorimeter containing 300 g of water ($c = 4.18 \text{ J g}^{-1} \text{ K}^{-1}$). The temperature of the water went up by 55 K. Calculate an estimate of the mass of propane burnt.

Tip: Remember — if the temperature has increased during the reaction (i.e. it's exothermic), you need to use a negative value for q in your calculations.

Practice Questions — Fact Recall

Q1 What two things need to be measured in order to calculate the enthalpy change for a reaction in a laboratory?

Q2 Sketch and label a calorimeter that could be used in the lab to measure the enthalpy change of a combustion.

Q3 a) In the equation $q = mc\Delta T$, what does 'q' stand for?

b) What are the units of q?

Q4 What conditions are needed to measure the standard enthalpy change of a reaction, ΔH_r°?

Q5 Explain how you would calculate ΔH_r° for a reaction, given a value for q and the number of moles, n, of a reactant used in the reaction.

4. Hess's Law

Learning Objective:

- Know Hess's Law and be able to use it to perform simple calculations, for example calculating enthalpy changes for reactions from enthalpies of combustion or enthalpies of formation.

Specification Reference 3.2.1

For some reactions, there is no easy way to measure enthalpy changes in the lab. For these, we can use Hess's Law.

What is Hess's Law?

Hess's Law says that:

> The total enthalpy change of a reaction is always the same, no matter which route is taken.

This law is handy for working out enthalpy changes that you can't find directly by doing an experiment — for example, the enthalpy change of the reaction that breaks down NO_2 into N_2 and O_2. We can call this reaction 'route 1'. But we can also think of the reaction as NO_2 breaking down into NO and O_2, and then reacting further to form N_2 and O_2. This longer route, with an intermediate step, can be called 'route 2' (see Figure 1).

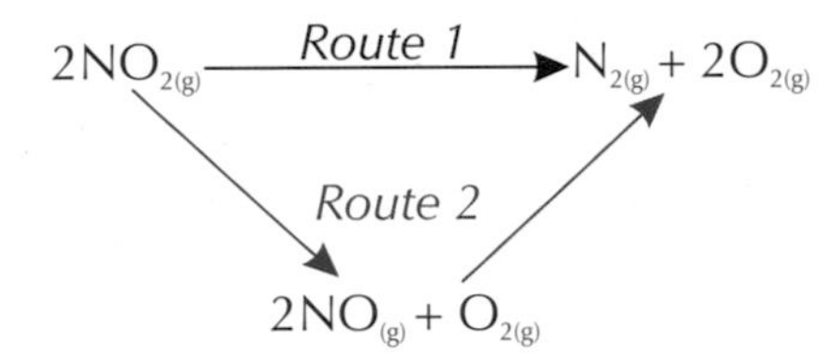

Figure 1: *Two possible routes for the formation of nitrogen and oxygen from nitrogen dioxide.*

Hess's Law says that the total enthalpy change for route 1 is the same as for route 2. So if you know the enthalpy changes for the stages of route 2, you can calculate the enthalpy change for route 1, as shown in the example below.

Example

Use Hess's Law to calculate the enthalpy change, ΔH_r°, for route 1 of the reaction shown below.

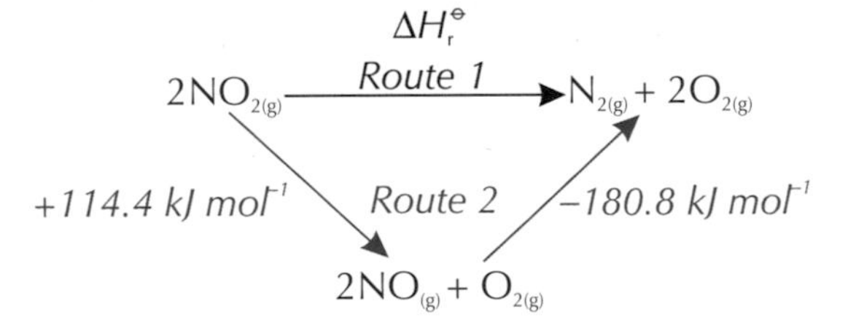

The total enthalpy change for route 1 is the same as the total enthalpy change for route 2. So the enthalpy change for route 1 is the sum of the steps in route 2:

ΔH_r° = 144.4 kJ + (–180.8 kJ) = –66.4 kJ mol^{-1}.

Using enthalpies of formation

Enthalpy changes of formation are useful for calculating enthalpy changes you can't find directly. You need to know ΔH_f° for all the reactants and products that are compounds. The value of ΔH_f° for elements is zero — the element's being formed from the element, so there's no change in enthalpy.
The standard enthalpy changes are all measured at 298 K.

Example

Calculate ΔH_r° for this reaction using the enthalpies of formation in Figure 2:

$$SO_{2(g)} + 2H_2S_{(g)} \rightarrow 3S_{(s)} + 2H_2O_{(l)}$$

- Write under the reaction a list of all the elements present in the reaction, balanced in their correct molar quantities, as shown below:

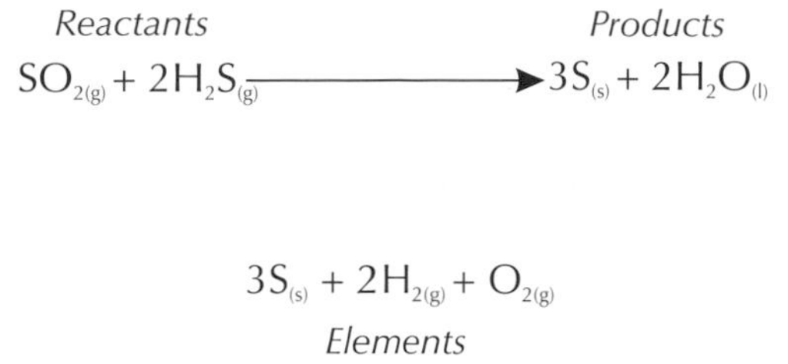

Reactants $SO_{2(g)} + 2H_2S_{(g)} \longrightarrow 3S_{(s)} + 2H_2O_{(l)}$ *Products*

$3S_{(s)} + 2H_{2(g)} + O_{2(g)}$
Elements

- Enthalpies of formation (ΔH_f°) tell you the enthalpy change going from the elements to the compounds. The enthalpy change of reaction (ΔH_r°) is the enthalpy change going from the reactants to the products. Draw and label arrows to show this on your diagram:

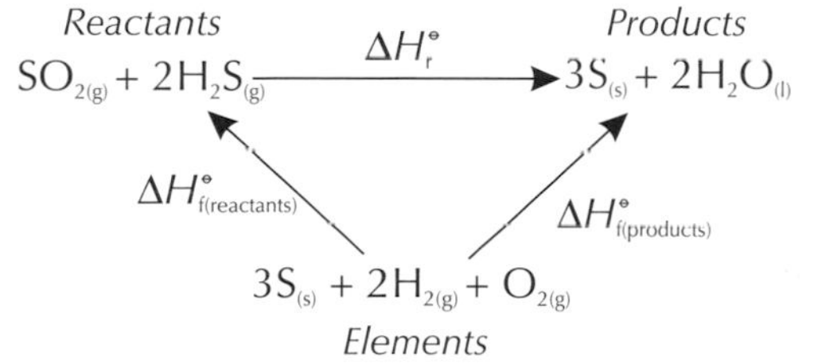

Reactants $SO_{2(g)} + 2H_2S_{(g)} \xrightarrow{\Delta H_r^\circ} 3S_{(s)} + 2H_2O_{(l)}$ *Products*

$\Delta H^\circ_{f(reactants)}$ $\Delta H^\circ_{f(products)}$

$3S_{(s)} + 2H_{2(g)} + O_{2(g)}$
Elements

- The calculation is often simpler if you keep the arrows end to end, so make both routes go from the elements to the products. Route 1 gets there via the reactants (and includes ΔH_r°), whilst route 2 gets there directly. Label the enthalpy changes along each arrow, as shown below. There are 2 moles of H_2O and 2 moles of H_2S, so their enthalpies of formation will need to be multiplied by 2. ΔH_f° of sulfur is zero because it's an element, but you can still label it on the diagram.

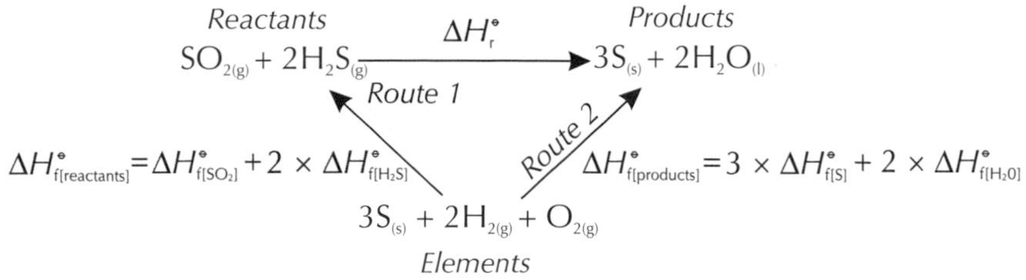

Reactants $SO_{2(g)} + 2H_2S_{(g)} \xrightarrow{\Delta H_r^\circ} 3S_{(s)} + 2H_2O_{(l)}$ *Products*

Route 1 *Route 2*

$\Delta H^\circ_{f[reactants]} = \Delta H^\circ_{f[SO_2]} + 2 \times \Delta H^\circ_{f[H_2S]}$ $\Delta H^\circ_{f[products]} = 3 \times \Delta H^\circ_{f[S]} + 2 \times \Delta H^\circ_{f[H_2O]}$

$3S_{(s)} + 2H_{2(g)} + O_{2(g)}$
Elements

- Use Hess's Law, Route 1 = Route 2, and plug the numbers from Figure 2 into the equation:

$$\Delta H^\circ_{f\,[SO_2]} + 2\Delta H^\circ_{f\,[H_2S]} + \Delta H_r^\circ = 3\Delta H^\circ_{f\,[S]} + 2\Delta H^\circ_{f\,[H_2O]}$$
$$-297 + (2 \times -20.2) + \Delta H_r^\circ = (3 \times 0) + (2 \times -286)$$
$$\Delta H_r^\circ = (3 \times 0) + (2 \times -286) - [-297 + (2 \times -20.2)] = -234.6 \text{ kJ mol}^{-1}.$$

Compound	ΔH_f°
$SO_{2(g)}$	–297 kJ mol^{-1}
$H_2S_{(g)}$	–20.2 kJ mol^{-1}
$H_2O_{(l)}$	–286 kJ mol^{-1}

Figure 2: *Table of enthalpies of formation for three compounds.*

Tip: You don't have to pick a route that follows the direction of the arrows. If your route goes against an arrow you can just change the signs (so negative enthalpies become positive and positive enthalpies become negative). There's an example of this on page 119.

Using enthalpies of combustion

You can use a similar method to find an enthalpy change from enthalpy changes of combustion, instead of using enthalpy changes of formation.

Substance	ΔH_c°
$C_{(s)}$	–394 kJ mol⁻¹
$H_{2(g)}$	–286 kJ mol⁻¹
$C_2H_5OH_{(l)}$	–1367 kJ mol⁻¹

Figure 3: *Table of enthalpies of combustion for three substances.*

Example

Calculate ΔH_f° of ethanol using the enthalpies of combustion in Figure 3.

- The desired reaction in this case is the formation of ethanol from its elements, so write out the balanced equation:

Reactants *Product*

$$2C_{(s)} + 3H_{2(g)} + \tfrac{1}{2}O_{2(g)} \longrightarrow C_2H_5OH_{(l)}$$

- Figure 3 tells you the enthalpy change when each of the 'reactants' and 'products' is burned in oxygen. Add these combustion reactions to your diagram, making sure they are balanced, as shown below:

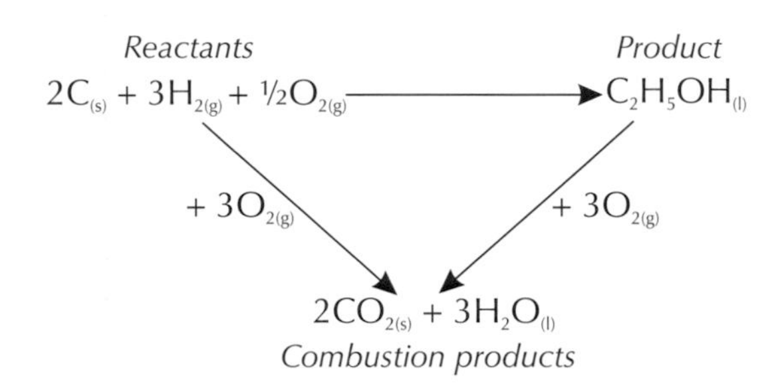

Tip: The products of a complete combustion are carbon dioxide (CO_2) and water (H_2O).

- Choose which reactions will form which route. Label the diagram with the enthalpy changes along each arrow as before (taking into account molar quantities):

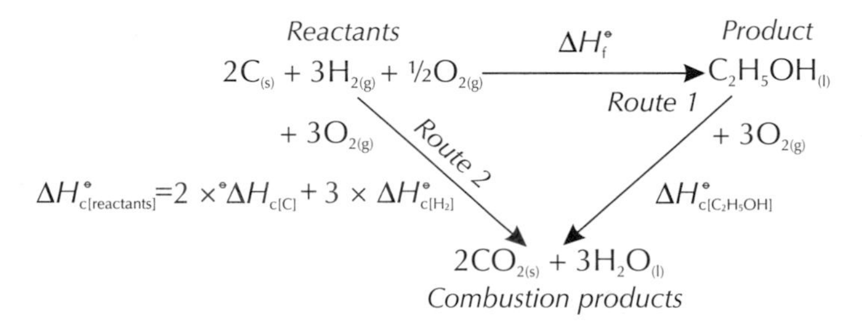

Tip: You can ignore the enthalpy change of combustion of oxygen in these calculations. Oxygen doesn't have an enthalpy change of combustion — you can't burn 1 mole of oxygen in oxygen.

- Use Hess's Law as follows: Route 1 = Route 2

$$\Delta H_f^{\circ}[\text{ethanol}] + \Delta H_c^{\circ}[C_2H_5OH] = 2\Delta H_c^{\circ}[C] + 3\Delta H_c^{\circ}[H_2]$$

$$\Delta H_f^{\circ}[\text{ethanol}] + (-1367) = (2 \times -394) + (3 \times -286)$$

$$\Delta H_f^{\circ}[\text{ethanol}] = -788 + -858 - (-1367)$$

$$\Delta H_f^{\circ}[\text{ethanol}] = -279 \text{ kJ mol}^{-1}.$$

Using enthalpies of reaction

You can also use Hess's Law to calculate enthalpy changes using a group of linked reactions, where all but one of the enthalpy changes for the reactions are known. The following example shows how to do this, this time choosing routes where the arrows don't run end to end.

Reaction	ΔH_r°
ΔH_1	+987 kJ mol^{-1}
ΔH_2	–366 kJ mol^{-1}
ΔH_3	–85 kJ mol^{-1}

Figure 4: Table of enthalpies of reaction for three reactions.

Examples

Calculate ΔH_r for the reaction below using the data given in Figure 4.

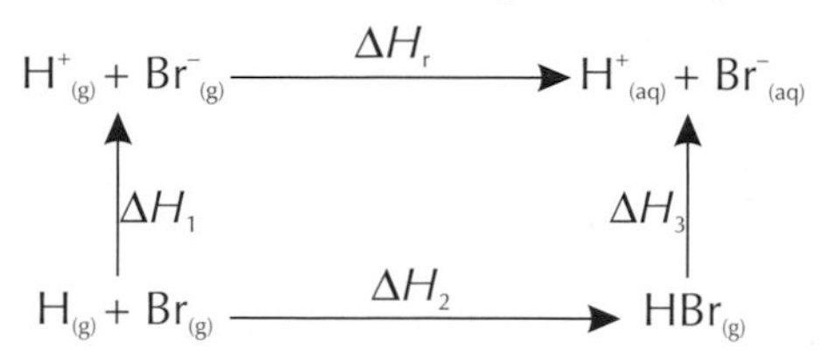

You are given three of the four enthalpies for these reactions, so use Hess's Law to find the unknown ΔH_r. First though, choose and label the two routes. For this example we will choose routes that go against the direction of the arrows, to show how this method works:

$H^+_{(g)} + Br^-_{(g)}$ —ΔH_r (Route 1)→ $H^+_{(aq)} + Br^-_{(aq)}$

$-\Delta H_1$ ↓ ↑ ΔH_1 ΔH_3 ↑

$H_{(g)} + Br_{(g)}$ —ΔH_2 (Route 2)→ $HBr_{(g)}$

The first step in the chosen route 2 goes against the direction of the arrow for ΔH_1. The enthalpy change for a backwards reaction is exactly the same size as for the forwards reaction — but with the opposite sign. So the enthalpy change for the first step in route 2 will be $-\Delta H_1$, as shown.

Now just use Hess's Law as before:

Route 1 = Route 2

$\Delta H_r = -\Delta H_1 + \Delta H_2 + \Delta H_3$

$\Delta H_r = -987 + (-366) + (-85)$

$\Delta H_r = -1438$ kJ mol^{-1}.

Exam Tip

It doesn't really matter how you pick your routes to do the Hess's Law calculation in an exam question, so choose a method that you're comfortable with. Just take care with the positives and negatives by labelling everything clearly and writing down each step of your working.

Practice Questions — Application

Q1 Calculate ΔH_r° for the following reactions using Hess's Law, and the enthalpies of formation given in Figure 5:

a) $2Na_{(s)} + 2H_2O_{(l)} \rightarrow 2NaOH_{(aq)} + H_{2(g)}$

b) $MgO_{(s)} + 2HCl_{(aq)} \rightarrow MgCl_{2(s)} + H_2O_{(l)}$

c) $NaOH_{(aq)} + HCl_{(aq)} \rightarrow NaCl_{(aq)} + H_2O_{(l)}$

Q2 Calculate ΔH_f° for the following organic compounds using Hess's Law, and the enthalpies of combustion given in Figure 6 and below:

a) propan-1-ol (C_3H_7OH): $\Delta H_c^\circ = -2021$ kJ mol^{-1}.

b) ethane-1,2-diol ($C_2H_4(OH)_2$): $\Delta H_c^\circ = -1180$ kJ mol^{-1}.

c) butan-2-one (C_4H_8O): $\Delta H_c^\circ = -2442$ kJ mol^{-1}.

Compound	ΔH_f°
$H_2O_{(l)}$	–286 kJ mol^{-1}
$NaOH_{(aq)}$	–469 kJ mol^{-1}
$MgO_{(s)}$	–602 kJ mol^{-1}
$HCl_{(aq)}$	–167 kJ mol^{-1}
$MgCl_{2(s)}$	–641 kJ mol^{-1}
$NaCl_{(aq)}$	–407 kJ mol^{-1}

Figure 5: Table of enthalpies of formation for six compounds.

Element	ΔH_c°
$C_{(s)}$	–394 kJ mol^{-1}
$H_{2(g)}$	–286 kJ mol^{-1}

Figure 6: Enthalpies of combustion for carbon and hydrogen.

Q3 The reaction scheme below involves 7 unknown substances, A-G:

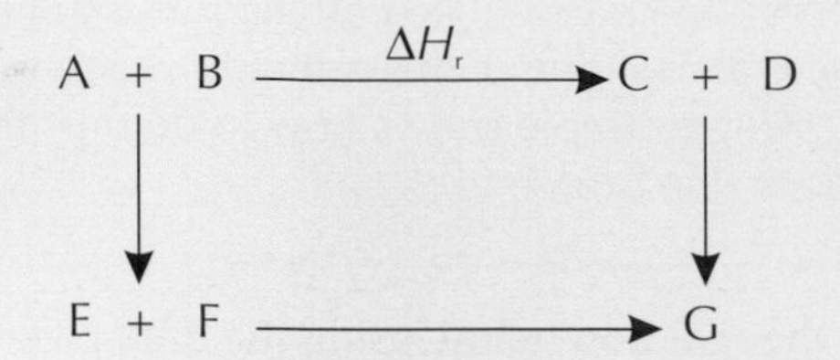

Reaction	ΔH (kJ mol^{-1})
A + B → E + F	–837
E + F → G	+89
C + D → G	+424

Use Hess's Law, along with the data in the table, to calculate the enthalpy change, ΔH_r, for the reaction A + B → C + D.

Section Summary

Make sure you know...

- That enthalpy change, ΔH (in kJ mol^{-1}), is the heat energy transferred in a reaction at constant pressure.
- That ΔH° is the enthalpy change for a reaction where the reactants and products are in their standard states and the measurements are made at 100 kPa pressure and a stated temperature (usually 298 K).
- That exothermic reactions give out energy, so ΔH is negative.
- That endothermic reactions absorb energy, so ΔH is positive.
- That mean bond enthalpies tell us the average energy (per mole) required to break the bond between two atoms.
- How to use mean bond enthalpies to calculate enthalpy changes for reactions, using the equation: Enthalpy change of reaction = Total energy absorbed – Total energy released.
- That ΔH_r° is the enthalpy change when a reaction occurs in the molar quantities shown in the chemical equation, under standard conditions with all reactants and products in their standard states.
- That ΔH_f° is the enthalpy change when 1 mole of a compound is formed from its elements in their standard states under standard conditions.
- That ΔH_c° is the enthalpy change when 1 mole of a substance is completely burned in oxygen under standard conditions.
- How to calculate the heat lost or gained (q) by a reaction in the laboratory using the equation $q = mc\Delta T$, where m is the mass of the reaction mixture, c is its specific heat capacity, and ΔT is the temperature change due to the reaction.
- That for a reaction at a constant pressure, the enthalpy change, ΔH, is the heat change, q, per mole.
- How to calculate the enthalpy change of combustion and the enthalpy change of reaction given values for q and n, the number of moles reacted.
- That Hess's Law says that:
  The total enthalpy change of a reaction is always the same, no matter which route is taken.
- How to use Hess's Law to calculate enthalpy changes for reactions from enthalpies of formation.
- How to use Hess's Law to calculate enthalpy changes for reactions from enthalpies of combustion.
- How to use Hess's Law to calculate enthalpy changes for reactions from other enthalpies of reaction.

Exam-style Questions

1 A teacher is demonstrating the following neutralisation reaction to her class:

$$HCl_{(aq)} + NH_{3(aq)} \rightarrow NH_4Cl_{(aq)}$$

She adds 0.005 mol of hydrochloric acid to an excess of ammonia in a polystyrene beaker, and measures the rise in temperature.

The solution in the beaker has a total mass of 50 g, and a specific heat capacity of 4.7 J g^{-1} K^{-1}.

1 (a) The temperature rises by 1 °C. Calculate the enthalpy change due to the reaction.

(3 marks)

1 (b) State two conditions necessary for the enthalpy change calculated in **1** part **(a)** to be the standard enthalpy change of reaction for the neutralisation.

(2 marks)

1 (c) The data book gives a value of –53.4 kJ mol^{-1} for the standard enthalpy change of this reaction.

Give two reasons why the teacher's experiment gives a different value.

(2 marks)

2 The table below shows the standard enthalpy change of combustion, ΔH_c°, for carbon, hydrogen and octane ($C_8H_{18(l)}$). The standard enthalpy of formation of octane can be calculated from this data using Hess's Law.

	ΔH_c°
$C_{(s)}$	–394 kJ mol^{-1}
$H_{2(g)}$	–286 kJ mol^{-1}
$C_8H_{18(l)}$	–5470 kJ mol^{-1}

2 (a) State Hess's Law.

(1 mark)

2 (b) Write out a balanced chemical equation for the complete combustion of octane.

(1 mark)

2 (c) (i) Use your answers to parts **(a)** and **(b)**, and the data in the table above, to calculate the standard enthalpy change of formation of octane, ΔH_f°.

(3 marks)

2 (c) (ii) State whether the formation of octane is exothermic or endothermic. Explain your answer.

(2 marks)

3 The structure of but-1-ene is shown below.

$$H-\underset{H}{\overset{H}{C}}-\underset{H}{\overset{H}{C}}-\overset{H}{C}=C\begin{matrix}H\\H\end{matrix}$$

But-1-ene will burn completely in oxygen to produce CO_2 and H_2O.

The table below shows bond enthalpies for the bonds present in the reactants and products of this combustion reaction.

Bond	Bond Enthalpy (Mean value except where stated)
C–H	413 kJ mol^{-1}
C=C	612 kJ mol^{-1}
C–C	347 kJ mol^{-1}
O=O	498 kJ mol^{-1}
C=O (in CO_2)	805 kJ mol^{-1}
O–H (in H_2O)	460 kJ mol^{-1}

These bond enthalpies can be used to calculate the standard enthalpy change of combustion for but-1-ene.

3 (a) Define the term 'standard enthalpy change of combustion'.

(3 marks)

3 (b) Use the data in the table to calculate a value for the standard enthalpy change of combustion for but-1-ene.

(3 marks)

3 (c) The standard enthalpy change of combustion for but-1-ene calculated from the mean bond enthalpies is different to the value given in the data book. Explain why.

(1 mark)

4 Potassium hydroxide reacts with sulphuric acid in the following way:

$$2KOH_{(s)} + H_2SO_{4(l)} \rightarrow K_2SO_{4(s)} + 2H_2O_{(l)}$$

The table below shows the standard enthalpies of formation of each of the reactants and products in this reaction.

	$\Delta H_f^\ominus$
$KOH_{(s)}$	–425 kJ mol^{-1}
$H_2SO_{4(l)}$	–814 kJ mol^{-1}
$K_2SO_{4(s)}$	–1438 kJ mol^{-1}
$H_2O_{(l)}$	–286 kJ mol^{-1}

4 (a) Define the term 'standard enthalpy of formation'.

(3 marks)

4 (b) Use the data in the table to calculate a value for the standard enthalpy change of the reaction, $\Delta H_r^\ominus$.

(3 marks)

Unit 2 Section 2: Kinetics and Equilibria

1. Reaction Rates

The rate of a reaction is how quickly the reaction happens.

Collision theory and activation energy

Particles in liquids and gases are always moving and colliding with each other. They don't react every time though — only when the conditions are right. **Collision theory** says that a reaction won't take place between two particles unless they collide in the right direction (they need to be facing each other the right way) and they collide with at least a certain minimum amount of kinetic (movement) energy.

The minimum amount of kinetic energy particles need to react is called the **activation energy**. The particles need this much energy to break the bonds to start the reaction. Reactions with low activation energies often happen pretty easily. But reactions with high activation energies don't. You need to give the particles extra energy by heating them.

Learning Objectives:

- Understand that most collisions do not lead to a reaction.
- Understand that reactions can only occur when collisions take place between particles having sufficient energy.
- Be able to define the term activation energy and understand its significance.
- Have a qualitative understanding of the Maxwell–Boltzmann distribution of molecular energies in gases.
- Be able to draw and interpret distribution curves for different temperatures.
- Understand the qualitative effect of temperature changes on the rate of reaction.
- Understand how small temperature increases can lead to a large increase in rate.
- Understand the qualitative effect of changes in concentration on rate of reaction.

Specification Reference 3.2.2

Enthalpy profile diagrams

To make things a bit clearer, we can draw an enthalpy profile diagram like the one shown below in Figure 1.

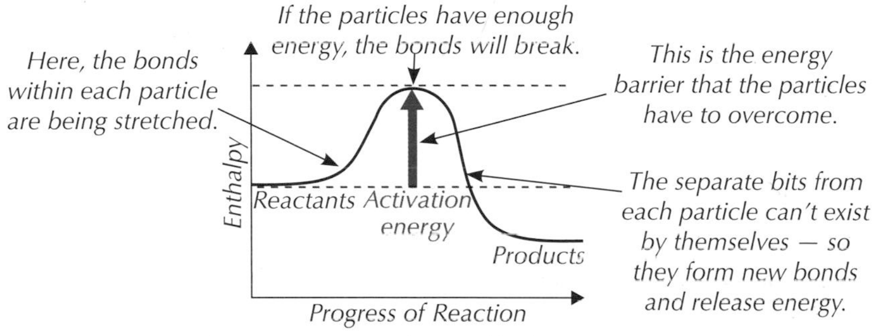

Figure 1: *An enthalpy profile diagram.*

Enthalpy profile diagrams can be used to work out the enthalpy change (ΔH) of a reaction, and whether it is exothermic or endothermic (see page 109). ΔH is the difference between the enthalpy of the reactants and the enthalpy of the products on the diagram. If the products have a lower enthalpy than the reactants, the reaction is exothermic. If the products have a higher enthalpy than the reactants, the reaction is endothermic.

Example

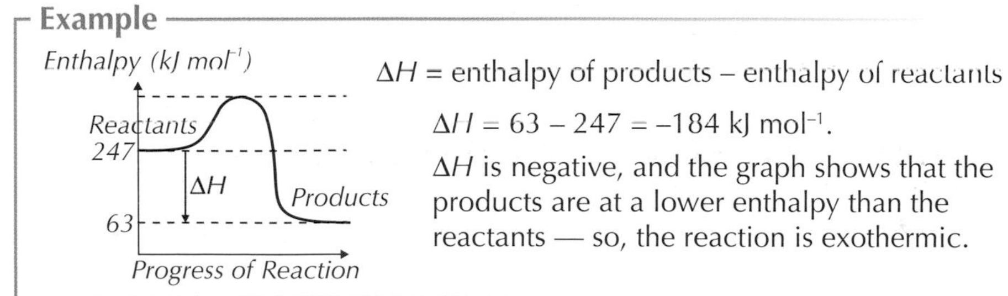

ΔH = enthalpy of products – enthalpy of reactants

$\Delta H = 63 - 247 = -184$ kJ mol^{-1}.

ΔH is negative, and the graph shows that the products are at a lower enthalpy than the reactants — so, the reaction is exothermic.

Figure 3: James Clerk Maxwell, the Scottish physicist who studied the motion of gas molecules.

Maxwell-Boltzmann distributions

Imagine looking down on Oxford Street when it's teeming with people. You'll see some people ambling along slowly, some hurrying quickly, but most of them will be walking with a moderate speed. It's the same with the molecules in a gas. Some don't have much kinetic energy and move slowly. Others have loads of kinetic energy and whizz along. But most molecules are somewhere in between. If you plot a graph of the numbers of molecules in a gas with different kinetic energies you get a **Maxwell-Boltzmann distribution**. The Maxwell-Boltzmann distribution is a theoretical model that has been developed to explain scientific observations. It looks like this —

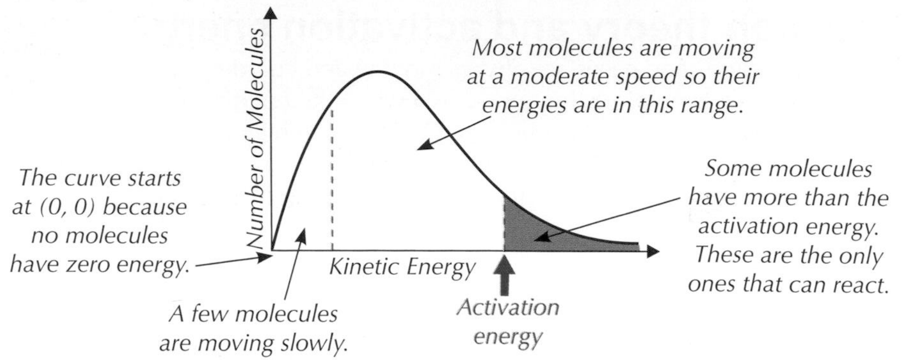

Figure 2: A Maxwell-Boltzmann distribution curve showing the different kinetic energies of molecules in a gas.

Figure 4: Ludwig Boltzmann, the Austrian physicist who developed Maxwell's ideas on the energy distribution of gas molecules.

The effect of temperature on reaction rate

If you increase the temperature of a gas, the molecules will on average have more kinetic energy and will move faster. So, a greater proportion of molecules will have at least the activation energy and be able to react. This changes the shape of the Maxwell-Boltzmann distribution curve — it pushes it over to the right (see Figure 5). The total number of molecules is still the same, which means the area under each curve must be the same.

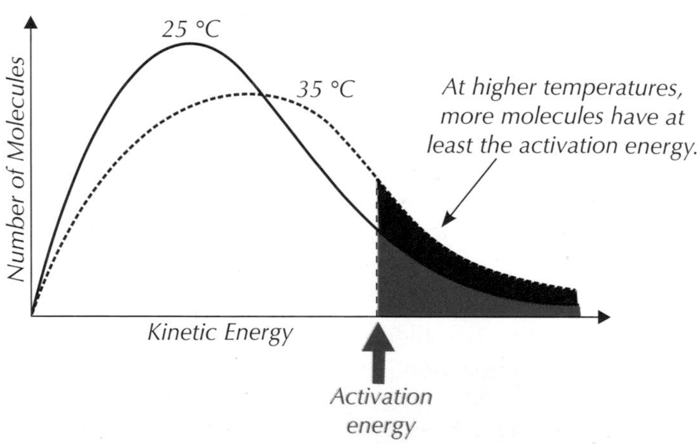

Figure 5: Two Maxwell-Boltzmann distribution curves for a gas at different temperatures. Increasing the temperature of the gas shifts the distribution of the kinetic energies of the molecules.

Because the molecules are flying about faster, they'll collide more often. This is another reason why increasing the temperature makes a reaction faster. So, small temperature increases can lead to large increases in reaction rate.

Exam Tip
You need to be able to draw distribution curves for different temperatures so remember — if the temperature **i**ncreases the curve moves to the **r**ight, if it d**e**creases the curve moves to the l**e**ft.

The effect of concentration on reaction rate

If you increase the concentration of reactants in a solution, the particles will on average be closer together. If they're closer, they'll collide more often. If there are more collisions, they'll have more chances to react.

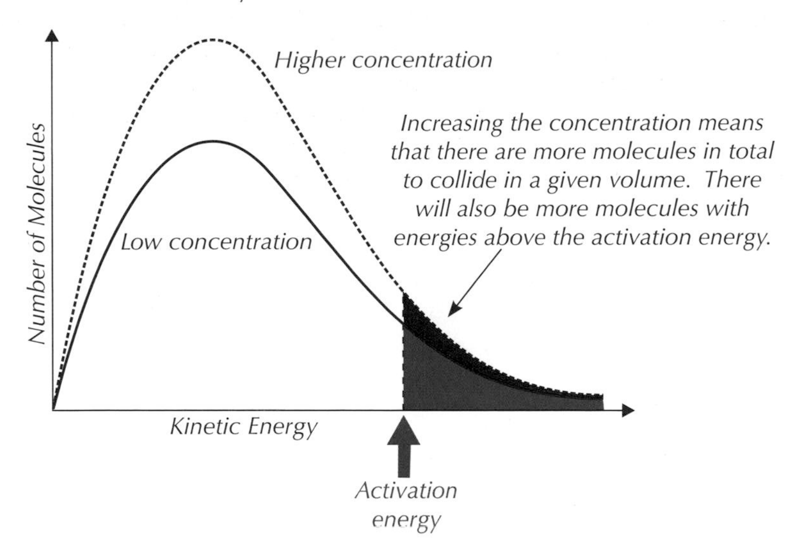

Figure 6: *Two Maxwell-Boltzmann distribution curves for a solution at different concentrations.*

Tip: Figure 6 refers to the number of molecules in a given volume. Changing the volume as well as the concentration means that two variables in the experiment have changed — you wouldn't be able to tell what was causing the change in the Maxwell-Boltzmann distribution. See page 204 for more on variables.

If the reaction involves gases, increasing the pressure of the gases works in just the same way. A higher pressure means that there are more molecules in total to collide in a given volume so there will be more molecules with energies above the activation energy.

Practice Questions — Application

Q1 a) Calculate the enthalpy change of the reaction shown in the enthalpy profile diagram below.

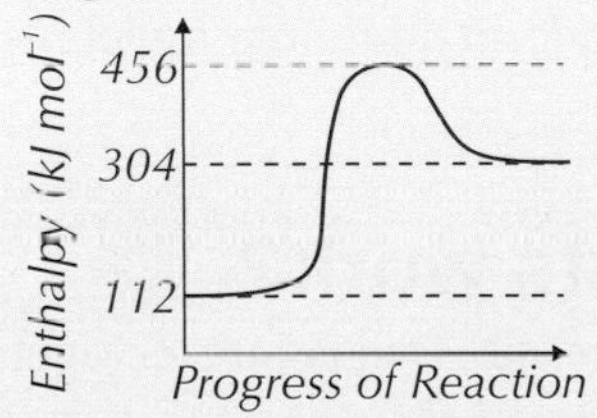

b) Is the reaction exothermic or endothermic? Explain your answer.

Q2 The two Maxwell-Boltzmann distribution curves shown in Figure 7 are for the same volume of the same gas. Which curve, A or B, is for the gas at a higher temperature? Explain your answer.

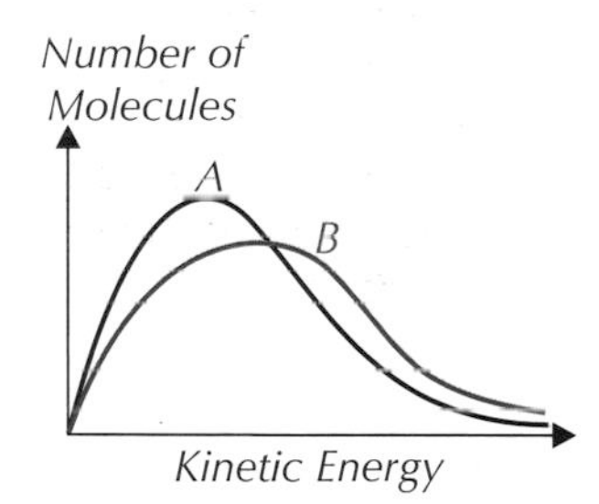

Figure 7: *Two Maxwell-Boltzmann distribution curves for a volume of gas at different temperatures.*

Practice Questions — Fact Recall

Q1 What conditions are required for a collision between two particles to result in a reaction?

Q2 What does the term 'activation energy' mean?

Q3 Explain why a small increase in temperature can lead to a large increase in reaction rate.

Q4 Describe and explain the effect that increasing the concentration of a solution has on the rate of a reaction involving that solution.

2. Catalysts

Learning Objectives:

- Know the meaning of the term catalyst.
- Understand that catalysts work by providing an alternative reaction route of lower activation energy.

Specification Reference 3.2.2

Sometimes you need to speed up a reaction, but you can't (or don't want to) increase the temperature, concentration or pressure any further. That's where catalysts come in.

What is a catalyst?

You can use **catalysts** to make chemical reactions happen faster. A catalyst increases the rate of a reaction by providing an alternative reaction pathway with a lower activation energy. The catalyst is chemically unchanged at the end of the reaction.

Catalysts are great. They don't get used up in reactions, so you only need a tiny bit of catalyst to catalyse a huge amount of stuff. They do take part in reactions, but they're remade at the end. Catalysts are very fussy about which reactions they catalyse. Many will usually only work on a single reaction. Catalysts save heaps of money in industrial processes.

Figure 1: Fritz Haber, the German chemist who developed the process of ammonia production with Carl Bosch.

Example

The Haber-Bosch process uses an iron catalyst to increase the rate of forming ammonia from nitrogen and hydrogen in the following reaction:

$$N_{2(g)} + 3H_{2(g)} \rightleftharpoons 2NH_{3(g)}$$

This reaction has a very high activation energy, due to a very strong N≡N bond in N_2. For the reaction rate to be high enough to make ammonia in any great quantity, the temperature and pressure would have to be extremely high — too high to be practical or profitable.

In reality, the reaction is performed with the use of an iron catalyst, which increases the reaction rate at a workable temperature and pressure (around 400-500 °C and 20 MPa).

The nitrogen and hydrogen molecules bind to the surface of the catalyst. This makes it easier to break the bonds at lower energies, and so the activation energy of the reaction decreases. The broken nitrogen and hydrogen molecules then form ammonia molecules, and break away from the surface of the catalyst.

Tip: The reaction used to make ammonia is a reversible reaction — there's more on reversible reactions on pages 128-130.

How do catalysts work?

If you look at an enthalpy profile (see Figure 2) together with a Maxwell-Boltzmann distribution (Figure 3 — next page), you can see why catalysts work.

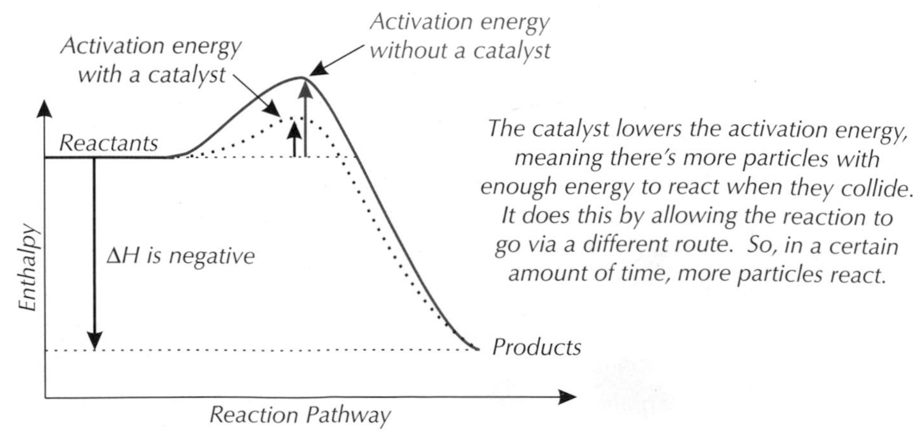

Figure 2: Enthalpy profile diagram for a reaction with and without a catalyst.

With a catalyst present, the molecules still have the same amount of energy, so the Maxwell-Boltzmann distribution curve is unchanged. But because the catalyst lowers the activation energy, more of the molecules have energies above this threshold and are able to react, as shown in Figure 3.

Tip: Catalysts speed up the reaction in a different way to increasing temperature, concentration or pressure. These things all change the energy distribution but the addition of a catalyst does not.

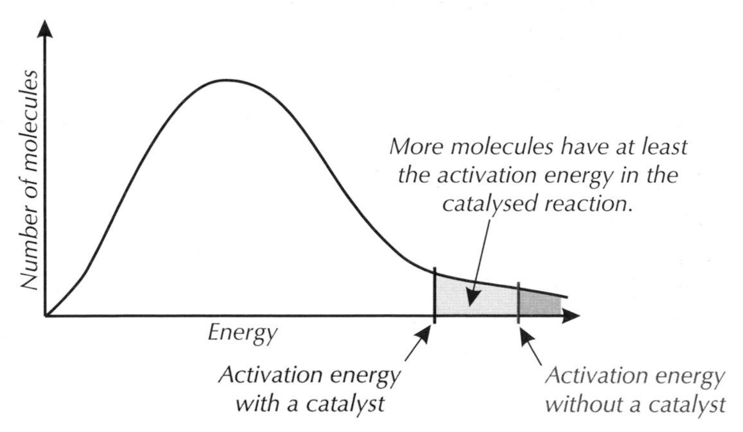

Figure 3: *A Maxwell-Boltzmann distribution curve for a reaction with and without a catalyst.*

Practice Question — Application

Q1 The enthalpy profile diagram shown below is for an uncatalysed chemical reaction to produce 'Product X'.

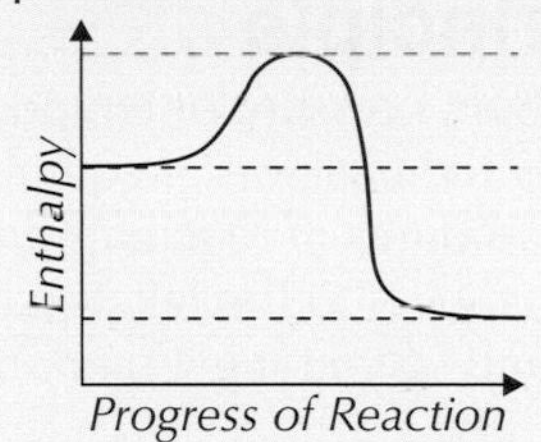

A company wants to produce 'Product X' on a large scale. They are considering using a catalyst.

a) Draw a sketch to show how the addition of a catalyst would affect the enthalpy profile diagram for the reaction.

b) The uncatalysed reaction will only take place at temperatures above 1000 °C. Suggest how adding a catalyst would improve the industrial process.

Tip: 'Uncatalysed' just means that no catalyst has been used.

Practice Questions — Fact Recall

Q1 What is a catalyst?

Q2 Explain why catalysts are used in many industrial processes.

Q3 Explain how a catalyst can speed up the rate of a reaction.

Exam Tip
You need to be able to give a full description of what a catalyst is.

3. Reversible Reactions

Learning Objectives:

- Know that many chemical reactions are reversible.
- Understand that for a reaction in equilibrium, although the concentrations of reactants and products remain constant, both forward and reverse reactions are still proceeding at equal rates.
- Be able to use Le Chatelier's principle to predict the effects of changes in temperature, pressure and concentration on the position of equilibrium in homogeneous reactions.
- Know that a catalyst does not affect the position of equilibrium.
- Be able to apply these concepts to given chemical processes.
- Be able to predict qualitatively the effect of temperature on the position of equilibrium from the sign of ΔH for the forward reaction.

Specification Reference 3.2.3

We usually think of a reaction as a one-way process to make products from reactants. In reality though, many reactions are reversible.

Dynamic equilibrium

Lots of chemical reactions are reversible — they go both ways. To show a reaction's reversible, you stick in a $\rightleftharpoons$.

Example

Hydrogen will react with iodine to produce hydrogen iodide:

$$H_{2(g)} + I_{2(g)} \rightleftharpoons 2HI_{(g)}$$

This reaction can go in either direction —

forwards: $H_{2(g)} + I_{2(g)} \rightarrow 2HI_{(g)}$ ...or backwards: $2HI_{(g)} \rightarrow H_{2(g)} + I_{2(g)}$

As the reactants get used up, the forward reaction slows down — and as more product is formed, the reverse reaction speeds up. After a while, the forward reaction will be going at exactly the same rate as the backward reaction. The concentration of reactants and products won't be changing any more, so it'll seem like nothing's happening. It's a bit like you're digging a hole, while someone else is filling it in at exactly the same speed. This is called a **dynamic equilibrium**. A dynamic equilibrium can only happen in a **closed system**. This just means nothing can get in or out.

Le Chatelier's principle

If you change the concentration, pressure or temperature of a reversible reaction, you're going to alter the position of equilibrium. This just means you'll end up with different amounts of reactants and products at equilibrium. If the position of equilibrium moves to the left, the backwards reaction is faster than the forwards reaction, and so you'll get more reactants.

Example

If the position of equilibrium in the reaction $H_{2(g)} + I_{2(g)} \rightleftharpoons 2HI_{(g)}$ shifts to the left, the backwards reaction is fastest, so more H_2 and I_2 are produced:

$$2HI_{(g)} \rightarrow H_{2(g)} + I_{2(g)}$$

If the position of equilibrium moves to the right, the forwards reaction is faster than the backwards reaction, and so you'll get more products.

Example

If the position of equilibrium in the reaction $H_{2(g)} + I_{2(g)} \rightleftharpoons 2HI_{(g)}$ shifts to the right, the forwards reaction is fastest, so more HI is produced:

$$H_{2(g)} + I_{2(g)} \rightarrow 2HI_{(g)}$$

Tip: $H_{2(g)} + I_{2(g)} \rightarrow 2HI_{(g)}$ is an example of a homogeneous reaction — the reactants and products are all in the same state (in this case they're all gases).

Le Chatelier's principle tells you how the position of equilibrium will change if a condition changes:

> If there's a change in concentration, pressure or temperature, the equilibrium will move to help counteract the change.

So, basically, if you raise the temperature, the position of equilibrium will shift to try to cool things down. And, if you raise the pressure or concentration, the position of equilibrium will shift to try to reduce it again. Catalysts have no effect on the position of equilibrium. They can't increase yield — but they do mean equilibrium is reached faster.

Using Le Chatelier's principle

Changing concentration

If you increase the concentration of a reactant, the equilibrium tries to get rid of the extra reactant. It does this by making more product. So the equilibrium's shifted to the right. If you increase the concentration of the product, the equilibrium tries to remove the extra product. This makes the reverse reaction go faster. So the equilibrium shifts to the left. Decreasing the concentrations has the opposite effect.

Examples

Sulfur dioxide reacts with oxygen to produce sulfur trioxide:

$$2SO_{2(g)} + O_{2(g)} \rightleftharpoons 2SO_{3(g)}$$

If you increase the concentration of SO_2 or O_2, the equilibrium tries to get rid of it by making more SO_3, so the equilibrium shifts to the right. If you increase the concentration of SO_3, the equilibrium shifts to the left to make the backwards reaction faster to get rid of the extra SO_3.

In the Haber process, nitrogen reacts with hydrogen to produce ammonia:

$$N_{2(g)} + 3H_{2(g)} \rightleftharpoons 2NH_{3(g)}$$

If you increase the concentration of N_2 or H_2, the equilibrium shifts to the right and you'll make more NH_3. If you increase the concentration of NH_3, the equilibrium shifts to the left and you'll make more N_2 and H_2.

Figure 1: *Henri Le Chatelier, the French physical chemist who developed Le Chatelier's principle in the 1880's.*

Changing pressure

Changing the pressure only affects equilibria involving gases. Increasing the pressure shifts the equilibrium to the side with fewer gas molecules. This reduces the pressure. Decreasing the pressure shifts the equilibrium to the side with more gas molecules. This raises the pressure again.

Examples

When sulfur dioxide reacts with oxygen you get sulfur trioxide:

$$2SO_{2(g)} + O_{2(g)} \rightleftharpoons 2SO_{3(g)}$$

There are 3 moles on the left, but only 2 on the right. So, an increase in pressure shifts the equilibrium to the right, making more SO_3 and reducing the pressure. Decreasing the pressure favours the backwards reaction, so the equilibrium shifts to the left and more SO_2 and O_2 will be made to increase the pressure.

Methane reacts with water to produce carbon monoxide and hydrogen:

$$CH_{4(g)} + H_2O_{(g)} \rightleftharpoons CO_{(g)} + 3H_{2(g)}$$

There are 2 moles on the left and 4 on the right. So for this reaction an increase in pressure shifts the equilibrium to the left, making more CH_4 and H_2O. Decreasing the pressure shifts the equilibrium to the right to make more CO and H_2. This reaction is used in industry to produce hydrogen. It is best performed at a low pressure to favour the forwards reaction so that more H_2 is produced.

Changing temperature

Increasing the temperature means adding heat. The equilibrium shifts in the endothermic (positive ΔH) direction to absorb this heat. Decreasing the temperature removes heat. The equilibrium shifts in the exothermic (negative ΔH) direction to try to replace the heat. If the forward reaction's endothermic, the reverse reaction will be exothermic, and vice versa.

Tip: An enthalpy change given with a reversible reaction always refers to the forwards reaction, unless you're told otherwise.

Exam Tip
In an exam question, make it clear exactly how the equilibrium shift opposes a temperature change — i.e. by removing or producing heat.

Tip: A lot of questions in this section ask about the effect of increasing temperature, pressure and concentration. But their effect on reaction rate is different to their effect on the position of equilibrium. Make sure you're clear which one you're being asked about.

Exam Tip
If you're asked to define something like 'dynamic equilibrium' in an exam, look at the number of marks allocated for the answer. If there's more than one, you'll need more than one point in your definition.

Examples

This reaction's exothermic in the forward direction, which means it is endothermic in the backward direction.

Exothermic→

$$2SO_{2(g)} + O_{2(g)} \rightleftharpoons 2SO_{3(g)} \qquad \Delta H = -197 \text{ kJ mol}^{-1}.$$

←Endothermic

If you increase the temperature, the equilibrium shifts to the left (the endothermic direction) to absorb the extra heat. This means more SO_2 and O_2 are produced.
If you decrease the temperature, the equilibrium shifts to the right (the exothermic direction) to produce more heat. This means more SO_3 is produced.

This reaction's endothermic in the forward direction (and so exothermic in the backward direction).

Endothermic→

$$C_{(s)} + H_2O_{(g)} \rightleftharpoons CO_{(g)} + H_{2(g)} \qquad \Delta H = +131 \text{ kJ mol}^{-1}.$$

←Exothermic

Increasing the temperature will shift the equilibrium to the right, producing more CO and H_2. Decreasing the temperature shifts the equilibrium to the left, producing more C and H_2O.

Practice Questions — Application

Q1 An industrial process uses the following reversible reaction:

$$A_{(g)} + 2B_{(g)} \rightleftharpoons C_{(g)} + D_{(g)} \qquad \Delta H = -189 \text{ kJ mol}^{-1}.$$

a) Explain the effect of increasing the concentration of A on the position of the equilibrium.

b) Explain the effect of increasing the pressure on the position of the equilibrium.

c) Explain the effect of increasing the temperature on the position of the equilibrium.

d) Briefly outline the best reaction conditions (in terms of high or low concentration, pressure and temperature) to maximise the production of product D.

Q2 What will be the effect of increasing the pressure on the position of equilibrium of the following reaction?

$$H_{2(g)} + I_{2(g)} \rightleftharpoons 2HI_{(g)}$$

Explain your answer.

Practice Questions — Fact Recall

Q1 What does it mean if a reaction is in dynamic equilibrium?

Q2 What is Le Chatelier's Principle?

Q3 How does the addition of a catalyst affect the position of equilibrium in a reversible reaction?

4. Industrial Processes

Le Chatelier's Principle can be applied to lots of industrial processes — like the production of ethanol and methanol.

Learning Objectives:

- Know about the hydration of ethene to form ethanol and the reaction of carbon monoxide with hydrogen to form methanol as important industrial examples where Le Chatelier's Principle can be applied.
- Understand why a compromise temperature and pressure may be used.
- Know the importance of ethanol and methanol as liquid fuels.

Specification Reference 3.2.3

Ethanol production

Ethanol is produced via a reversible exothermic reaction between ethene and steam:

$$C_2H_{4(g)} + H_2O_{(g)} \rightleftharpoons C_2H_5OH_{(g)} \qquad \Delta H = -46 \text{ kJ mol}^{-1}$$

The industrial conditions for the reaction are:

- a pressure of 60-70 atmospheres
- a temperature of 300 °C
- a phosphoric acid catalyst.

Because it's an exothermic reaction, lower temperatures favour the forward reaction. This means that at lower temperatures more ethene and steam is converted to ethanol — you get a better **yield**. But lower temperatures mean a slower rate of reaction. You'd be daft to try to get a really high yield of ethanol if it's going to take you 10 years. So the 300 °C is a compromise between maximum yield and a faster reaction.

Higher pressures favour the forward reaction, so a pressure of 60-70 atmospheres is used — high pressure moves the reaction to the side with fewer molecules of gas. Increasing the pressure also increases the rate of reaction. Cranking up the pressure as high as you can sounds like a great idea so far. But high pressures are expensive to produce. You need stronger pipes and containers to withstand high pressure. And, in this process, increasing the pressure can also cause side reactions to occur. So the 60-70 atmospheres is a compromise between maximum yield and expense. In the end, it all comes down to minimising costs.

Only a small proportion of the ethene reacts each time the gases pass through the catalyst. To save money and raw materials, the unreacted ethene is separated from the liquid ethanol and recycled back into the reactor. Thanks to this around 95% of the ethene is eventually converted to ethanol.

Tip: The yield is the amount of product you get from a reaction. Increasing the reaction rate will give you a higher yield in a given time, but you need to shift the equilibrium to increase the maximum yield.

Methanol production

Methanol is also made industrially in a reversible reaction. It's made from hydrogen and carbon monoxide:

$$2H_{2(g)} + CO_{(g)} \rightleftharpoons CH_3OH_{(g)} \qquad \Delta H = -90 \text{ kJ mol}^{-1}$$

The industrial conditions for the reaction are:

- a pressure of 50-100 atmospheres
- a temperature of 250 °C
- a catalyst of a mixture of copper, zinc oxide and aluminium oxide.

Just like with the production of ethanol, the conditions used are a compromise between keeping costs low and yield high. A high pressure favours the forward reaction, and also increases the reaction rate, so the pressure is kept as high as is reasonable given the cost. As with ethanol production, low temperatures favour the forward (exothermic) reaction, so the temperature is kept as low as possible without reducing the reaction rate too much. The catalyst is used to increase the reaction rate without affecting the position of equilibrium.

Figure 1: Methanol has many uses. For example, it is widely used as a solvent.

> **Tip:** Something is carbon neutral if it has no net annual carbon (greenhouse gas) emissions to the atmosphere.

The importance of methanol and ethanol

Methanol is mainly used to make other chemicals, but both methanol and ethanol can also be used as fuels for cars — either on their own, or added to petrol. Ethanol and methanol are thought of as greener than petrol — they can be made from renewable resources and they produce fewer pollutants (like NO_x and CO). Methanol and ethanol can both be carbon neutral fuels (pretty much) — see page 186 for more on this.

Figure 2: *A methanol powered bus in New York City.*

Practice Questions — Fact Recall

Q1 Describe the industrial conditions for:
a) the hydration of ethene to form ethanol,
b) the reaction of carbon monoxide to form methanol.

Q2 Explain why the temperature used for the production of both ethanol and methanol is a compromise.

Q3 Describe the main advantages of using ethanol and methanol as fuels.

Section Summary

Make sure you know...

- That most collisions between particles don't result in a reaction.
- That collision theory says that a collision will only result in a reaction if it's in the right direction and has at least a certain minimum amount of kinetic energy.
- That the minimum amount of kinetic energy required for a reaction is called the activation energy.
- How to interpret an enthalpy profile diagram for a reaction, by identifying the activation energy, the enthalpy change of the reaction, and whether the reaction is exothermic or endothermic.
- That the Maxwell-Boltzmann distribution describes the spread of energies of the molecules in a gas.
- How to draw and interpret Maxwell-Boltzmann distribution curves for gases at different temperatures.
- That even a small increase in temperature can increase the reaction rate, by increasing the number of molecules with energies above the activation energy so that more will react when they collide.
- That increasing the concentration of reactants (or the pressure if they're gases) will increase the reaction rate, because the molecules will be closer together and so more likely to collide and react.
- That a catalyst is a substance that increases the rate of a reaction by providing an alternative pathway with a lower activation energy, and is chemically unchanged at the end of the reaction.
- That reversible reactions can reach an equilibrium, where the concentrations of reactants and products stay constant and the forwards and backwards reactions have the same reaction rate.
- Le Chatelier's principle states that "if there's a change in concentration, pressure or temperature, the equilibrium will move to help counteract the change."
- That a catalyst does not affect the position of equilibrium in a reversible reaction.
- That increasing the concentration of a reactant shifts the equilibrium to remove the extra reactant.
- That increasing the pressure shifts the equilibrium in favour of the reaction that produces the fewest moles of gas, in order to reduce the pressure.
- That increasing the temperature shifts the equilibrium in favour of the endothermic reaction, to remove the excess heat. (Low temperatures favour exothermic reactions.)
- The industrial conditions for the production of ethanol and methanol, and why there is a compromise in the temperatures and pressured used, in terms of rate, equilibrium and production costs.
- That ethanol and methanol are important as liquid fuels, because they can be produced from renewable sources and give out fewer pollutants than petrol.

Exam-style Questions

1 The enthalpy profile diagram for a reaction between two gases is shown below.

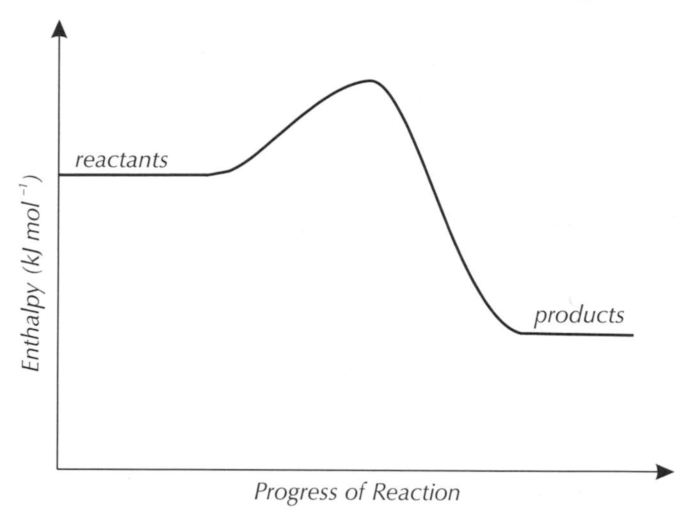

The reaction has an activation energy of 90 $kJ\ mol^{-1}$.

The enthalpy change for the reaction is –150 $kJ\ mol^{-1}$.

1 (a) (i) What is meant by the term 'activation energy'?

(2 marks)

1 (a) (ii) Label the enthalpy profile diagram with arrows showing the activation energy and the enthalpy change of the reaction.

(2 marks)

1 (b) A catalyst is added to the reaction.

1 (b) (i) Define the term catalyst.

(1 mark)

1 (b) (ii) How will the addition of a catalyst affect the shape of the enthalpy profile diagram?

(1 mark)

1 (c) The reactants are heated.

Explain the effect this will have on the rate of the reaction.

(3 marks)

1 (d) For this particular reaction, the best yield is obtained by keeping the pressure as low as possible.

Explain the effect that lowering the pressure has on the rate of the reaction.

(3 marks)

2 A chemical factory produces ethanol (C_2H_5OH) from ethene (C_2H_4) and water (H_2O) using the following reversible reaction:

$$C_2H_{4(g)} + H_2O_{(g)} \rightleftharpoons C_2H_5OH_{(g)} \qquad \Delta H = -46 \text{ kJ mol}^{-1}$$

The reaction is carried out under the following conditions:

Pressure = 60 atm

Temperature = 300 °C

Catalyst = phosphoric acid

2 (a) Without the phosphoric acid catalyst the rate of reaction is so slow that dynamic equilibrium takes a very long time to occur. Describe what it means for a reaction to be at dynamic equilibrium.

(2 marks)

2 (b) The process conditions for the reaction were chosen with consideration to Le Chatelier's principle. State Le Chatelier's principle.

(1 mark)

2 (c) Explain why the pressure chosen for the process is a compromise.

(3 marks)

2 (d) A leak in one of the pipes reduces the amount of H_2O in the reaction mixture. Explain the effect this has on the maximum yield of ethanol.

(3 marks)

3 Ammonia (NH_3) is produced industrially using the Haber-Bosch process. It uses the following reaction between nitrogen and hydrogen:

$$N_{2(g)} + 3H_{2(g)} \rightleftharpoons 2NH_{3(g)} \qquad \Delta H = -92 \text{ kJ mol}^{-1}$$

The reaction is usually carried out under the following conditions:

Pressure = 200 atm

Temperature = 400 °C – 500 °C

Catalyst = iron

3 (a) What effect does the iron catalyst have on the position of equilibrium?

(1 mark)

3 (b) The reaction needs to be carried out at a reasonably high temperature in order to keep the reaction rate high. As well as affecting the rate, increasing the temperature also affects the position of equilibrium for the reaction.

3 (b) (i) State whether this reaction is endothermic or exothermic.

(1 mark)

3 (b) (ii) Explain the effect that increasing the temperature has on the position of equilibrium.

(3 marks)

3 (b) (iii) Other than changing the temperature, suggest two ways to shift the position of equilibrium in order to get an increased yield of ammonia from the reaction.

(2 marks)

1. Redox Reactions

This'll probably ring a bell from GCSE, but don't go thinking you know it all already — there's plenty to learn about redox reactions.

Learning Objectives:
- Know that oxidation is the process of electron loss.
- Know that oxidising agents are electron acceptors.
- Know that reduction is the process of electron gain.
- Know that reducing agents are electron donors.
- Know and be able to apply the rules for assigning oxidation states in order to work out the oxidation state of an element in a compound from its formula.
- Understand oxidation and reduction reactions of s and p block elements.

Specification Reference 3.2.4

What are redox reactions?

A loss of electrons is called **oxidation**. A gain in electrons is called **reduction**. Reduction and oxidation happen simultaneously — hence the term "redox" reaction. An **oxidising agent** accepts electrons and gets reduced. A **reducing agent** donates electrons and gets oxidised (see Figure 1).

Example

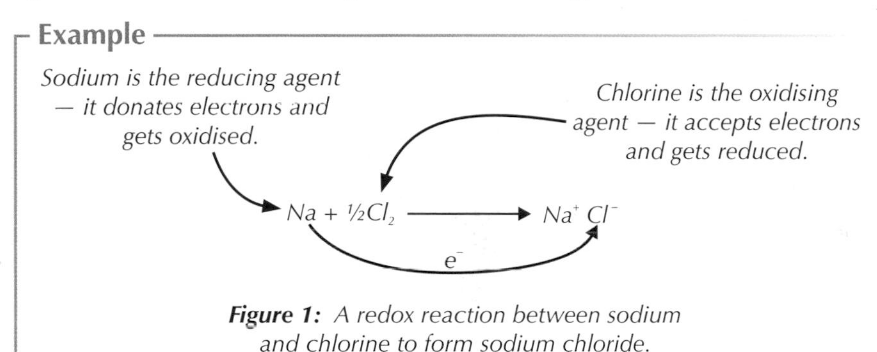

***Figure 1:** A redox reaction between sodium and chlorine to form sodium chloride.*

Oxidation states

The **oxidation state** of an element tells you the total number of electrons it has donated or accepted. Oxidation states are also called oxidation numbers. There are lots of rules for working out oxidation states. Take a deep breath...

Uncombined elements have an oxidation state of 0. Elements just bonded to identical atoms also have an oxidation state of 0.

Examples

The oxidation state of a simple monatomic ion is the same as its charge.

Examples

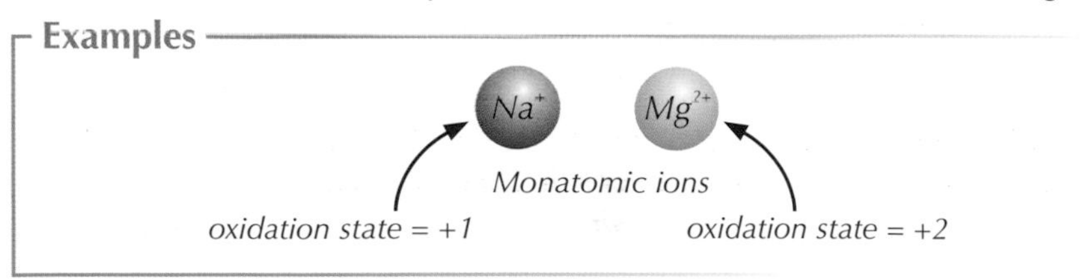

Tip: Now's your chance to learn the most famous memory aid thingy in the world...

OIL RIG
Oxidation Is Loss
Reduction Is Gain
(of electrons)

Tip: Take a look back at page 70 for more about electronegativity.

In compounds or compound ions, the overall oxidation state is just the ion charge (see Figure 2). Within an ion, the most electronegative element has a negative oxidation state (equal to its ionic charge). Other elements have more positive oxidation states.

Example

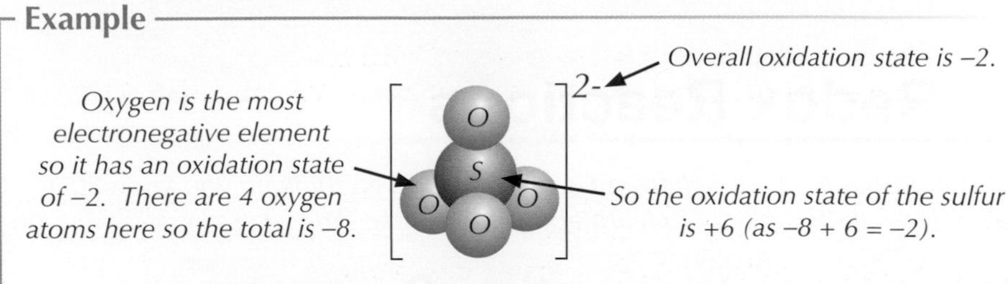

Figure 2: *Oxidation states of elements in the SO_4^{2-} ion.*

The sum of the oxidation states for a neutral compound is 0 (see Figure 3).

Example

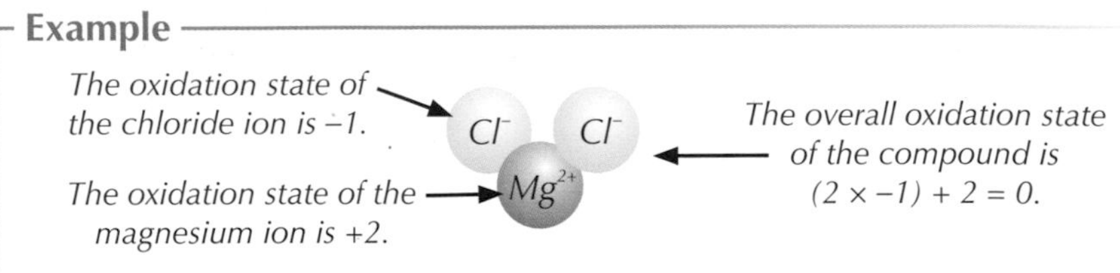

Figure 3: *Oxidation states of elements in magnesium chloride ($MgCl_2$).*

Tip: There are other exceptions for combined oxygen — in OF_2 it's +2, and in O_2F_2 it's +1. And don't forget O_2, where it's 0.

Combined oxygen is nearly always –2, except in peroxides, where it's –1 (see Figure 4). Combined hydrogen is +1, except in metal hydrides where it is –1 and H_2 where it's 0 (see Figures 4 and 5).

Examples

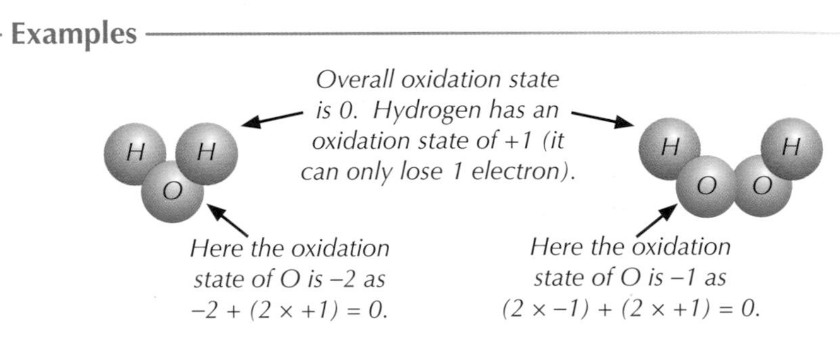

Figure 4: *Oxidation states of hydrogen and oxygen in water (H_2O) and hydrogen peroxide (H_2O_2).*

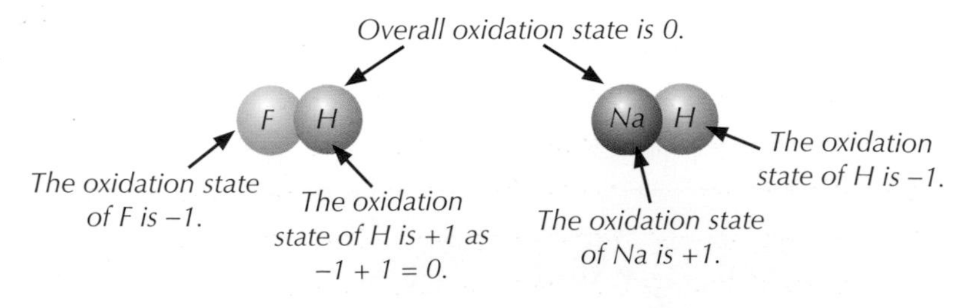

Figure 5: *Oxidation states of hydrogen in hydrogen fluoride (HF) and sodium hydride (NaH).*

Exam Tip
You may get a question asking you to work out the oxidation state of one element in a compound. Just follow all the rules and you'll be fine.

E.g. 'Give the oxidation state of Zn in $Zn(OH)_2$.'

- $Zn(OH)_2$ is neutral, so its overall oxidation state is 0.
- Oxygen's oxidation state is usually –2, and hydrogen's usually +1.
- So the oxidation state of zinc in $Zn(OH)_2$ is: 0 – (2 × (–2 + 1) = +2

Showing oxidation states

Sometimes, oxidation states aren't clear from the formula of a compound. If you see Roman numerals in a chemical name, it's an oxidation number.

Examples

Copper has oxidation state +2 in copper(II) sulfate.
Manganese has oxidation state +7 in a manganate(VII) ion (MnO_4^-)

Practice Questions — Application

Q1 Give the oxidation states of the following ions.
a) Na^+ b) F^- c) Ca^{2+}

Q2 Give the overall oxidation states of the following ions.
a) OH^- b) CO_3^{2-} c) NO_3^-

Q3 Work out the oxidation states of all the elements in the following compounds and compound ions.
a) HCl b) SO_2 c) CO_3^{2-}
d) ClO_4^- e) Cu_2O f) HSO_4^-

Q4 Work out the oxidation states of carbon in the following.
a) CO b) CO_2 c) CCl_4
d) C e) $CaCO_3$ f) C_3H_6

Q5 Work out the oxidation states of phosphorus in the following.
a) P_4 b) PH_3 c) PO_4^{2-}
d) P_2F_4 e) PBr_5 f) P_2H_4

Q6 Look at the reaction below.

$$Cu + H_2SO_4 \rightarrow CuSO_4 + H_2$$

Give the oxidation states at the beginning and end of the reaction for the following elements:
a) Cu b) S c) H

Tip: The oxidation state of an atom doesn't always change when it reacts, so don't be alarmed if your answer is the same for the beginning and end of the reaction.

Practice Questions — Fact Recall

Q1 What is oxidation?
Q2 What is reduction?
Q3 Describe the role of an oxidising agent in a redox reaction.
Q4 Describe the role of a reducing agent in a redox reaction.
Q5 Give the oxidation state of an element bonded to an identical atom.
Q6 What is the sum of the oxidation states for a neutral compound?
Q7 What is the oxidation state of oxygen in a peroxide?
Q8 Give the oxidation state of hydrogen in a metal hydride.

Exam Tip
It's really important to remember the basic rules for working out oxidation states, as well as the exceptions — it's the kind of thing that could easily trip you up in exam questions.

2. Redox Equations

Learning Objectives:

- Be able to write half-equations identifying the oxidation and reduction processes in redox reactions when the reactants and products are specified.
- Be able to combine half-equations to give an overall redox equation.

Specification Reference 3.2.4

In redox reactions, oxidation and reduction go on simultaneously. You can write separate equations to show the two things happening, or you can package them up into one nice, neat redox equation.

Half-equations and redox equations

Ionic half-equations show oxidation or reduction (see Figure 1). The electrons are shown in a half-equation so that the charges balance.

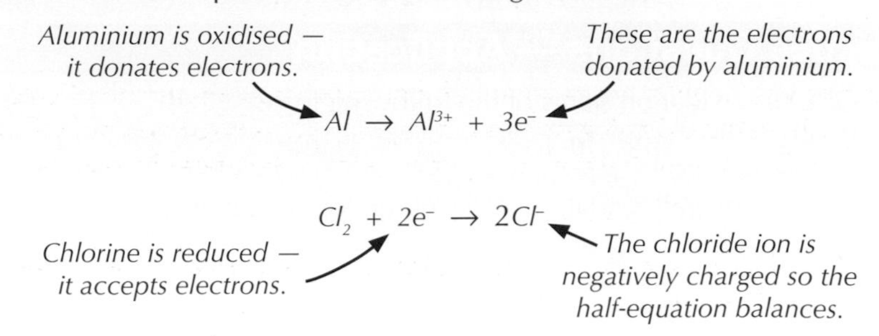

***Figure 1:** Half equations showing the oxidation of aluminium and the reduction of chlorine.*

Tip: Remember — the charges as well as the number of atoms must be balanced in a balanced equation. See pages 36-37 for more on balancing equations.

You can combine half-equations for oxidising and reducing agents to make full equations for redox reactions. Just make sure both half equations have the same number of electrons in, stick them together and cancel out the electrons.

Tip: In any redox reaction the number of electrons released by the oxidation reaction must be the same as the number used up by the reduction reaction.

Example

Aluminium reacts with chlorine to form aluminium chloride ($AlCl_3$).

You can see the half equations for the oxidation of aluminium and the reduction of chlorine in Figure 1. Oxidising aluminium produces three electrons — but to reduce chlorine you only need two.

If you multiply the aluminium equation by two and the chlorine equation by three then they'll both have six electrons in:

$$Al \rightarrow Al^{3+} + 3e^- \xrightarrow{\times 2} 2Al \rightarrow 2Al^{3+} + 6e^-$$

$$Cl_2 + 2e^- \rightarrow 2Cl^- \xrightarrow{\times 3} 3Cl_2 + 6e^- \rightarrow 6Cl^-$$

Now you can combine them. If you stick them together you get:

$$2Al + 3Cl_2 + 6e^- \rightarrow 2Al^{3+} + 6e^- + 6Cl^-$$

But the electrons on each side cancel out:

$$2Al + 3Cl_2 + \cancel{6e^-} \rightarrow 2Al^{3+} + \cancel{6e^-} + 3Cl^-$$

So the full redox equation for this reaction is:

$$2Al + 3Cl_2 \rightarrow 2AlCl_3$$

You can also work out the half-equations for a given equation — just make sure the atoms and charges balance.

Example

Magnesium burns in oxygen to form magnesium oxide:

$$2Mg + O_2 \rightarrow 2MgO$$

Write half-equations for the oxidation and reduction reactions that are part of this process.

Start with oxygen being reduced to O^{2-}: $\mathbf{O_2 \rightarrow 2O^{2-}}$
Now balance the charges by adding some electrons in: $O_2 + \mathbf{4e^-} \rightarrow 2O^{2-}$

Then do the same for magnesium being oxidised to Mg^{2+}: $\mathbf{2Mg \rightarrow 2Mg^{2+}}$
Balance it by adding in the electrons: $2Mg \rightarrow 2Mg^{2+} + \mathbf{4e^-}$

Overall, four electrons are involved in the reaction — but they're not included in the full redox equations because they cancel out:

$$2Mg + O_2 + \cancel{4e^-} \rightarrow 2MgO + \cancel{4e^-}$$

Tip: Take your time balancing half equations and always double check them — it's easy to get confused and end up with electrons all over the place.

Sometimes you might have to write half equations for a more complicated reaction where the oxidising or reducing agent contains oxygen or hydrogen. If so, you might need to add in H_2O and H^+ ions to balance the equation.

Tip: The only things you're allowed to add to half equations to balance them are electrons, H^+ ions and water.

Example

Write a half equation for the conversion of manganate(VIII) ions (MnO_4^-) in acid solution into Mn^{2+} ions.

Start by writing out the basic reaction:

$$MnO_4^- \rightarrow Mn^{2+}$$

Add some H_2O to the right side to balance the oxygen in MnO_4^-:

$$MnO_4^- \rightarrow Mn^{2+} + 4H_2O$$

Next, add H^+ ions to the left side to balance the hydrogen:

$$MnO_4^- + 8H^+ \rightarrow Mn^{2+} + 4H_2O$$

Finally, add electrons in to balance the charges:

$$MnO_4^- + 8H^+ + 5e^- \rightarrow Mn^{2+} + 4H_2O$$

Exam Tip
If you're told that it's an acid solution, that's a really big hint that you need to have H^+ ions in the equation somewhere.

Tip: If you come across other reactions like this with complicated oxidising or reducing agents, just follow the same steps and you'll be fine.

Practice Questions — Application

Q1 Combine the 2 half equations below to give the full redox equation for the displacement of silver by zinc:

$Zn \rightarrow Zn^{2+} + 2e^-$ and $Ag^+ + e^- \rightarrow Ag$

Q2 Write the oxidation and reduction half-equations for this reaction:

$$Ca + Cl_2 \rightarrow CaCl_2$$

Q3 Balance this half-equation: $NO_3^- + H^+ + e^- \rightarrow N_2 + H_2O$

Q4 Write a half equation for the reduction of $Cr_2O_7^{2-}$ ions in acid solution to Cr^{3+} ions.

Q5 H_2SO_4 can act as an oxidising agent. Give the half-equation for the reduction of H_2SO_4 to H_2S and water.

Practice Questions — Fact Recall

Q1 What does an ionic half-equation show?

Q2 Which of these (A, B or C) is a half-equation?

A $2Li + O_2 \rightarrow 2MgO$

B $Fe \rightarrow Fe^{3+} + 3e^-$

C $2Mg + O_2 + 4e^- \rightarrow 2MgO + 4e^-$

3. Group 7 — The Halogens

The halogens are highly-reactive non-metals found in Group 7 of the periodic table. You need to know about their properties and trends — oh, and just how much we rely on chlorine to give us nice clean water.

Learning Objectives:

- Understand the trends in electronegativity and boiling point of the halogens.
- Understand that the ability of the halogens (from fluorine to iodine) to oxidise decreases down the group (e.g. the displacement reactions with halide ions in aqueous solution).
- Know the reaction of chlorine with cold, dilute, aqueous NaOH and the uses of the solutions formed.
- Know the reactions of chlorine with water and the use of chlorine in water treatment.
- Appreciate that the benefits to health of water treatment by chlorine outweigh its toxic effects.

Specification Reference 3.2.5

Properties of halogens

The table below gives some of the main properties of the first four halogens, at room temperature.

halogen	formula	colour	physical state	electronic structure
fluorine	F_2	pale yellow	gas	$1s^2\ 2s^2\ 2p^5$
chlorine	Cl_2	green	gas	$1s^2\ 2s^2\ 2p^6\ 3s^2\ 3p^5$
bromine	Br_2	red-brown	liquid	$1s^2\ 2s^2\ 2p^6\ 3s^2\ 3p^6\ 3d^{10}\ 4s^2\ 4p^5$
iodine	I_2	grey	solid	$1s^2\ 2s^2\ 2p^6\ 3s^2\ 3p^6\ 3d^{10}\ 4s^2\ 4p^6\ 4d^{10}\ 5s^2\ 5p^5$

Boiling points

The boiling points of the halogens increase down the group. This is due to the increasing strength of the van der Waals forces as the size and relative mass of the atoms increases. This trend is shown in the changes of physical state from fluorine (gas) to iodine (solid).

Electronegativity

Electronegativity decreases down the group. Electronegativity, remember, is the tendency of an atom to attract a bonding pair of electrons. The halogens are all highly electronegative elements. But larger atoms attract shared electrons less than smaller ones. So, going down the group, as the atoms become larger, the electronegativity decreases.

Tip: There's lots more about electronegativity on page 70 if you need a reminder.

Displacement reactions

When the halogens react, they gain an electron. This means they are oxidising agents. They get less reactive down the group, because the atoms become larger (and less electronegative). So you can say that the halogens become less oxidising down the group.

The relative oxidising strengths of the halogens can be seen in their displacement reactions with the halide ions. A halogen will displace a halide from solution if the halide is below it in the periodic table — e.g. chlorine will displace bromine but will be displaced by fluorine. You can see this if you add a few drops of an aqueous halogen to a solution containing halide ions. A colour change is seen if there's a reaction:

	Potassium chloride solution $KCl_{(aq)}$ — colourless	Potassium bromide solution $KBr_{(aq)}$ — colourless	Potassium iodide solution $KI_{(aq)}$ — colourless
Chlorine water $Cl_{2(aq)}$ — colourless	no reaction	orange solution (Br_2) formed	brown solution (I_2) formed
Bromine water $Br_{2(aq)}$ — orange	no reaction	no reaction	brown solution (I_2) formed
Iodine solution $I_{2(aq)}$ — brown	no reaction	no reaction	no reaction

Tip: The word <u>halogen</u> should be used when describing the atom (X) or molecule (X_2), but the word <u>halide</u> is used to describe the negative ion (X^-).

These displacement reactions can be used to help identify which halogen (or halide) is present in a solution. Halide ions are colourless in solution, but when the halogen is displaced it shows a distinctive colour, e.g. when bromide ions come out of solution to form bromine the colour changes from colourless to orange.

Figure 1: Green chlorine gas.

Examples

Chlorine

If you add chlorine to a solution containing bromide ions (e.g. potassium bromide), it will displace the bromine — and there will be a colour change.

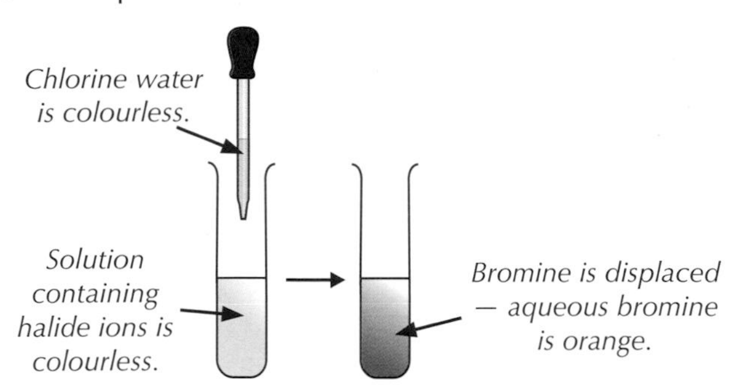

The equation for this reaction is: $Cl_{2(aq)} + 2KBr_{(aq)} \rightarrow 2KCl_{(aq)} + Br_{2(aq)}$

It can also be written as an ionic equation: $Cl_{2(aq)} + 2Br^{-}_{(aq)} \rightarrow 2Cl^{-}_{(aq)} + Br_{2(aq)}$

Figure 2: Red-brown bromine liquid.

If you add chlorine to a solution of potassium iodide ions, it will displace the iodine. This time the colour change will be from colourless to brown.

The equation for this reaction is: $Cl_{2(aq)} + 2KI_{(aq)} \rightarrow 2KCl_{(aq)} + I_{2(aq)}$

The ionic equation is: $Cl_{2(aq)} + 2I^{-}_{(aq)} \rightarrow 2Cl^{-}_{(aq)} + I_{2(aq)}$

Bromine

If you add bromine to a solution of potassium iodide, it will displace the iodine — and there will be a colour change.

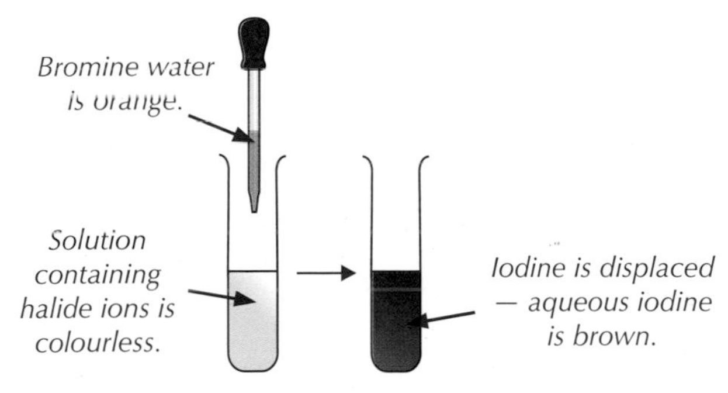

The equation for this reaction is: $Br_{2(aq)} + 2KI_{(aq)} \rightarrow 2KBr_{(aq)} + I_{2(aq)}$

The ionic equation is: $Br_{2(aq)} + 2I^{-}_{(aq)} \rightarrow 2Br^{-}_{(aq)} + I_{2(aq)}$

There's no reaction if you add bromine water to a solution of chloride ions. Chlorine is above bromine in Group 7 so is more reactive and can't be displaced by it.

Figure 3: Grey iodine crystals.

Iodine

Iodine is below chlorine and bromine in Group 7, so it's less reactive than them and won't displace either halogen.

Tip: Take a look at pages 135-137 for more on oxidation states and how to work them out.

Making bleach

If you mix chlorine gas with dilute sodium hydroxide at room temperature, you get sodium chlorate(I) solution, $NaClO_{(aq)}$, which just happens to be common household bleach. In this reaction some of the chlorine is oxidised and some of it is reduced. This is called **disproportionation**.

$$2NaOH_{(aq)} + Cl_{2\,(g)} \rightarrow NaClO_{(aq)} + NaCl_{(aq)} + H_2O_{(l)}$$

Chlorine is bonded to chlorine so its oxidation state is 0.

ClO^- is the chlorate(I) ion. Chlorine's oxidation state is +1 in this ion.

Here, chlorine's oxidation state is −1.

The sodium chlorate(I) solution (bleach) has loads of uses — it's used in water treatment, to bleach paper and textiles... and it's good for cleaning toilets, too. Handy...

Chlorine and water

When you mix chlorine with water, it undergoes disproportionation. You end up with a mixture of hydrochloric acid and chloric(I) acid (also called hypochlorous acid).

$$Cl_{2(g)} + H_2O_{(l)} \rightleftharpoons HCl_{(aq)} + HClO_{(aq)}$$

Chlorine's oxidation state is 0.

In hydrochloric acid chlorine's oxidation state is −1.

In chloric(I) acid chlorine's oxidation state is +1.

Aqueous chloric(I) acid ionises to make chlorate(I) ions (also called hypochlorite ions):

$$HClO_{(aq)} + H_2O_{(l)} \rightleftharpoons ClO^-_{(aq)} + H_3O^+_{(aq)}$$

In bright sunlight, chlorine and water undergo an additional reaction:

$$2Cl_2 + 2H_2O \xrightarrow{U.V.} 4HCl + O_2$$

Figure 4: Chlorine is used to treat tap water in the UK.

Water treatment

Chlorate(I) ions kill bacteria. So, adding chlorine (or a compound containing chlorate(I) ions) to water can make it safe to drink or swim in. In the UK our drinking water is treated to make it safe.

Chlorine is an important part of water treatment. It kills disease-causing microorganisms (and some chlorine persists in the water and prevents reinfection further down the supply). It also prevents the growth of algae, eliminating bad tastes and smells, and removes discolouration caused by organic compounds.

Tip: See page 4 for more about weighing up the benefits and risks of scientific techniques (like using chlorine to treat drinking water).

However, there are risks from using chlorine to treat water. Chlorine gas is very harmful if it's breathed in — it irritates the respiratory system. Liquid chlorine on the skin or eyes causes severe chemical burns. Accidents involving chlorine could be really serious, or fatal. Water contains a variety of organic compounds, e.g. from the decomposition of plants. Chlorine reacts with these compounds to form chlorinated hydrocarbons, e.g. chloromethane (CH_3Cl), and many of these chlorinated hydrocarbons are carcinogenic (cancer-causing). However, this increased cancer risk is small compared to the risks from untreated water — a cholera epidemic, say, could kill thousands of people. There are ethical considerations too. We don't get a choice about having our water chlorinated — some people object to this as forced 'mass medication'.

Figure 5: The distinctive 'swimming pool smell' is due to the chlorine in the water.

Practice Questions — Application

Q1 Three test tubes, A, B and C, contain different halide solutions. Several drops of chlorine water are added to each test tube and the following colour changes are observed.

Tube A — colourless to orange

Tube B — no colour change

Tube C — colourless to brown

a) Name the halide ion present in each solution.

b) The test is repeated, but iodine solution ($I_{2(aq)}$) is added to the test tubes instead of chlorine water. Explain how the results would be different.

Q2 Chlorine gas is mixed with sodium hydroxide solution. The solution is tested with litmus paper, which turns white. Explain why.

Practice Questions — Fact Recall

Q1 Describe the trend in the boiling points of the halogens.

Q2 Name the most electronegative halogen.

Q3 Which halide ions are displaced by reaction with chlorine water?

Q4 a) Describe the colour change when bromine water is added to potassium iodide solution.

b) Give the full equation for this reaction.

c) Give the ionic equation for this reaction.

Q5 a) Name three products of the reaction between sodium hydroxide and chlorine.

b) Give the balanced equation for this reaction.

Q6 Describe the reactions that occur when chlorine is mixed with water.

Q7 a) Explain why chlorine is used to treat water.

b) Describe the disadvantages of using chlorine to treat water.

4. Halide Ions

Halides — the nifty name for the 1– ions formed by the halogens. Different halide ions react slightly differently in solution, so telling them apart is easier than you might think. Now's your chance to get learning those details...

Learning Objectives:

- Understand the trend in reducing ability of the halide ions.
- Know the different products formed by reaction of NaX and H_2SO_4.
- Understand why acidified silver nitrate solution is used as a reagent to identify and distinguish between F^-, Cl^-, Br^- and I^-.
- Know the trend in solubility of the silver halides in ammonia.

Specification Reference 3.2.5

Halide ion formation and oxidation

You'll remember from your chemistry basics that the elements in Group 7 form ions by gaining one electron. They end up as 1– ions with a full outer shell. For example:

Chlorine atom → *Chloride ion*

When a halide ion takes part in a **redox reaction**, it reduces something and is oxidised itself. To reduce something, the halide ion needs to lose an electron from its outer shell — think OIL RIG (see page 135).

The reducing power of halides

How easy it is for a halide ion to lose an electron depends on the attraction between the nucleus and the outer electrons. As you go down the group, the attraction gets weaker because the ions get bigger, so the electrons are further away from the positive nucleus. There are extra inner electron shells too, so there's a greater shielding effect (see Figure 1). Therefore, the reducing power of the halides increases down the group.

Tip: You already know one good example of halide ions as reducing agents — it's the good old halogen / halide displacement reaction. For example:
$Cl_2 + 2Br^- \rightarrow 2Cl^- + Br_2$

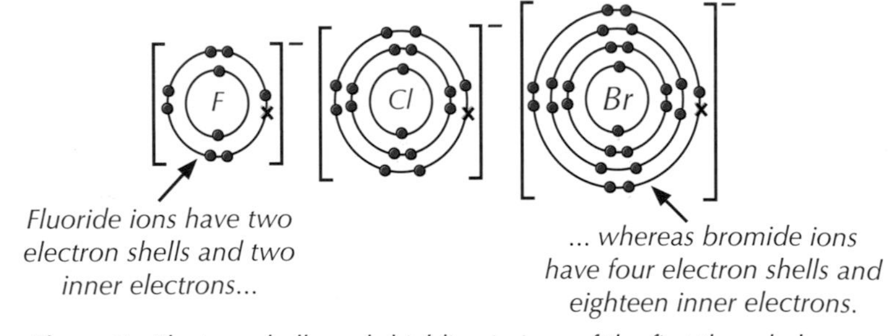

Figure 1: *Electron shells and shielding in ions of the first three halogens.*

Reactions with sulfuric acid

All the halides react with concentrated sulfuric acid to give a hydrogen halide as a product to start with.

$$NaX + H_2SO_4 \rightarrow NaHSO_4 + HX$$

A sodium halide with the halogen labelled as 'X'. — *A hydrogen halide is produced.*

Tip: In chemistry, X is often used to stand for 'any halogen'.

But what happens next depends on which halide you've got. Some halide ions are strong enough reducing agents that they can reduce the sulfuric acid to water and sulfur dioxide. Overall the reaction is:

$$2HX + H_2SO_4 \rightarrow X_2 + SO_2 + 2H_2O$$

The half equations are:

$$2X^-_{(g)} \rightarrow X_{2(s)} + 2e^-$$ ← *The halide is oxidised.*

$$H_2SO_4 + 2H^+ + 2e^- \rightarrow SO_2 + 2H_2O$$ ← *The sulfuric acid is reduced.*

Exam Tip
You don't need to learn these half equations by heart — they're just here to help you understand the reaction.

And iodine is such a strong reducing agent that it can reduce the SO_2 to H_2S.

Examples

Reaction of NaF or NaCl with H_2SO_4

$$NaF_{(s)} + H_2SO_{4(aq)} \rightarrow NaHSO_{4(s)} + HF_{(g)}$$

$$NaCl_{(s)} + H_2SO_{4(aq)} \rightarrow NaHSO_{4(s)} + HCl_{(g)}$$

Hydrogen fluoride (HF) or hydrogen chloride gas (HCl) is formed. You'll see misty fumes as the gas comes into contact with moisture in the air. But HF and HCl aren't strong enough reducing agents to reduce the sulfuric acid, so the reaction stops there. It's not a redox reaction — the oxidation states of the halide and sulfur stay the same (–1 and +6).

Reaction of NaBr with H_2SO_4

$$NaBr_{(s)} + H_2SO_{4(aq)} \rightarrow NaHSO_{4(s)} + HBr_{(g)}$$

The first reaction gives misty fumes of hydrogen bromide gas (HBr). But the HBr is a stronger reducing agent than HCl and reacts with the H_2SO_4 in a redox reaction.

$$2HBr_{(aq)} + H_2SO_{4(aq)} \rightarrow Br_{2(g)} + SO_{2(g)} + 2H_2O_{(l)}$$

Oxidation state of S:	*+6*	→	*+4*	*reduction*
Oxidation state of Br:	*–1*	→	*0*	*oxidation*

The reaction produces choking fumes of SO_2 and orange fumes of Br_2.

Reaction of NaI with H_2SO_4

$$NaI_{(s)} + H_2SO_{4(aq)} \rightarrow NaHSO_{4(s)} + HI_{(g)}$$

Same initial reaction giving HI gas. The HI then reduces H_2SO_4, as above.

$$2HI_{(g)} + H_2SO_{4(aq)} \rightarrow I_{2(s)} + SO_{2(g)} + 2H_2O_{(l)}$$

Oxidation state of S:	*+6*	→	*+4*	*reduction*
Oxidation state of I:	*–1*	→	*0*	*oxidation*

But HI (being the strongest reducing agent) keeps going and reduces the SO_2 to H_2S.

$$6HI_{(g)} + SO_{2(g)} \rightarrow H_2S_{(g)} + 3I_{2(s)} + 2H_2O_{(l)}$$

Oxidation state of S:	*+4*	→	*–2*	*reduction*
Oxidation state of I:	*–1*	→	*0*	*oxidation*

Tip: This may seem like an awful lot of information at first glance. Don't worry though — just learn the principles and keep referring back to the generic equations on the previous page. What you need to learn is the pattern — you can work out oxidation states if you need to (see pages 135-136) so you'll always be able to figure out what's reduced and what's oxidised.

Tip: This is no one's favourite reaction — H_2S is toxic and smells of bad eggs.

Testing for halides

The halogens are pretty distinctive to look at (see pages 140 and 141). Unfortunately, the same can't be said of halide solutions, which are colourless. You can test for halides using the **silver nitrate test** — it's dead easy. First you add dilute nitric acid to remove ions which might interfere with the test. Then you just add silver nitrate solution ($AgNO_{3\ (aq)}$). A precipitate is formed (of the silver halide).

$$Ag^+_{(aq)} + X^-_{(aq)} \rightarrow AgX_{(s)}$$ ...where X is F, Cl, Br or I

Tip: You can't use hydrochloric acid instead of nitric acid because the silver nitrate would just react with the chloride ions from the HCl — and that would mess up your results completely.

The colour of the precipitate identifies the halide (see Figures 2 and 3).

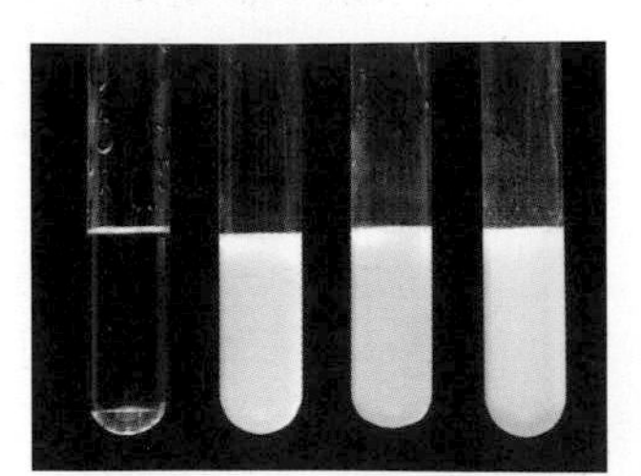

Figure 3: *Results of silver nitrate tests for solutions containing (L-R) fluoride, chloride, bromide and iodide ions.*

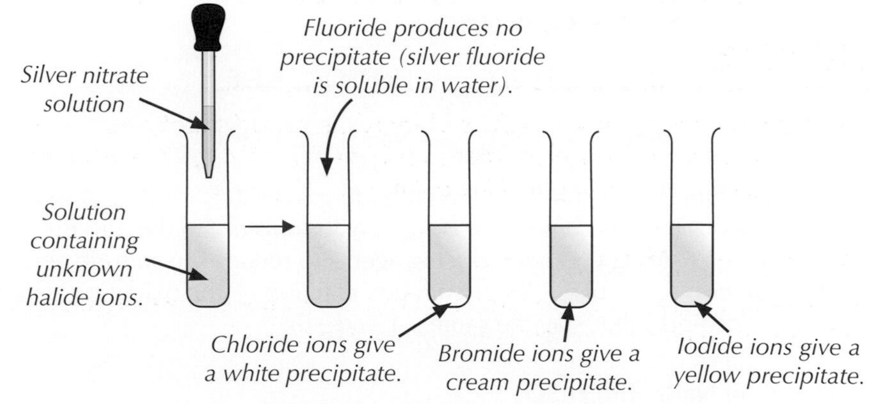

Figure 2: *The silver nitrate test for identifying an unknown halide ion in solution.*

Then to be extra sure, you can test your results by adding ammonia solution. Each silver halide has a different solubility in ammonia (see Figures 4 and 5).

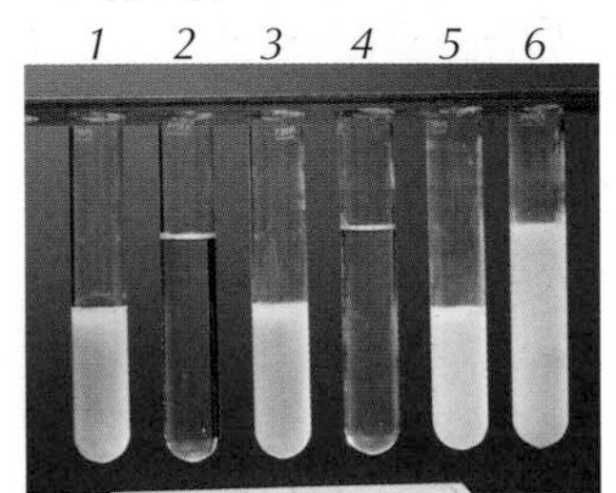

Figure 5: *The chloride, bromide and iodide test tubes from Figure 3 (1, 3 and 5), and the same tubes with $NH_{3(aq)}$ added (2, 4 and 6).*

Halide	Result
Chloride Cl–	precipitate dissolves in dilute $NH_{3(aq)}$
Bromide Br–	precipitate dissolves in conc. $NH_{3(aq)}$
Iodide I–	precipitate insoluble in conc. $NH_{3(aq)}$

Figure 4: *Solubility of silver halide precipitates in ammonia.*

Practice Questions — Application

Q1 Sunil carries out a reaction between solid sodium bromide and aqueous sulfuric acid. Then he does the same reaction with sodium chloride. He predicts that the only gaseous product of both reactions will be a hydrogen halide.
Explain whether Sunil's prediction is correct.

Q2 An experiment is carried out to identify the halide ions in three different solutions. The results are shown in the table below.

Sample	Colour of precipitate following addition of silver nitrate	Effect of adding concentrated NH_3 solution to the precipitate
A	yellow	no change
B	no precipitate	no change
C	cream	precipitate dissolves

Identify the halide ion in each sample.

Practice Questions — Fact Recall

Q1 Explain why the reducing power of the halide ions increases down the group.

Q2 Write the equation(s) for the reaction of sulfuric acid with:
a) sodium fluoride. b) sodium iodide.

Q3 a) Describe a test that could be used to distinguish between solutions of fluoride ions and chloride ions.
b) Describe how you could use ammonia solution to confirm the result for the chloride ion.

5. Group 2 — The Alkaline Earth Metals

Learning Objective:
- Understand the trends in atomic radius, first ionisation energy and melting point of the elements Mg – Ba.

Specification Reference 3.2.6

The alkaline earth metals are in the s block of the periodic table. You have to know the trends in their properties as you go down Group 2 — in atomic radius, ionisation energy and melting points.

Atomic radius

Atomic radius increases down Group 2. This is because of the extra electron shells as you go down the group (see Figures 2 and 3).

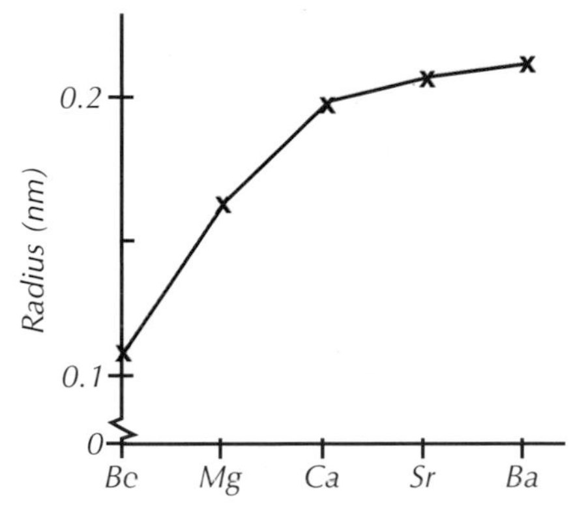

Figure 2: *Atomic radii of the first five elements in Group 2.*

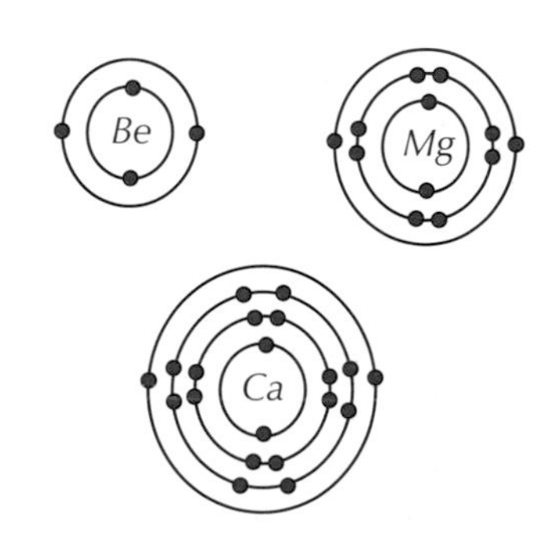

Figure 3: *Electron configurations of the first three elements in Group 2.*

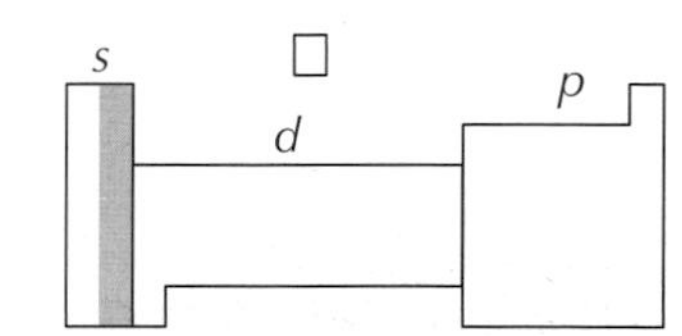

Figure 1: *The s, p and d blocks of the periodic table (see page 79 for more on this). Group 2 is highlighted in grey.*

Ionisation energy

Group 2 elements all have two electrons in their outer shell (s^2). They can lose their two outer electrons to form 2+ ions. Their ions then have every atom's dream electronic structure — that of a noble gas (see Figure 4).

Element	Atom	Ion
Be	$1s^2\ 2s^2$	$1s^2$
Mg	$1s^2\ 2s^2\ 2p^6\ 3s^2$	$1s^2\ 2s^2\ 2p^6$
Ca	$1s^2\ 2s^2\ 2p^6\ 3s^2\ 3p^6\ 4s^2$	$1s^2\ 2s^1\ 2p^6\ 3s^2\ 3p^6$

Figure 4: *Electronic structures of Group 2 atoms and ions.*

Tip: See pages 22-23 for more on ionisation energies.

Ionisation energy decreases down the group (see Figure 5). This is because each element down Group 2 has an extra electron shell compared to the one above. The extra inner shells shield the outer electrons from the attraction of the nucleus. Also, the extra shell means that the outer electrons are further away from the nucleus, which greatly reduces the nucleus's attraction. Both of these factors make it easier to remove outer electrons, resulting in a lower ionisation energy. The positive charge of the nucleus does increase as you go down a group (due to the extra protons), but this effect is overridden by the effect of the extra shells.

Group 2 element	*1st ionisation energy / kJ mol⁻¹*
Be	900
Mg	738
Ca	590
Sr	550
Ba	503

Figure 5: *First ionisation energies of Group 2 elements.*

Example

The first and second ionisation energies of calcium are lower than the first and second ionisation energies of magnesium (see Figure 6).

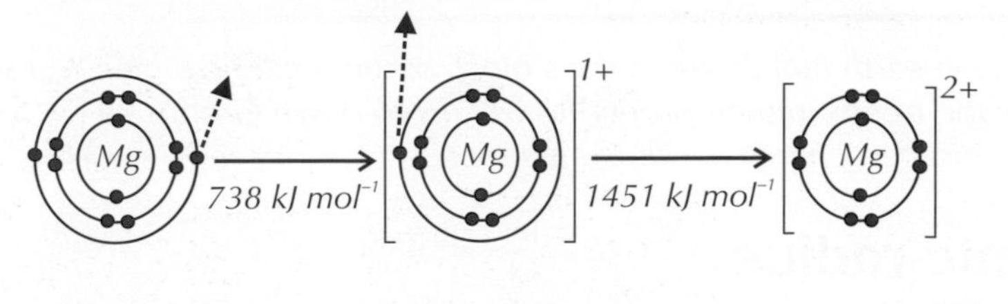

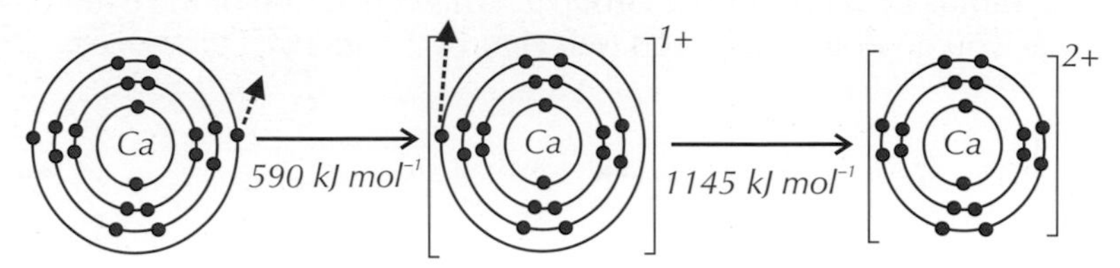

Figure 6: *First and second ionisation energies of magnesium and calcium.*

A magnesium atom has three electron shells, whereas a calcium atom has four electron shells. This means that the outer shell electrons are further from the nucleus in calcium than in magnesium. Also, a calcium atom has 18 electrons in inner shells, compared to only 10 in a magnesium atom. This means that shielding is greater in calcium atoms. So, less energy is needed to remove an electron from calcium than from magnesium.

Figure 7: *Magnesium ribbon reacting with hydrochloric acid.*

Figure 8: *Calcium reacting with hydrochloric acid.*

Reactivity

When Group 2 elements react they lose electrons, forming positive ions. The easier it is to lose electrons (i.e. the lower the first and second ionisation energies), the more reactive the element, so reactivity increases down the group (see Figures 7 and 8).

Melting point

Melting points generally decrease down the group (see Figure 9). The Group 2 elements have typical metallic structures, with the electrons of their outer shells being delocalised. Going down the group the metallic ions get bigger. But the number of delocalised electrons per atom doesn't change (it's always 2) — so the delocalised electrons get further away from the positive ions. These two factors mean there's reduced attraction of the positive ions to the 'sea' of delocalised electrons. So it takes less energy to break the bonds, which means lower melting points generally down the group. However, there's a big 'blip' at magnesium, because the crystal structure (the arrangement of the metallic ions) changes.

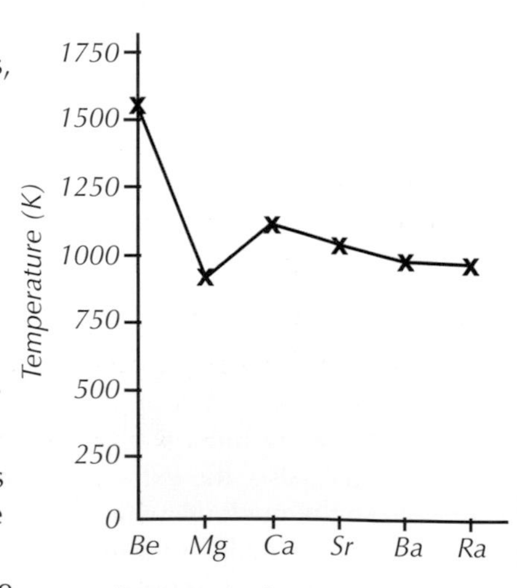

Figure 9: *Melting points of Group 2 elements.*

Exam Tip

There's no need to memorise the graphs on this page and page 147, but you do need to know their shapes and be able to explain them.

Example

The atomic radii increase from beryllium to magnesium to calcium, but there are still only two delocalised electrons per ion (see Figure 10). So melting point decreases.

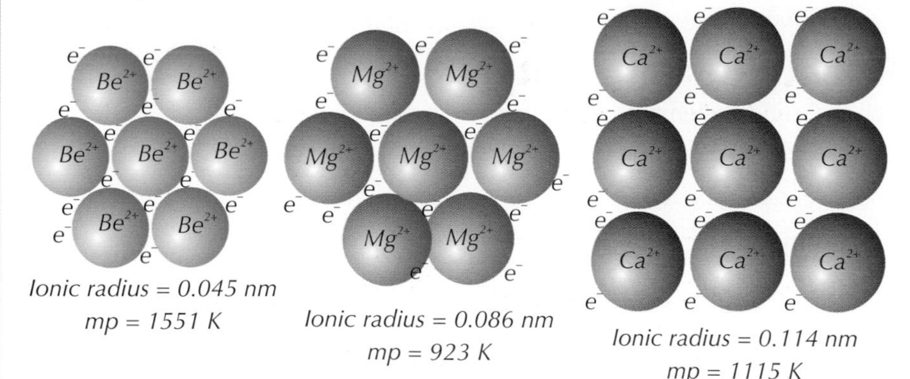

Figure 10: *Comparison of beryllium, magnesium and calcium crystals. ('mp' means melting point.)*

Exam Tip

There's no need to memorise these structures and numbers, but you do have to understand how atomic radius affects melting point.

Practice Questions — Application

Q1 Calcium and strontium are reacted with dilute hydrochloric acid. Explain which reaction you would expect to occur more rapidly.

Q2 The table below shows the atomic radii of three elements from Group 2.

Element	*Atomic radius/nm*
X	0.089
Y	0.198
Z	0.176

a) Explain which element you would expect to have the highest first ionisation energy.

b) Explain which element you would expect to have the lowest melting point.

Practice Questions — Fact Recall

Q1 Describe the trend in atomic radius in Group 2.

Q2 Explain the trend in first ionisation energy in Group 2.

Q3 Is beryllium more or less reactive that barium?

Q4 Why is the melting point of barium higher than the melting point of radium?

Learning Objectives:

- Know the reactions of the elements Mg – Ba with water and recognise the trend.
- Know the relative solubilities of the hydroxides of the elements Mg – Ba and that $Mg(OH)_2$ is sparingly soluble.
- Know the relative solubilities of the sulfates of the elements Mg – Ba.
- Understand why acidified $BaCl_2$ solution is used as a reagent to test for sulfate ions.
- Know the use of $BaSO_4$ in medicine.
- Know the use of $Mg(OH)_2$ in medicine and of $Ca(OH)_2$ in agriculture.

Specification Reference 3.2.6

6. Group 2 Compounds

Here's a bit more about the alkaline earth metals and their compounds to follow on from what you learned in the previous topic. It's just a bit of a Group 2 bonus.

Reactions with water

When Group 2 elements react, they are oxidised from a state of 0 to +2, forming M^{2+} ions.

$$M \rightarrow M^{2+} + 2e^-$$

Oxidation state: $0 \rightarrow +2$

Example

$$\mathbf{Ca \rightarrow Ca^{2+} + 2e^-}$$

Oxidation state: $0 \rightarrow +2$

The Group 2 metals react with water to give a metal hydroxide and hydrogen.

$$M_{(s)} + 2H_2O_{(l)} \rightarrow M(OH)_{2\,(aq)} + H_{2\,(g)}$$

Oxidation state: $0 \rightarrow +2$

Example

Calcium reacts with water to form calcium hydroxide and hydrogen.

$$\mathbf{Ca_{(s)} + 2H_2O_{(l)} \rightarrow Ca(OH)_{2\,(aq)} + H_{2\,(g)}}$$

Oxidation state: $0 \rightarrow +2$

The elements react more readily down the group because the ionisation energies decrease (see Figure 1).

Group 2 element	1st ionisation energy / kJ mol^{-1}	Rate of reactivity with water
Be	900	doesn't react
Mg	738	VERY slow
Ca	590	steady
Sr	550	fairly quick
Ba	503	rapid

Figure 1: *Comparison of first ionisation energies and reactivity with water for Group 2 elements.*

Solubility of compounds

The solubility of Group 2 compounds depends on the anion (negative ion) in the compound. Generally, compounds of Group 2 elements that contain singly charged negative ions (e.g. OH^-) increase in solubility down the group, whereas compounds that contain doubly charged negative ions (e.g. SO_4^{2-}) decrease in solubility down the group (see Figure 2).

Group 2 element	hydroxide (OH^-)	sulfate (SO_4^{2-})
magnesium	least soluble ↓	most soluble ↑
calcium		
strontium		
barium	most soluble	least soluble

Figure 2: *Solubility of Group 2 anions.*

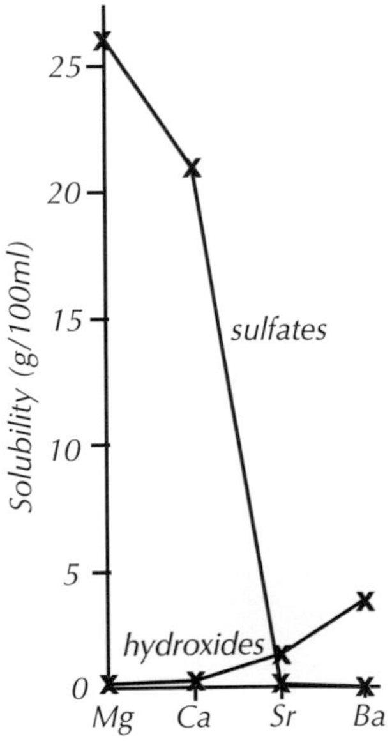

Figure 3: *Solubilities of Group 2 compounds.*

Compounds like magnesium hydroxide which have very low solubilities are said to be sparingly soluble.

Most sulfates are soluble in water, but barium sulfate is insoluble. The test for sulfate ions makes use of this property. If acidified barium chloride ($BaCl_2$) is added to a solution containing sulfate ions then a white precipitate of barium sulfate is formed (see Figure 4).

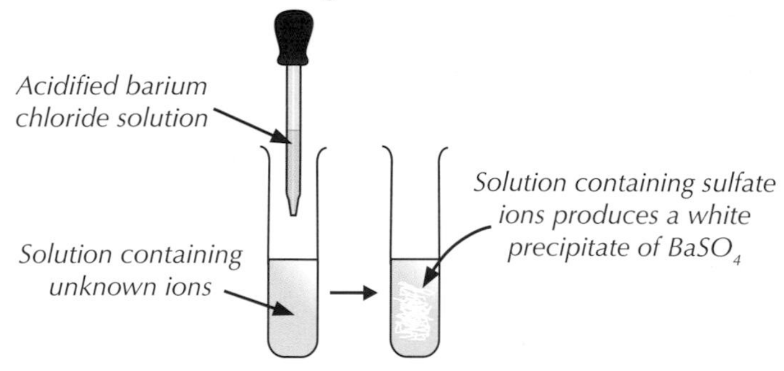

Figure 4: *The test for identifying sulfate ions in solution.*

Tip: You need to acidify the barium chloride (with, say, hydrochloric acid) to get rid of any lurking sulfites or carbonates.

Barium meals

The fact that barium sulfate is insoluble is also useful in medicine. X-rays are great for finding broken bones, but they pass straight through soft tissue — so soft tissues, like the digestive system, don't show up on conventional X-ray pictures. Barium sulfate is opaque to X-rays — they won't pass through it. It's used in 'barium meals' to help diagnose problems with the oesophagus, stomach or intestines. A patient swallows the barium meal, which is a suspension of barium sulfate. The barium sulfate coats the tissues, making them show up on the X-rays, showing the structure of the organs (see Figure 5). You couldn't use other barium compounds for this because solutions containing barium ions are poisonous — barium sulfate is insoluble so forms a suspension rather than a solution.

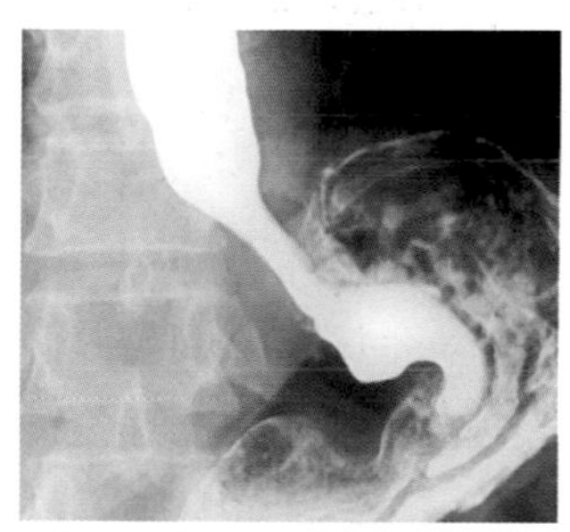

Figure 5: *X-ray showing the oesophagus and stomach following a barium meal.*

Other uses of Group 2 compounds

Group 2 elements are known as the alkaline earth metals, and many of their common compounds are used for neutralising acids. Calcium hydroxide (slaked lime, $Ca(OH)_2$) is used in agriculture to neutralise acidic soils. Magnesium hydroxide ($Mg(OH)_2$) is used in some indigestion tablets as an antacid.

Practice Questions — Application

Q1 One Group 2 element has a first ionisation energy of 550 kJ mol^{-1} and another has a first ionisation energy of 738 kJ mol^{-1}. Explain which element you would expect to react most rapidly with water.

Q2 Acidified barium chloride is added to a solution. No precipitate forms. What does this result show?

Practice Questions — Fact Recall

Q1 Describe the trend in reactivity of Group 2 elements with water.

Q2 How does the solubility of hydroxides change down Group 2?

Q3 What is a 'barium meal'?

Q4 Give two uses of Group 2 hydroxides.

7. Extraction of Metals

Extracting metals may not be glamorous but it is pretty handy...

Learning Objectives:

- Know that metals are found in ores, usually as oxides or sulfides and that sulfide ores are usually converted into oxides by roasting in air.
- Understand the environmental problems associated with the conversion of sulfides into oxides and also that the sulfur dioxide produced can be used to manufacture sulfuric acid.
- Understand that extraction of metals involves reduction.
- Understand that carbon and carbon monoxide are cheap and effective reducing agents that are used in the extraction of iron, manganese and copper.
- Know why carbon reduction is not used for extraction of titanium, aluminium and tungsten.
- Understand how aluminium is manufactured from purified bauxite.
- Understand how titanium is extracted from TiO_2 via $TiCl_4$.
- Understand how tungsten is extracted from WO_3 by reduction with hydrogen.

Specification Reference 3.2.7

Ores

An **ore** is a natural substance that a metal can be economically extracted from. In other words, a rock you can get quite a bit of metal out of. Metals are often found in ores as sulfides (such as lead sulfide and zinc sulfide), or oxides (like titanium dioxide and iron(III) oxide).

Sulfide ores

The metal element needs to be removed from these compounds — that's where the chemistry comes in. The first step to extract a metal from a sulfide ore is to turn it into an oxide. This is done by roasting the sulfide in air, which also produces sulfur dioxide.

Example

Zinc can be found as a sulfide. The first stage in extracting the zinc is:

$$\text{zinc sulfide} + \text{oxygen} \rightarrow \text{zinc oxide} + \text{sulfur dioxide}$$

$$2ZnS_{(s)} + 3O_{2(g)} \rightarrow 2ZnO_{(s)} + 2SO_{2(g)}$$

The zinc oxide can then be processed further — see below.

Here's the bad news: sulfur dioxide gas causes acid rain. Acid rain can cause harm to plants and aquatic life, and damage limestone buildings, so the sulfur dioxide can't be released into the atmosphere. But here's the good news: by converting the sulfur dioxide to sulfuric acid a pollutant is avoided, and a valuable product is made — sulfuric acid's in demand because it's used in many chemical and manufacturing processes.

Reducing metal oxides

Once you've got a metal oxide, either made from a sulfide ore or straight out of the ground, you can reduce it to extract the metal. The method for reducing the oxide depends on the metal you're trying to extract. Carbon (as coke — a solid fuel made from coal) and carbon monoxide are used as reducing agents for quite a few metals — usually the ones that are less reactive than carbon. You need to know three examples of the extraction of metals with carbon and carbon monoxide.

Reduction of iron(III) oxide

Iron(III) oxide is reduced by carbon or carbon monoxide to iron and carbon dioxide.

$$2Fe_2O_{3(s)} + 3C_{(s)} \rightarrow 4Fe_{(l)} + 3CO_{2(g)}$$

Oxidation state of Fe:	+3		→	0		reduction
Oxidation state of C:		0	→		+4	oxidation

$$Fe_2O_{3(s)} + 3CO_{(g)} \rightarrow 2Fe_{(l)} + 3CO_{2(g)}$$

Oxidation state of Fe:	+3		→	0		reduction
Oxidation state of C:		+2	→		+4	oxidation

These reactions happen in a blast furnace at temperatures greater than 700 °C.

Tip: 'Roasting' in this context has nothing to do with potatoes. It just means the ore is heated in plenty of air.

Reduction of manganese(IV) oxide (manganese dioxide)

Manganese(IV) oxide is reduced with carbon (as coke) or carbon monoxide in a blast furnace.

$$MnO_{2(s)} + C_{(s)} \rightarrow Mn_{(l)} + CO_{2(g)}$$

Oxidation state of Mn: +4 → 0 *reduction*

Oxidation state of C: 0 → +4 *oxidation*

$$MnO_{2(s)} + 2CO_{(g)} \rightarrow Mn_{(l)} + 2CO_{2(g)}$$

Oxidation state of Mn: +4 → 0 *reduction*

Oxidation state of C: +2 → +4 *oxidation*

This needs higher temperatures than iron(III) oxide — about 1200 °C.

Figure 1: *A blast furnace.*

Reduction of copper carbonate and copper(II) oxide

Copper can be extracted using carbon. One ore of copper is malachite, containing $CuCO_3$. This can be heated directly with carbon.

$$2CuCO_{3(s)} + C_{(s)} \rightarrow 2Cu_{(l)} + 3CO_{2(g)}$$

Oxidation state of Cu: +2 → 0 *reduction*

Oxidation state of C: 0 → +4 *oxidation*

Another method involves heating the carbonate until it decomposes to copper(II) oxide and CO_2, then reducing the oxide with carbon.

$$CuCO_{3(s)} \rightarrow CuO_{(s)} + CO_{2(g)}$$

$$2CuO_{(s)} + C_{(s)} \rightarrow 2Cu_{(l)} + CO_{2(g)}$$

Oxidation state of Cu: +2 → 0 *reduction*

Oxidation state of C: 0 → +4 *oxidation*

Carbon and carbon monoxide are the first choice for extracting metals because they're cheap. But they're not always suitable — some metals have to be extracted by other methods.

Exam Tip

You need to learn the reduction equations and the conditions used for iron, manganese and copper extraction.

Tip: Don't forget — if an element has Roman numerals after it (e.g. copper(II) oxide), the Roman numerals show the oxidation state of that element in that particular compound (e.g. 2+).

Extracting tungsten

Tungsten can be extracted from its oxide with carbon, but that can leave impurities which make the metal more brittle. If pure tungsten is needed, the ore is reduced using hydrogen instead.

$$WO_{3(s)} + 3H_{2(g)} \rightarrow W_{(s)} + 3H_2O_{(g)}$$

Oxidation state of W: +6 → 0 *reduction*

Oxidation state of H: 0 → +1 *oxidation*

This happens in a furnace at temperatures above 700 °C. Tungsten is the only metal reduced on a large scale using hydrogen. Hydrogen is more expensive than carbon but it's worth the extra cost to get pure tungsten, which is much easier to work with. Hydrogen is highly explosive when mixed with air though, which is a bit of a hazard.

Extracting aluminium

Aluminium is too reactive to extract using reduction by carbon. A very high temperature is needed, so extracting aluminium by reduction is too expensive to make it worthwhile. Instead, it's extracted by electrolysis.

You'll probably remember electrolysis from GCSE. It involves passing an electric current through the electrolyte (an ionic substance that's molten or in solution) so that it breaks down into its elements. It relies on the flow of electrons from ions at the positive electrode (**anode**) to ions at the negative electrode (**cathode**). This is the reason the electrolyte has to be a liquid — the ions have to be free to move. As the ions gain or lose electrons they become atoms (or molecules) and are released. In the case of aluminium extraction, the electrolyte is the ore.

Figure 2: *Bauxite.*

Aluminium's ore is called **bauxite** (see Figure 2) — it's aluminium oxide, Al_2O_3, with various impurities. First of all, these impurities are removed. Next, it's dissolved in molten cryolite (sodium aluminium fluoride, Na_3AlF_6), which lowers its melting point from a scorching 2050 °C, to a cool 970 °C. This reduces the operating costs — energy is needed to heat the ore and that's expensive. The equipment used for the extraction is shown in Figure 3.

Tip: The current used in electrolysis is high (200 000 A), so the process is carried out where cheap electricity is available, often near hydroelectric power stations.

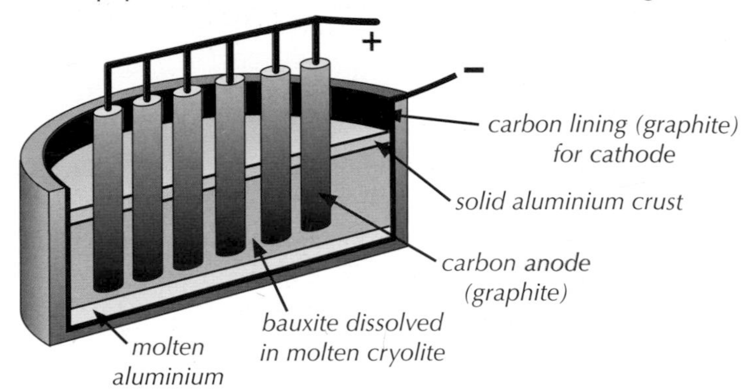

Figure 3: *Equipment used for the extraction of aluminium from its ore.*

Exam Tip
You don't need to be able to draw the equipment, but you do need to know the energy considerations, electrode equations and conditions for the extraction of aluminium from bauxite.

At the cathode, aluminium ions gain electrons and are reduced:

$$Al^{3+} + 3e^- \rightarrow Al$$

The pure aluminium collects as molten metal at the bottom of the cell.

At the anode, oxide ions lose electrons and are oxidised, producing oxygen gas:

$$2O^{2-} \rightarrow O_2 + 4e^-$$

The anode has to be replaced frequently because the carbon reacts with the oxygen produced.

Extracting titanium

Titanium is a pretty abundant metal in the Earth's crust. In its pure form, titanium is a strong, light metal that is highly resistant to corrosion. Pretty much perfect really, so how come it's not used more? Well basically, it's just a bit too difficult and expensive to produce. The main ore is rutile (titanium(IV) oxide, TiO_2). You can't extract titanium from it by carbon reduction because you get titanium carbide which ruins it:

$$TiO_{2\,(s)} + 3C_{(s)} \rightarrow TiC_{(s)} + 2CO_{(g)}$$

Tip: A batch process is where a specific quantity (a batch) of a product is made.

The extraction of titanium is a batch process with several stages. The ore is converted to titanium(IV) chloride by heating it to about 900 °C with carbon in a stream of chlorine gas.

$$TiO_{2\,(s)} + 2Cl_{2\,(g)} + 2C_{(s)} \rightarrow TiCl_{4\,(g)} + 2CO_{(g)}$$

The titanium chloride is purified by fractional distillation under an inert atmosphere of argon. Then the chloride gets reduced in a furnace at almost 1000 °C. It's heated with a more reactive metal such as sodium or magnesium — they act as reducing agents.

$$TiCl_{4\,(g)} + 4Na_{(l)} \rightarrow Ti_{(s)} + 4NaCl_{(l)}$$

Oxidation state of Ti:	*+4*		*→ 0*		*reduction*
Oxidation state of Na:		*0*	*→*	*+1*	*oxidation*

$$TiCl_{4\,(g)} + 2Mg_{(l)} \rightarrow Ti_{(s)} + 2MgCl_{2\,(l)}$$

Oxidation state of Ti:	*+4*		*→ 0*		*reduction*
Oxidation state of Mg:		*0*	*→*	*+2*	*oxidation*

An inert atmosphere of argon is also used for this stage to prevent the titanium chloride, reducing agent and titanium metal from reacting with oxygen or water vapour from the air.

Figure 4: *Titanium production. A vehicle removing a glowing hot ingot of titanium from a furnace.*

Exam Tip
You could be asked for the equations and conditions for titanium extraction, with either Na or Mg as a reducing agent — so make sure you learn both.

Practice Questions — Fact Recall

Q1 What is an ore?

Q2 a) How would you turn a sulfide ore into an oxide?

b) Give one disadvantage of doing this.

Q3 Iron can be extracted from its oxide using carbon or carbon monoxide.

a) Give the conditions needed for the reduction of iron oxide.

b) Write the equation for the reduction of iron oxide with carbon.

c) Write the equation for the reduction of iron oxide with carbon monoxide.

Q4 a) Give the equation for the reduction of manganese(IV) oxide with carbon monoxide.

b) Give the conditions used for this reaction.

Q5 a) Give the equation for the reduction of malachite ($CuCO_3$) with carbon.

b) Give the equation for the reduction of copper(II) oxide (CuO) with carbon.

Q6 a) Describe the process of extracting tungsten from its oxide.

b) Give one risk associated with this process.

Q7 a) Explain why electrolysis is used to extract aluminium rather than reduction with carbon.

b) Write the ionic equations for the anode and cathode reactions during the extraction of aluminium.

Q8 Give the equation for the extraction of titanium from its chloride using magnesium as a reducing agent.

8. Recycling Metals

Learning Objectives:
- Understand the environmental and economic advantages and disadvantages of recycling scrap metals compared with the extraction of metals.
- Understand the environmental advantages of using scrap iron to extract copper from aqueous solutions compared with the high-temperature carbon reduction of copper oxide.
- Know that the usual source of such aqueous solutions is low grade ore.

Specification Reference 3.2.7

You probably know about recycling metals from recycling cans at home. But metal recycling happens on a big scale in industry too.

Advantages and disadvantages

Once you've got the metal out of the ore, you can keep recycling it again and again. As usual, there are pros and cons:

Advantages of recycling metals

- Saves raw materials — ores are a finite resource.
- Saves energy — recycling metals takes less energy than extracting metal. This saves money too.
- Reduces waste sent to landfill.
- Mining damages the landscape and spoil heaps are ugly. Recycling metals reduces this.

Disadvantages of recycling metals

- Collecting and sorting metals from other waste can be difficult and expensive.
- The purity of recycled metal varies — there's usually other metals and other impurities mixed in.
- Recycling metals may not produce a consistent supply to meet demand.

Tip: There's more on page 4 about how decisions are made on things like whether we should recycle.

Using scrap iron

Some scrap metal can be put to other uses. For example, scrap iron can be used to extract copper from solution. This method is mainly used with low grade ore — ore that only contains a small percentage of copper. Acidified water dissolves the copper compounds in the ore. The solution is collected and scrap iron is then added. The iron dissolves and reduces the copper(II) ions. The copper precipitates out of the solution.

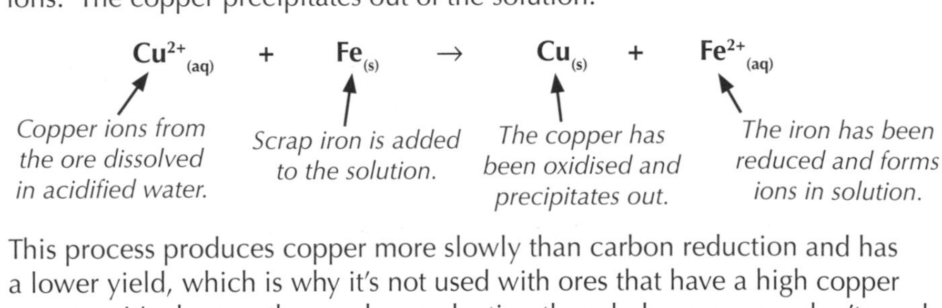

This process produces copper more slowly than carbon reduction and has a lower yield, which is why it's not used with ores that have a high copper content. It's cheaper than carbon reduction though, because you don't need high temperatures, and better for the environment because there's no CO_2 produced.

Figure 1: Pile of scrapped cars awaiting processing at a metal recycling centre.

Practice Questions — Fact Recall

Q1 Describe the advantages and disadvantages of recycling metals.

Q2 a) Describe how scrap iron can be used to extract copper from aqueous solution.

b) What is the usual source of the aqueous copper solution?

Section Summary

Make sure you know...

- That loss of electrons is called oxidation and gain of electrons is called reduction.
- What redox reactions are.
- That oxidising agents are electron acceptors and reducing agents are electron donors.
- How to work out the oxidation state of an element in a compound.
- How to combine half-equations to make a full redox equation.
- How to write half-equations for the oxidation and reduction parts of a redox reaction.
- That the elements of Group 7 are known as the halogens.
- Why the boiling points of the halogens increase as you go down the group.
- Why the electronegativity of the halogens decreases as you go down the group.
- That the oxidising ability of the halogens decreases down the group, and how this can be demonstrated by halide ion displacement reactions.
- The products of the reaction between chlorine and cold dilute sodium hydroxide and their uses.
- How chlorine reacts with water.
- Why chlorine is used in water treatment, even though it can be toxic.
- Why the reducing ability of the halide ions increases down the group.
- The reactions between sulfuric acid and the sodium halides, plus the reasons for the different products made with different halides.
- What the silver nitrate test is.
- The results of the silver nitrate test for solutions containing fluoride, chloride, bromide and iodide ions.
- The trend in the solubility of silver halides in ammonia and why this is useful.
- Why atomic radius increases as you go down Group 2.
- Why first ionisation energy decreases as you go down Group 2.
- How and why melting point changes as you go down Group 2.
- The reactions of Group 2 metals with water and what the reactivity trend is as you go down the group.
- How the solubilities of Group 2 hydroxides and sulfates vary.
- What the barium chloride test for sulfate ions is and what a positive test result is.
- How barium sulfate and magnesium hydroxide are used in medicine.
- How calcium hydroxide is used in agriculture.
- What ores are and that most ores are oxides or sulfides.
- How sulfide ores are converted to oxides and what happens to the sulfur dioxide produced.
- That ores are reduced to extract the metal.
- How carbon and carbon monoxide are used as reducing agents in the extraction of iron, manganese and copper.
- How tungsten is extracted by reduction with hydrogen.
- How aluminium is extracted from bauxite.
- How titanium is extracted from its oxide.
- The advantages and disadvantages of recycling scrap metal.
- Why scrap iron is used to extract copper from aqueous copper solution.
- That aqueous copper solutions for this process are prepared from low grade copper ore.

Exam-style Questions

1 Chlorine and bromine are halogens.

1 (a) The halogens have different boiling points.

State whether chlorine has a higher or lower boiling point than bromine and explain why.

(3 marks)

1 (b) Chlorine water and bromine water are added to solutions **A** and **B**. Each solution contains a potassium halide. The table below shows the results.

	Solution A	Solution B
Chlorine water	solution turns orange	solution turns brown
Bromine water	no change	solution turns brown

1 (b) (i) Identify solution **A** and explain your reasoning.

(3 marks)

1 (b) (ii) Identify solution **B** and write an ionic equation for its reaction with chlorine water.

(2 marks)

1 (c) Chlorine can undergo the following reaction:

$$2NaOH_{(aq)} + Cl_{2\,(g)} \rightarrow NaClO_{(aq)} + NaCl_{(aq)} + H_2O_{(l)}$$

1 (c) (i) Deduce the oxidation states of chlorine in Cl_2, ClO^- and NaCl.

(3 marks)

1 (c) (ii) Give one use for the NaClO formed.

(1 mark)

1 (d) Silver nitrate can be used to identify halide ions in solution.

1 (d) (i) Explain why dilute nitric acid (HNO_3) is added to the solution.

(1 mark)

1 (d) (ii) State what you would observe if bromide ions are present in the solution being tested.

(1 mark)

1 (d) (iii) Explain how ammonia solution can be used to confirm the result you gave in **(d) (ii)**.

(1 mark)

2 Samples of three of the alkaline earth metals, strontium, calcium and magnesium, are placed in jars labelled **D**, **E** and **F**. Some information about the three metals is shown in the table below.

	D	**E**	**F**
Atomic radius	0.16 nm	0.19 nm	0.215 nm
1st ionisation energy	738 kJ mol^{-1}	590 kJ mol^{-1}	550 kJ mol^{-1}
Melting point	923 K	1115 K	1050 K

2 (a) Which of the elements in the table is magnesium?

(1 mark)

2 (b) Explain why the first ionisation energy of **D** is higher than the first ionisation energy of **E**.

(3 marks)

2 (c) Using the information in the table, explain how the reactivity of metal **F** with water will compare with **E**.

(2 marks)

2 (d) Barium has a lower melting point than metal **F**.
Explain why this is the case.

(3 marks)

2 (e) (i) State the solubility of magnesium hydroxide in water.

(1 mark)

2 (e) (ii) How would you expect the solubility of the hydroxide of metal **E** to compare to the solubility of magnesium hydroxide?

(1 mark)

2 (f) Describe how magnesium hydroxide is used in medicine.

(2 marks)

2 (g) Sodium is used as a reducing agent in the reaction with titanium(IV) chloride.

2 (g) (i) Write the equation for this reaction.

(1 mark)

2 (g) (ii) Explain what is meant by the term reducing agent.

(1 mark)

3 Manganese (Mn) is an element that occurs in many minerals and can be used to make alloys such as stainless steel.

Manganese can be reduced from its ore pyrulosite (MnO_2) using carbon monoxide.

3 (a) State what an ore is.

(1 mark)

3 (b) Explain why carbon monoxide is used as a reducing agent in metal extraction.

(1 mark)

3 (c) Write an equation for the reduction of pyrulosite (MnO_2) with carbon monoxide.

(1 mark)

3 (d) Give the conditions used for the extraction of manganese from manganese(IV) dioxide using carbon monoxide.

(1 mark)

3 (e) Carbon monoxide is not used to extract tungsten from its ore. Describe the conditions used for the extraction of tungsten and give one hazard associated with this process.

(3 marks)

4 Aluminium is the third most abundant metal in the Earth's crust. It is extremely reactive and occurs naturally in many different minerals, the most common of which is bauxite.

4 (a) Aluminium reacts with chlorine (Cl_2) to form aluminium chloride ($AlCl_3$).

Write the ionic half-equations for this reaction.

Identify which half-equation is the reduction process and which is the oxidation process.

(4 marks)

4 (b) Aluminium is extracted from bauxite (Al_2O_3) using electrolysis.

Describe the process used to extract aluminium from bauxite.

Explain why this process is very expensive.

(5 marks)

4 (c) Aluminium cans can be recycled.

Describe the advantages and disadvantages of recycling aluminium cans.

(4 marks)

1. Synthesis of Chloroalkanes

Chloroalkanes are alkanes with one or more hydrogen atoms substituted by a chlorine atom. They are pretty important to chemists so it's important to understand how they're made. That's where the synthesis part comes in — a synthesis is just a step-wise method detailing how to create a chemical.

Learning Objectives:

- Understand the reaction mechanism of methane with chlorine as a free-radical substitution reaction in terms of initiation, propagation and termination steps.
- Know that chloroalkanes and chlorofluoroalkanes can be used as solvents.
- Understand that ozone formed naturally in the upper atmosphere is beneficial.
- Be able to use equations to explain why chlorine atoms catalyse the decomposition of ozone and contribute to the formation of a hole in the ozone layer.
- Know that chlorine atoms are formed in the upper atmosphere when energy from ultraviolet radiation causes C–Cl bonds in chlorofluorocarbons (CFCs) to break.
- Know that legislation to ban the use of CFCs was supported by chemists and that they have now developed alternative chlorine-free compounds.

Specification Reference 3.2.8

Reactivity of alkanes

A chemical is **polar** when the bonding electrons in the molecule are pulled towards more electronegative atoms creating a dipole (see page 70). Opposite dipoles on different molecules can attract each other and cause the molecules to react.

The C–C bonds and C–H bonds in alkanes are pretty non-polar. But most chemicals are polar — like water, haloalkanes, acids and alkalis. Polar chemicals are attracted to the polar groups on molecules they attack. Alkanes don't have any polar groups, so they don't react with polar chemicals. Alkanes will react with some non-polar things though — such as oxygen or the halogens. But they'll only bother if you give them enough energy.

Photochemical reactions

Halogens react with alkanes in photochemical reactions to form haloalkanes (see page 164 for more on haloalkanes). Photochemical reactions are started by ultraviolet light. A hydrogen atom is substituted (replaced) by chlorine or bromine. This is a **free radical** substitution reaction. Free radicals are particles with an unpaired electron, written like this — Cl· or $CH_3\cdot$. You get them when bonds split equally, and they're highly reactive.

Synthesis of chloromethane

A mixture of methane and chlorine will not react on its own but when exposed to UV light it reacts with a bit of a bang to form chloromethane. The overall equation for this reaction is shown below.

$$CH_4 + Cl_2 \xrightarrow{UV} CH_3Cl + HCl$$

A reaction mechanism shows each step in the synthesis of a chemical. The reaction mechanism for the synthesis of chloromethane by a photochemical reaction has three stages — initiation, propagation and termination.

Initiation

In the initiation step, free radicals are produced. Sunlight provides enough energy to break some of the Cl–Cl bonds — this is photodissociation.

$$Cl_2 \xrightarrow{UV} 2Cl\bullet$$

The bond splits equally and each atom gets to keep one electron. The atom becomes a highly reactive free radical, Cl·, because of its unpaired electron.

Exam Tip
When you're writing radical equations you need to make sure that there's the same number of radicals on each side of the equation or that two radicals are combining to create a non-radical.

Propagation

During propagation, free radicals are used up and created in a chain reaction. First, Cl· attacks a methane molecule:

$$Cl\bullet + CH_4 \rightarrow CH_3\bullet + HCl$$

The new methyl free radical, $CH_3\cdot$, can then attack another Cl_2 molecule:

$$CH_3\bullet + Cl_2 \rightarrow CH_3Cl + Cl\bullet$$

The new Cl· can attack another CH_4 molecule, and so on, until all the Cl_2 or CH_4 molecules are used up.

Substitutions

If the chlorine's in excess, the hydrogen atoms on methane will eventually be replaced by chlorine atoms. This means you'll get dichloromethane CH_2Cl_2, trichloromethane $CHCl_3$, and tetrachloromethane CCl_4.

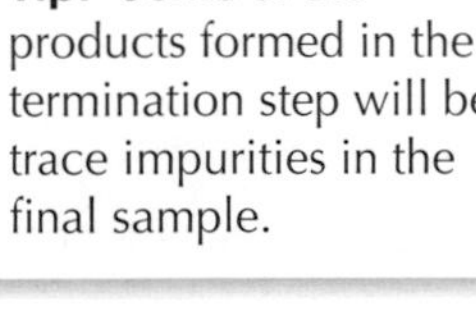

Tip: Some of the products formed in the termination step will be trace impurities in the final sample.

$$CH_4 + Cl_2 \rightarrow CH_3Cl + HCl$$

$$CH_3Cl + Cl_2 \rightarrow CH_2Cl_2 + HCl$$

$$CH_2Cl_2 + Cl_2 \rightarrow CHCl_3 + HCl$$

$$CHCl_3 + Cl_2 \rightarrow CCl_4 + HCl$$

But if the methane's in excess, then the chlorine will be used up quickly and the product will mostly be chloromethane.

$$CH_4 + Cl_2 \rightarrow CH_3Cl + HCl$$

Termination

In the termination step, free radicals are mopped up. If two free radicals join together, they make a stable molecule — this terminates the chain reaction. There are heaps of possible termination reactions. Here's a couple of them to give you the idea:

$$CH_3\bullet + Cl\bullet \rightarrow CH_3Cl$$

$$CH_3\bullet + CH_3\bullet \rightarrow C_2H_6$$

Chlorofluorocarbons

Chlorofluorocarbons (CFCs) are haloalkane molecules where all of the hydrogen atoms have been replaced by chlorine and fluorine atoms.

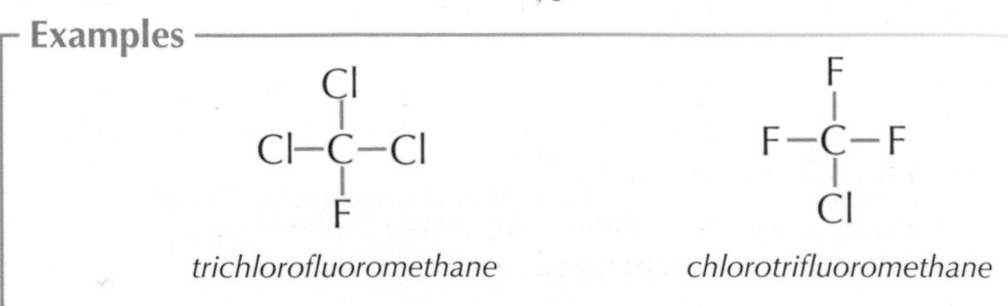

Figure 1: *Household solvents or a really lame tombola.*

Both CFCs and chloroalkanes can be used as solvents — they both used to be used in dry cleaning and degreasing.

Chlorofluorocarbons and the ozone layer

Ozone (O_3) in the upper atmosphere acts as a chemical sunscreen. It absorbs a lot of the ultraviolet radiation which can cause sunburn or even skin cancer. Ozone's formed naturally when an oxygen molecule is broken down into two free radicals by ultraviolet radiation:

$$O_2 + h\nu \rightarrow O\bullet + O\bullet$$

The free radicals attack other oxygen molecules forming ozone:

$$O_2 + O\bullet \rightarrow O_3$$

Tip: The hν in the first equation is the notation for a quantum of UV radiation — a photon. It just means that the reaction needs to be initiated by electromagnetic radiation.

You've heard of how the ozone layer's being destroyed by CFCs, right. Well, here's what's happening. Chlorine free radicals, Cl·, are formed when the C–Cl bonds in CFCs are broken down by ultraviolet radiation, like this:

$$CCl_3F_{(g)} \rightarrow CCl_2F\bullet_{(g)} + Cl\bullet_{(g)}$$

These free radicals are **homogeneous catalysts** — they're in the same phase as the ozone molecules. They react with ozone to form an **intermediate** (ClO·), and an oxygen molecule.

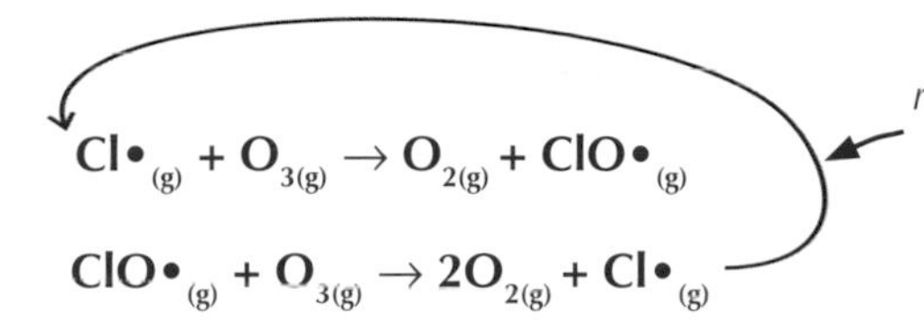

The chlorine free radical is regenerated. It goes straight on to attack another ozone molecule.

Because the Cl· free radical is regenerated, it only takes one little chlorine free radical to destroy loads of ozone molecules. So, the overall reaction is...

$$2O_{3(g)} \rightarrow 3O_{2(g)}$$

... and Cl· is the catalyst.

Environmental problems of CFCs

CFCs are pretty unreactive, non-flammable and non-toxic. They used to be used in fire extinguishers, as propellants in aerosols, as the coolant gas in fridges and to foam plastics to make insulation and packaging materials. In the 1970s scientists discovered that CFCs were causing damage to the ozone layer. The advantages of CFCs couldn't outweigh the environmental problems they were causing, so they were banned. Chemists have developed alternatives to CFCs. HCFCs (hydrochlorofluorocarbons) and HFCs (hydrofluorocarbons) are less dangerous than CFCs, so they're being used as temporary alternatives until safer products are developed. Most aerosols now have been replaced by pump spray systems or use nitrogen as the propellant. Many industrial fridges use ammonia or hydrocarbons as the coolant gas, and carbon dioxide is used to make foamed polymers.

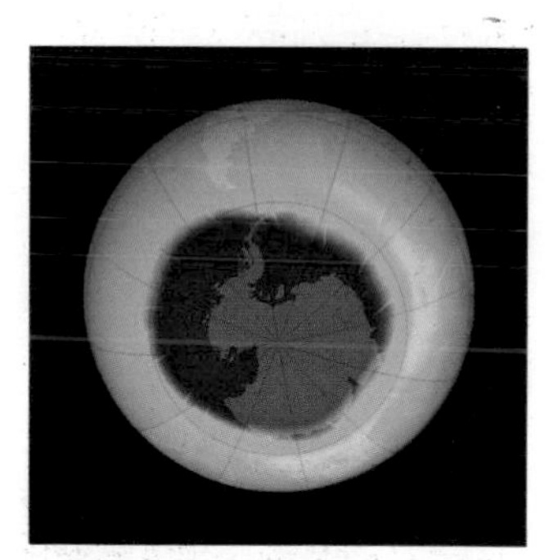

Figure 2: *Antarctic ozone hole, 2009. On the diagram, green indicates areas with a high ozone concentration and blue indicates areas with a low ozone concentration.*

Practice Questions — Fact Recall

Q1 What is a photochemical reaction?

Q2 Write an equation for the initiation step of the synthesis of chloromethane by a photochemical reaction.

Q3 Name the catalyst that aids the destruction of ozone in the upper atmosphere.

Learning Objective:

- Understand that haloalkanes contain polar bonds.

Specification Reference 3.2.8

2. Haloalkanes

Haloalkanes pop up a lot in chemistry so it's important that you know exactly what they are and how they react.

What are haloalkanes?

A haloalkane is an alkane with at least one halogen atom in place of a hydrogen atom.

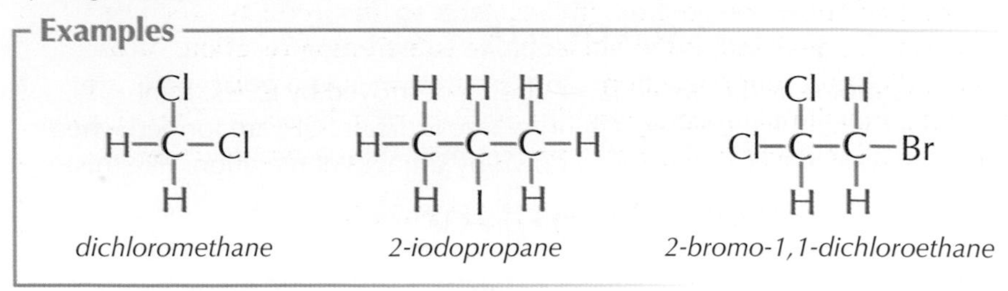

Tip: Don't worry if you see haloalkanes called halogenoalkanes. It's a government conspiracy to confuse you.

Polarity of haloalkanes

Halogens are much more electronegative than carbon.
So, the carbon-halogen bond is **polar**.

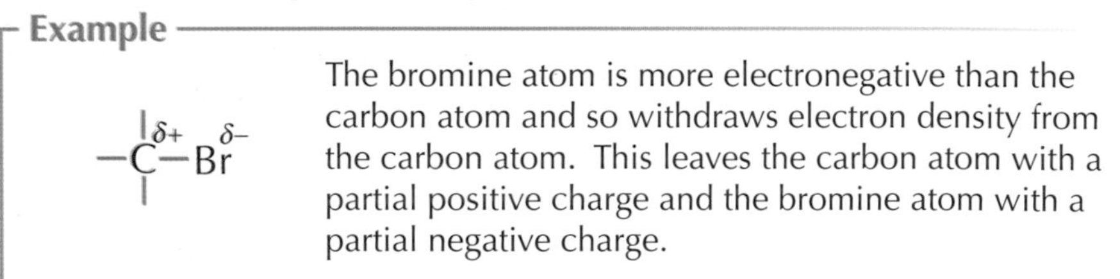

The δ+ carbon doesn't have enough electrons. This means it can be attacked by a **nucleophile**. A nucleophile's an electron-pair donor. It donates an electron pair to somewhere without enough electrons.

Tip: Nucleophiles are often negative ions — because they form by gaining electrons they have extra electrons that they can donate. They don't <u>have</u> to be ions though. For example, NH_3 is a nucleophile — it's got a non-bonding pair of electrons that it can donate.

Examples

Here are some examples of nucleophiles that will react with haloalkanes.

$:\bar{C}N$	$:NH_3$	$:\bar{O}H$
cyanide ion	*ammonia*	*hydroxide ion*

The pairs of dots represent lone pairs of electrons.

There are examples of reactions where nucleophiles react with haloalkanes on the next few pages.

Practice Questions — Fact Recall

Q1 What is a haloalkane?

Q2 Explain why halogen-carbon bonds are polar.

Q3 What is a nucleophile?

Q4 Give two examples of nucleophiles that will react with haloalkanes.

Q5 What does a pair of dots represent on a nucleophile?

3. Nucleophilic Substitution

Nucleophilic substitution is a reaction mechanism that substitutes one functional group for another.

Learning Objectives:

- Understand that haloalkanes are susceptible to nucleophilic attack, by ^{-}OH, ^{-}CN and NH_3.
- Understand the mechanism of nucleophilic substitution in primary haloalkanes.
- Understand that the carbon–halogen bond enthalpy influences the rate of hydrolysis.

Specification Reference 3.2.8

Nucleophilic substitution reactions

Mechanisms are diagrams that show how a reaction works. They show how the bonds in molecules are made and broken, how the electrons are transferred and how you get from the reactants to the products. The first mechanism we deal with is the **nucleophilic substitution reaction**. In a nucleophilic substitution reaction, a nucleophile attacks a polar molecule, kicks out a functional group and settles itself down in its place. The equation for the overall reaction of a general nucleophilic substitution reaction is:

$$CH_3CH_2X + Nu^- \rightarrow CH_3CH_2Nu + X^-$$

And here's how it all works:

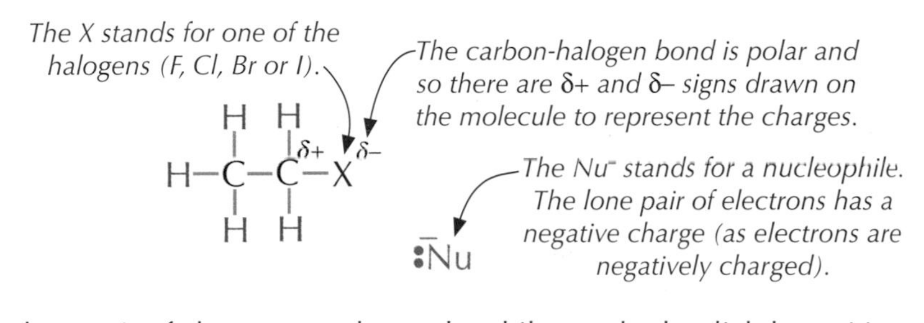

The lone pair of electrons on the nucleophile attacks the slightly positive charge on the carbon — this is shown by a black curly arrow. In mechanisms, curly arrows always show the movement of an electron pair. The lone pair of electrons creates a new bond between the nucleophile and the carbon.

$$CH_3CH_2^{\delta+}X^{\delta-} + :Nu^- \longrightarrow CH_3CH_2Nu + :X^-$$

The carbon can only be bonded to four other atoms so the addition of the nucleophile breaks the bond between the carbon and the halogen — this is shown by another curly arrow. The pair of electrons from the carbon-halogen bond are taken by the halogen and become a lone pair.

Exam Tip

You <u>must</u> draw the curly arrows coming from the <u>lone pair</u> of electrons or from the <u>bond</u>. If you don't — you won't get the marks for the mechanism in the exam.

Hydrolysis of haloalkanes

In hydrolysis reactions, molecules are split into two parts by water molecules (which are also split into two parts). Haloalkanes can be hydrolysed to make alcohols.

Example

Bromoethane can be hydrolysed to ethanol in a nucleophilic substitution reaction. You have to use warm aqueous sodium or potassium hydroxide or it won't work. Here's the equation for this reaction:

$$CH_3CH_2Br + H_2O \rightarrow CH_3CH_2OH + HBr$$

And here's the general equation for this type of reaction:

$$R\text{–}X + H_2O \rightarrow ROH + HX$$

R represents an alkyl group. X stands for one of the halogens (F, Cl, Br or I). As it's a nucleophilic substitution reaction, the nucleophile (^-OH) kicks out the halogen (X) from the R–X molecule and takes its place. You can ignore the H^+ ions because they don't take part in the mechanism. So the overall reaction can just be written as:

$$\mathbf{R{-}X + {}^-OH \rightarrow ROH + X^-}$$

Here's how it happens:

1. The C–Br bond is polar. The $C^{\delta+}$ attracts a lone pair of electrons from the OH^- ion.

3. A new bond forms between the C and the OH^- ion.

4. The C–Br bond breaks and both the electrons from the bond are taken by the Br.

2. The OH^- ion acts as a nucleophile, attacking the slightly positive carbon atom.

Tip: When you're drawing mechanisms make sure the charges balance. That way you'll know if you've managed to lose electrons along the way. In this example, the left hand side of the equation has one negative charge on the hydroxide nucleophile and the right hand side has one negative charge from a bromine ion — so it's balanced.

Reactivity of haloalkanes

The carbon-halogen bond strength (or enthalpy) decides reactivity. For any reaction to occur the carbon-halogen bond needs to break. The C–F bond is the strongest — it has the highest bond enthalpy. So fluoroalkanes are hydrolysed more slowly than other haloalkanes. The C–I bond has the lowest bond enthalpy, so it's easier to break. This means that iodoalkanes are hydrolysed more quickly.

bond	bond enthalpy kJ mol^{-1}
C–F	467
C–Cl	346
C–Br	290
C–I	228

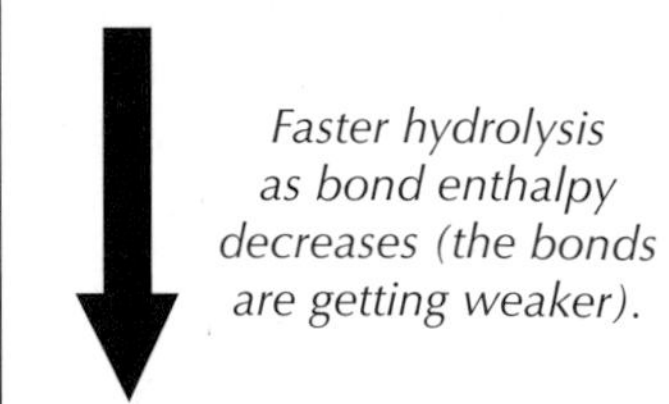

Figure 1: *Carbon-halogen bond enthalpies.*

Tip: If you've got a molecule with more than one halogen in it, the halogen with the lowest bond enthalpy will get replaced first.

Synthesising amines

An amine has the structure R_3N. The R groups can be hydrogens or another group. In amines, the nitrogen always has a lone pair (shown as a pair of dots next to the nitrogen atom).

Examples

The molecules below are both amines.

methylamine

ethylamine

Tip: Amines are derivatives of the ammonia molecule — shown below:

If you warm a haloalkane with excess ethanolic ammonia (ammonia dissolved in ethanol) in a sealed tube, the ammonia swaps places with the halogen to form an amine — yes, it's another one of those nucleophilic substitution reactions.

Example

In this reaction bromoethane is reacting with ammonia to form ethylamine. The first step is the same as in the mechanism on the previous page, except this time the nucleophile is NH_3. The nitrogen atom donates its lone pair of electrons to the carbon atom to create a bond. The nitrogen atom was neutral to begin with, so this means the nitrogen is left with a positive charge.

$$CH_3CH_2^{\delta+}-Br^{\delta-} + :NH_3 \xrightarrow{\text{ethanol}} CH_3CH_2NH_3^+ \quad :Br^-$$

In the second step, a second ammonia molecule removes a hydrogen from the NH_3 group to form an ammonium ion (NH_4^+) and an amine. The ammonia molecule donates its lone pair of electrons to the hydrogen to form a bond, so the nitrogen atom in the ammonium ion now has a positive charge, and the amine has no charge.

$$CH_3CH_2NH_3^+ + :NH_3 \rightleftharpoons CH_3CH_2\ddot{N}H_2 + NH_4^+$$

amine *ammonium ion*

The ammonium ion can react with the bromide ion to form ammonium bromide. Ammonium bromide is held together by an ionic bond (see page 56).

$$[NH_4^+ \quad :Br^-]$$

So the overall reaction is:

$$CH_3CH_2Br + 2\ :NH_3 \xrightarrow{\text{ethanol}} CH_3CH_2\ddot{N}H_2 + NH_4Br$$

Exam Tip

When you're drawing amines in the exam, it's a good idea to draw the lone pair of electrons in so that you don't forget that they're there. And if the amine's part of a mechanism you'll <u>have</u> to draw them in to get all the marks.

Exam Tip

This example shows ammonia reacting with bromoethane, but in the exam you could be given a question that involves a different haloalkane. Don't panic though — the mechanism is exactly the same.

Exam Tip

You could be asked for the mechanism for this reaction, or for the overall reaction equation, so make sure that you know them both.

Synthesising nitriles

Nitriles have CN groups. The carbon atom and nitrogen atom are held together with a triple bond.

Examples

Nitriles are derived from hydrogen cyanide:

H—C≡N

hydrogen cyanide

Here is the nitrile, ethane nitrile:

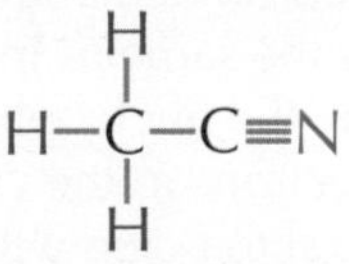

CH_3—C≡N (H—C(H)(H)—C≡N)

ethanenitrile

> **Tip:** Hydrogen cyanide could also be called methane nitrile. Hydrogen cyanide is the molecule's old name and methane nitrile is its name assigned by the IUPAC naming conventions. Either name is correct.

If you warm a haloalkane with ethanolic potassium cyanide you get a nitrile. It's yet another nucleophilic substitution reaction — the cyanide ion, CN^-, is the nucleophile.

Example

Reacting bromoethane with ethanolic potassium cyanide under reflux will produce propanenitrile and potassium bromide.

$$CH_3CH_2Br + KCN \rightarrow CH_3CH_2CN + KBr$$

The potassium cyanide dissociates to form a K^+ ion and a CN^- ion. It's the CN^- ion that acts as the nucleophile in the reaction.

$$KCN \rightarrow K^+ + CN^-$$

The reaction mechanism is the same as the ones on pages 165-167.

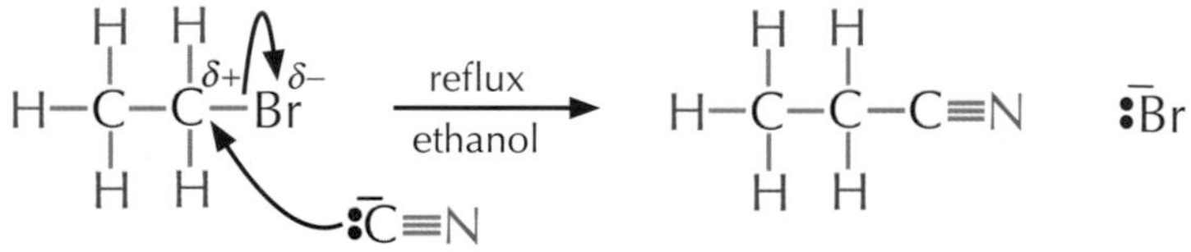

H—C(H)(H)—C(H)(H)$^{\delta+}$—Br$^{\delta-}$ + :$\bar{C}$≡N —(reflux, ethanol)→ H—C(H)(H)—C(H)(H)—C≡N + :$\bar{B}$r

> **Tip:** When you heat a liquid mixture eventually it will start to boil and some of the mixture will be lost as vapour. When you heat under reflux you use equipment that stops the vapour escaping from the reaction mixture. There's more on heating under reflux on page 190.

You have to use ethanol as a solvent here instead of water. If you used water, the hydroxide ion could act as a competing nucleophile and you'd get some alcohol product.

Summary of nucleophilic substitution

- Nucleophilic substitution reactions can occur between a haloalkane and a nucleophile.
- The nucleophile attacks the δ+ carbon atom, which breaks the carbon-halogen bond.
- One new bond is formed (between the nucleophile and the δ+ carbon atom) and one bond is broken (the carbon-halogen bond).
- When you're drawing mechanisms for nucleophilic substitution reactions it's important to draw the curly arrows coming from the electrons and going to an atom. The electrons can come from either a bond or from a lone pair on an atom or ion.
- Make sure the charges are balanced at every stage of a mechanism — if you start with a negative charge you should end up with one too.
- And finally, it doesn't matter which nucleophile you use (^-CN, ^-OH or NH_3), the mechanism for nucleophilic substitution of a haloalkane is always the same.

> **Exam Tip**
> In the exam you could be asked to draw a mechanism for a nucleophilic substitution reaction you haven't seen before. You should practice drawing mechanisms for lots of different reactions before the exam so that you get into the swing of it.

Practice Questions — Application

Q1 Draw the mechanism for the reaction of 1-chlorobutane with warm ethanolic potassium cyanide. The molecule 1-chlorobutane is shown below.

```
  H H H H
  | | | |
H-C-C-C-C-Cl
  | | | |
  H H H H
```

Q2 Which of the following reactions would be quickest? Explain your answer.

A: $CH_3CH_2Cl + H_2O \rightarrow CH_3CH_2OH + HCl$

B: $CH_3CH_2Br + H_2O \rightarrow CH_3CH_2OH + HBr$

C: $CH_3CH_2I + H_2O \rightarrow CH_3CH_2OH + HI$

Q3 Draw the mechanism for the reaction of iodopropane with ammonia. The reaction is done in a sealed tube in warm ethanol. The reactants are shown below.

```
  H H H                H
  | | |δ+ δ-           |
H-C-C-C-I            :N-H
  | | |                |
  H H H                H
```

Q4 Draw the mechanism for the hydrolysis of chloroethane by warm aqueous sodium hydroxide.

Practice Questions — Fact Recall

Q1 Briefly describe a nucleophilic substitution reaction.

Q2 What chemical would you react with bromoethane to get ethanol?

Q3 Explain why fluoroalkanes are hydrolysed more slowly than other haloalkanes.

Q4 Under what reaction conditions do you react bromoethane with ammonia to form ethylamine?

Q5 Name the nucleophile that is present when bromoethane reacts with ethanolic potassium cyanide under reflux.

4. Elimination Reactions

Learning Objectives:

- Understand concurrent substitution and elimination in the reaction of a haloalkane and the role of the reagent as both nucleophile and base.
- Appreciate the usefulness of elimination and nucleophilic substitution reactions in organic synthesis.

Specification Reference 3.2.8

In an elimination reaction, a small group of atoms breaks away from a larger molecule. This small group is not replaced by anything else (whereas it would be in a substitution reaction).

Elimination of a halogen from a haloalkane

If you warm a haloalkane with hydroxide ions dissolved in ethanol instead of water, an elimination reaction happens, and you end up with an alkene.

Example

Reacting bromoethane with potassium hydroxide dissolved in warm ethanol under **reflux** produces an elimination reaction and forms ethene, water and potassium bromide. Here's the equation for this reaction.

$$CH_3CH_2Br + KOH \rightarrow C_2H_4 + H_2O + KBr$$

In the reaction, H and Br are eliminated from neighbouring carbon atoms in CH_3CH_2Br to leave $CH_2{=}CH_2$. Here's how the reaction works:

1. OH^- acts as a base and takes a proton, H^+, from the carbon on the left. This makes water.

3. To form the double bond, the right carbon has to let go of the Br, which drops off as a Br^- ion.

$$CH_3CH_2Br \xrightarrow[\text{ethanol}]{\text{reflux}} CH_2{=}CH_2 \quad H_2O \quad :\!Br^-$$

2. The left carbon now has a spare pair of electrons, so it forms a double bond with the other carbon.

Tip: This elimination reaction takes place under anhydrous conditions — that means there's no water.

Nucleophilic substitution vs elimination

You can control what type of reaction happens by changing the conditions. By reacting a haloalkane with water under reflux, the molecule will predominantly undergo a nucleophilic substitution reaction to form an alcohol. You'll still get a bit of elimination to form an alkene but not a lot.

Example

Reacting bromoethane with water under reflux will produce ethanol.

$$CH_3CH_2Br \xrightarrow[\text{reflux}]{\text{NaOH or KOH, water}} CH_3CH_2OH$$

This is because under aqueous conditions, the OH^- acts as a nucleophile — it donates an electron pair to δ+ carbon atom.

Here the OH^- nucleophile is attacking the δ+ carbon atom.

Exam Tip
It's really important that you know the difference between nucleophilic substitution and elimination. So learn one first, then the other, then make sure you can describe the differences between them. You don't want to get them muddled up in the exam — that's the way to lose yourself marks.

By reacting a haloalkane with ethanol under reflux, the molecule will predominantly undergo an elimination reaction to form an alkene.

Example

Reacting bromoethane with ethanol under reflux will produce ethene.

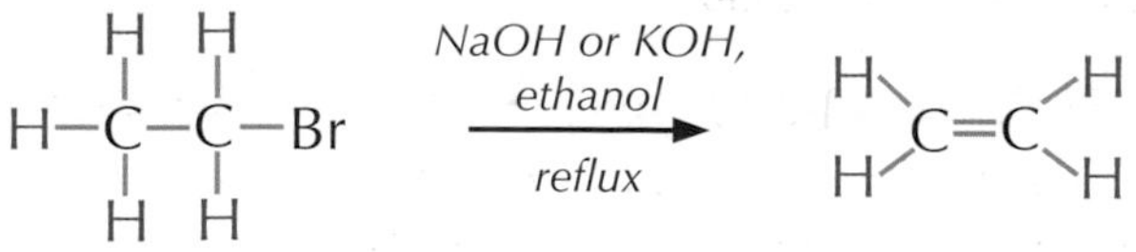

$$CH_3CH_2Br \xrightarrow[\text{reflux}]{\text{NaOH or KOH, ethanol}} H_2C{=}CH_2$$

This is because under anhydrous conditions, the OH^- acts as a base — it removes a hydrogen atom from the haloalkane.

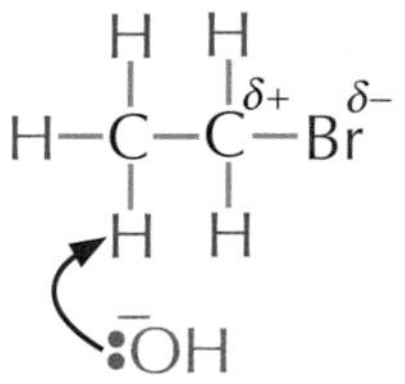

Here the OH^- is acting as a base and pulling the hydrogen off the haloalkane.

Tip: Bases just love to grab hydrogens when they're in solution. There's lots more on bases in the A2 course but for now you don't need to worry about it.

Both of these reactions have their uses. The elimination reaction is a good way of getting a double bond into a molecule. Loads of other organic synthesis reactions use alkenes, so the elimination reaction is a good starting point for making lots of different organic chemicals. The substitution reaction allows you to produce any alcohol molecule that you need. And alcohols can be the starting point for synthesis reactions that produce aldehydes, ketones, esters, and carboxylic acids. So haloalkanes are very useful as a starting material for making other organic compounds.

Practice Question — Application

Q1 Draw the mechanism for the main reaction of 1-bromopropane with ethanol under reflux. A molecule of 1-bromopropane is shown below.

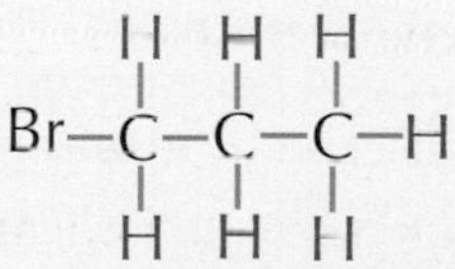

$$Br{-}CH_2{-}CH_2{-}CH_3$$

Practice Questions — Fact Recall

Q1 Briefly describe an elimination reaction.

Q2 Reacting bromoethane with water under reflux will produce mainly ethanol. What type of reagent does the ^-OH act as in this reaction? Name the type of reaction that is occurring.

Q3 Reacting bromoethane with ethanol under reflux will produce mainly ethene. What type of reagent does the ^-OH act as in this reaction? Name the type of reaction that is occurring.

Q4 Briefly describe why elimination reactions and nucleophilic substitution reactions are useful in organic synthesis

5. Reactions of Alkenes

Remember those alkenes from page 98 — well they're back and this time they're reacting.

Learning Objectives:

- Know that alkenes are unsaturated hydrocarbons.
- Know that bonding in alkenes involves a double covalent bond.
- Understand that the double bond in an alkene is a centre of high electron density.
- Understand the mechanism of electrophilic addition of alkenes with H_2SO_4 and Br_2.
- Know that bromine can be used to test for unsaturation.
- Understand that alcohols are produced industrially by hydration of alkenes in the presence of an acid catalyst.
- Know the typical conditions for the industrial production of ethanol from ethene.

Specification Reference 3.2.9

Alkenes

Alkenes have the general formula C_nH_{2n}. They're just made of carbon and hydrogen atoms, so they're hydrocarbons. Alkene molecules all have at least one C=C double covalent bond. Molecules with C=C double bonds are unsaturated because they can make more bonds with extra atoms in **addition reactions**. Because there are two pairs of electrons in the C=C double bond, it has a really high electron density. This makes alkenes pretty reactive.

Examples

Here are a few pretty diagrams of alkenes:

propene

penta-1,3-diene

cyclopentene

A cyclic alkene has two fewer hydrogen atoms than an open-chain alkene. Carbons can only have four bonds — a double bond means that the carbons can make one less bond with a hydrogen.

Electrophilic addition reactions

Electrophilic addition reactions aren't too complicated. The double bond in an alkene opens up and atoms are added to the carbon atoms. Electrophilic addition reactions happen because the double bond has got plenty of electrons and is easily attacked by **electrophiles**. Electrophiles are electron-pair acceptors — they're usually a bit short of electrons, so they're attracted to areas where there's lots of them about.

Examples

Here are a few examples of electrophiles.

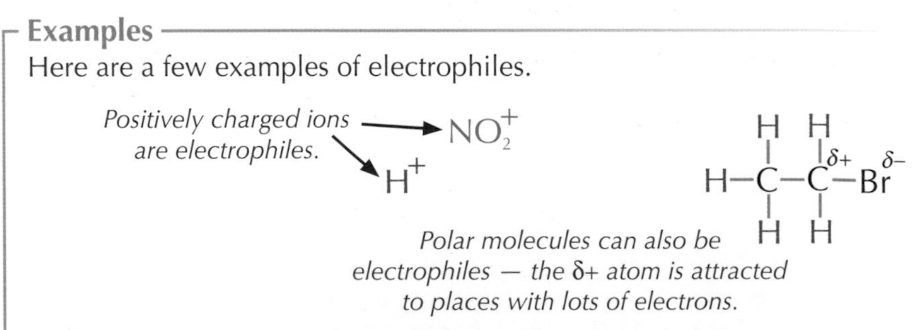

The double bond is also nucleophilic — it's attracted to places that don't have enough electrons.

Tip: Just as nucleophiles are often negatively charged ions (see page 164), electrophiles are often positively charged ions. Electrons were lost as the ions were formed, so positive ions are ready and waiting to accept any electrons that come their way.

You need to learn the mechanism for electrophilic addition.
Here is the general electrophilic addition reaction equation.

$$CH_2CH_2 + X\text{–}Y \rightarrow CH_2XCH_2Y$$

$H_2C_1{=}C_2H_2$

$X^{\delta+}\text{—}Y^{\delta-}$

The carbon-carbon double bond repels the electrons in X–Y, which polarises the X–Y bond (or the bond could already be polar, like in HBr).

Two electrons from the carbon-carbon double bond attack the δ+ X atom creating a new bond between carbon 1 and the X atom. The X–Y bond breaks and the electrons from the bond are taken by the Y atom to form a negative ion with a lone pair of electrons. Carbon 2 is left electron deficient — when the double bond was broken carbon 1 took the electrons to form a bond with the X atom, which left carbon 2 as a positively charged **carbocation intermediate**.

$H_2C_1{=}C_2H_2 + X^{\delta+}\text{—}Y^{\delta-} \longrightarrow H\text{–}C_1HX\text{–}C_2H_2^{+} \quad :Y^{-}$

Tip: A carbocation is an organic ion containing a positively charged carbon atom.

Tip: Reaction intermediates are short-lived, reactive molecules which occur in the middle of a step-wise reaction mechanism — you can't easily isolate them from the reaction mixture.

The Y^- ion then acts as a nucleophile, attacking the positively charged carbocation intermediate, donating its lone pair of electrons and forming a new bond with carbon 2.

$H\text{–}C_1HX\text{–}C_2H_2^{+} \;\; :Y^{-} \longrightarrow H\text{–}CHX\text{–}CHY\text{–}H$

So overall, the X–Y molecule has been added to the alkene across the double bond to form a saturated compound.

Testing for unsaturation

When you shake an alkene with orange bromine water, the solution quickly turns from orange to colourless (see Figure 1). Bromine is added across the double bond to form a colourless dibromoalkane — this happens by electrophilic addition.

***Figure 1:** Adding bromine water to a solution containing a carbon-carbon double bond turns the bromine water colourless.*

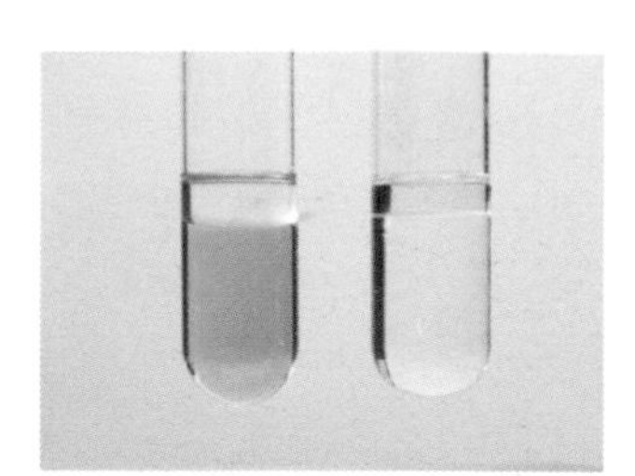

***Figure 2:** Bromine water has been added to two test tubes. The one on the right contains a compound with a C=C, that has decolourised the bromine water. The one on the left contains a substance that doesn't react with bromine.*

Example

When you shake ethene with orange bromine water, the solution turns from orange to colourless. Here's the equation for this reaction:

$$H_2C{=}CH_2 + Br_2 \rightarrow CH_2BrCH_2Br$$

Here's the mechanism...

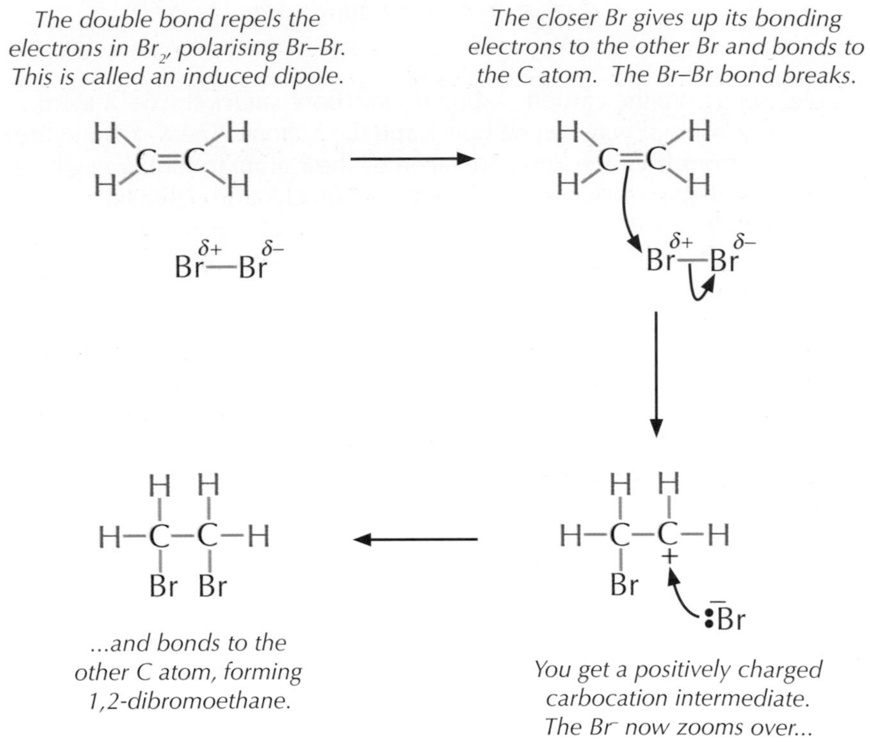

The double bond repels the electrons in Br_2, polarising Br–Br. This is called an induced dipole.

$H_2C{=}CH_2$ and $Br^{\delta+}{-}Br^{\delta-}$ →

The closer Br gives up its bonding electrons to the other Br and bonds to the C atom. The Br–Br bond breaks.

↓

$H{-}CH(Br){-}C^{+}H{-}H$ + $:Br^-$

You get a positively charged carbocation intermediate. The Br^- now zooms over...

←

$H{-}CH(Br){-}CH(Br){-}H$

...and bonds to the other C atom, forming 1,2-dibromoethane.

Exam Tip
Make sure the first curly arrow comes from the carbon-carbon double bond.

Exam Tip
You could get asked to draw the mechanism for the reaction between bromine water and any alkene — it might not be ethene. It's not too hard though — the mechanism is the same for all alkenes, and you'll always end up with a Br atom added to each of the carbon atoms that were double bonded. Simple as that.

Synthesising alcohols

Alcohols can be produced industrially by two different methods — by the steam hydration of ethene, and by hydrating alkenes in the presence of an acid catalyst, such as sulfuric acid.

1. Steam hydration of ethene

Steam hydration of ethene is used industrially to produce ethanol. Ethene can be hydrated by steam at 300 °C and a pressure of 60 atm. It needs a solid phosphoric(V) acid catalyst. The reaction's reversible and the reaction yield is low — only about 5%. This sounds rubbish, but you can recycle the unreacted ethene gas, making the overall yield a much more profitable 95%.

$$CH_2{=}CH_{2(g)} + H_2O_{(g)} \underset{\text{300 °C, 60 atm}}{\overset{H_3PO_4}{\rightleftharpoons}} CH_3CH_2OH_{(g)}$$

Tip: Remember that a catalyst is a substance that speeds up the rate of a reaction without being used up.

2. Hydration of alkenes in the lab

You can also synthesise alcohols in the lab by reacting an alkene with water in the presence of cold concentrated sulfuric acid.

Example

Reacting ethene with water in the presence of cold concentrated sulfuric acid produces ethanol. The overall equation for this reaction is shown below.

$$CH_2{=}CH_2 + H_2O \xrightarrow{H_2SO_4} C_2H_5OH$$

You have to do the reaction in two steps. First, cold concentrated sulfuric acid reacts with ethene in an electrophilic addition reaction. This forms ethyl hydrogen sulfate.

$$CH_2{=}CH_2 + H_2SO_4 \rightarrow CH_3CH_2OSO_2OH$$

If you then add cold water and warm the product, it's hydrolysed to form ethanol.

$$CH_3CH_2OSO_2OH + H_2O \rightarrow CH_3CH_2OH + H_2SO_4$$

Tip: A hydration reaction is a reaction where water is added to a compound. Hydrolysis is the breaking up of a molecule by reaction with water.

Mechanism

In the first step of this reaction, the carbon-carbon double bond attacks a δ+ hydrogen atom on the sulfuric acid molecule. A new bond is formed between one of the carbons and the hydrogen, and the electrons from the O–H bond are taken by the oxygen atom to form a lone pair. The second carbon is left with a positive charge because it has lost the electron from the double bond.

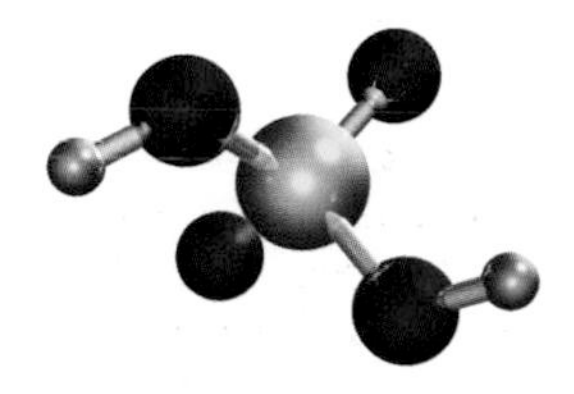

Figure 3: *A molecular model of a sulphuric acid molecule.*

The negative ion created in the first step then acts as a nucleophile and attacks the carbocation creating a new intermediate.

Exam Tip
When you're drawing out this mechanism in the exam make sure you draw out the structure of the sulfuric acid ion fully — you won't get all the marks for just writing out HSO_4^-.

This intermediate then reacts with water to produce sulfuric acid and ethanol.

The sulfuric acid in this reaction is never used up — it acts as a catalyst.

Tip: Remember to be careful where your curly arrows start and finish — they should come from bonds or lone pairs, and go to atoms.

Practice Questions — Application

Q1 Draw the mechanism for the reaction of propene with bromine water. The structures of the reactants are shown below.

```
   H  H
   |  |      H
H—C—C=C<
   |         H
   H
```

Br—Br

Q2 Draw the mechanism for the reaction of but-1-ene with water in the presence of a sulfuric acid catalyst. The structures of the reactants and the structure of the catalyst are shown below.

```
   H  H  H
   |  |  |     H
H—C—C—C=C<
   |  |        H
   H  H
```

```
    H
:O<
    H
```

```
H
|
O    O—H
  \ /
   S
  // \\
 O     O
```

Practice Questions — Fact Recall

Q1 Give the general formula for an alkene.

Q2 Explain why alkenes are unsaturated.

Q3 Explain why alkenes can undergo electrophilic addition reactions.

Q4 What is an electrophile?

Q5 Give two examples of electrophiles.

Q6 What can you use bromine water to test for?

Q7 Write the equation for the hydration of ethene by steam. Include the conditions for this reaction in your answer.

Q8 What can you do to increase the yield of ethanol production by steam hydration?

6. More Reactions of Alkenes

Sometimes a chemical reaction has more than one product — you've got to be able to decide which product is more likely to form. Don't panic, it's not just a wild stab in the dark — there are some handy rules to help you out.

Learning Objectives:
- Understand the mechanism of electrophilic addition of alkenes with HBr.
- Be able to predict the products of addition to unsymmetrical alkenes by reference to the relative stabilities of primary, secondary and tertiary carbocation intermediates.

Specification Reference 3.2.9

Synthesising bromoalkanes

Alkenes undergo addition reactions with hydrogen bromide to form bromoalkanes.

Example

This is the reaction between ethene and hydrogen bromide.

$$C_2H_4 + HBr \rightarrow C_2H_5Br$$

It's an electrophilic addition reaction so the mechanism is the same as the one in the previous topic (see pages 172-175).

$H_2C{=}CH_2$ + $H^{\delta+}{-}Br^{\delta-}$ → $H_3C{-}CH_2^{+}$ + $:Br^{-}$ → $CH_3{-}CH_2Br$

Exam Tip
Other alkenes react in a similar way with HBr. Don't be put off if they give you a different alkene in the exam — the mechanism works in exactly the same way.

Addition of hydrogen halides to unsymmetrical alkenes

If the HBr adds to an unsymmetrical alkene, there are two possible products.

Example

If you add hydrogen bromide to propene, the bromine atom could add to either the first carbon or the second carbon. This means you could produce 1-bromopropane or 2-bromopropane.

$H_2C{=}CH{-}CH_3$ (*propene*) + HBr → $BrCH_2{-}CH_2{-}CH_3$ (*1-bromopropane*) or $CH_3{-}CHBr{-}CH_3$ (*2-bromopropane*)

The amount of each product formed depends on how stable the carbocation formed in the middle of the reaction is. The three possible carbocations are:

$R{-}C^{+}H_2$ — *primary carbocation*

$R_2C^{+}H$ — *secondary carbocation*

R_3C^{+} — *tertiary carbocation*

R is an alkyl group — an alkane with a hydrogen removed, e.g. CH_3.

Tip: "Primary carbocation" can also be written as 1° carbocation — the 1° stands for primary. Secondary carbocation can be written as 2° carbocation, and tertiary as 3° carbocation.

> **Tip:** The alkyl groups don't give up their electrons to the carbon atom — they just move some of their negatively charged electrons nearer to it, which helps to stabilise the positive charge.

Carbocations with more alkyl groups are more stable because the alkyl groups feed electrons towards the positive charge. You can show that an alkyl group is donating electrons by drawing an arrow on the bond that points to where the electrons are donated.

primary carbocation	secondary carbocation	tertiary carbocation
$R\rightarrow \overset{+}{C}H_2$	$R\rightarrow \overset{+}{C}H(\leftarrow R)$	$R\rightarrow \overset{+}{C}(\leftarrow R)_2$

Least stable ⟶ **Most stable**

More stable carbocations are much more likely to form that less stable ones. This means that there will be more of the product formed via the more stable carbocation than there is via the less stable carbocation.

> **Tip:** The product that there's most of is called the major product, or the Markovnikov product — after the Russian scientist Vladimir Markovnikov who came up with the theory that the product formed most often is formed via a more stable carbocation.

Examples

Here's how hydrogen bromide reacts with propene:

$H_2C{=}CHCH_3 + HBr \rightarrow CH_3CHBrCH_3$ — *2-bromopropane major product*

$H_2C{=}CHCH_3 + HBr \rightarrow CH_2BrCH_2CH_3$ — *1-bromopropane minor product*

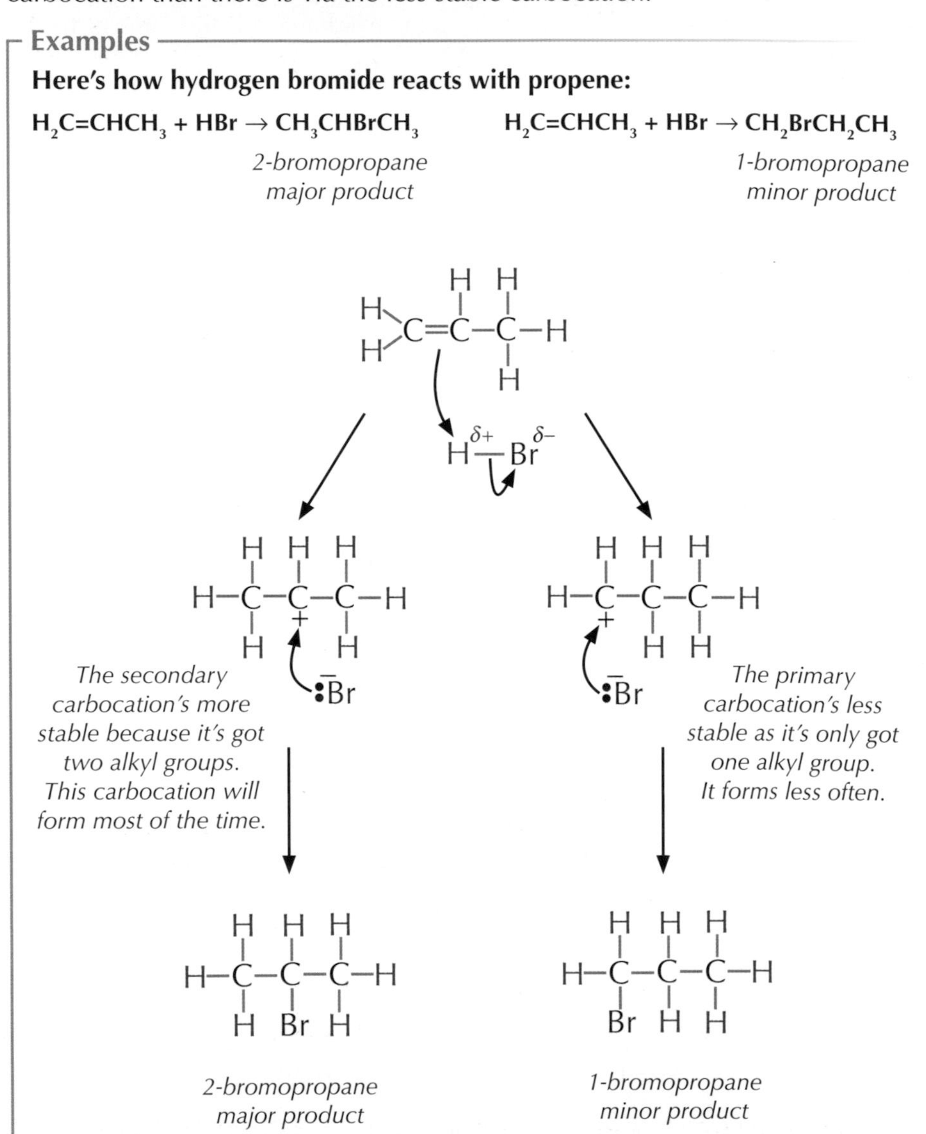

> **Exam Tip**
> It makes it easier to see what the main product is if you draw out all the possible cations each time — then there's less chance of making a mistake.

Here's how hydrogen bromide reacts with 2-methylbut-2-ene:

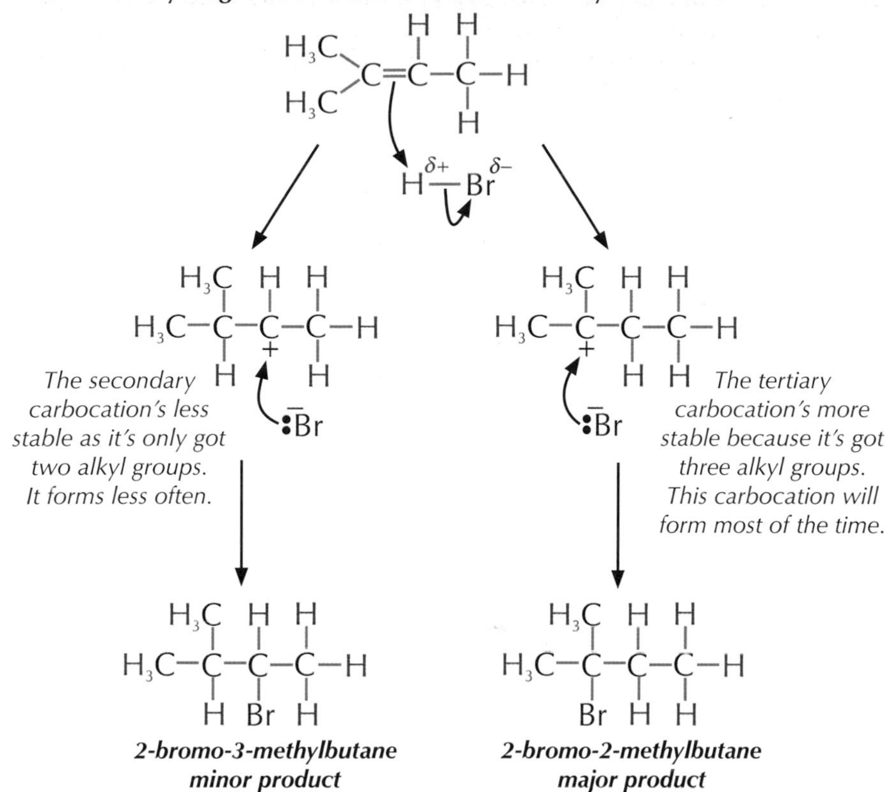

Tip: The bigger the difference in stability of the carbocations, the more of the major product you'll get at the end.

Practice Questions — Application

Q1 a) Draw the mechanism for the reaction between but-2-ene and hydrogen bromide. The reactants for this reaction are shown below.

```
     H     H  H
     |     |  |
  H—C—C=C—C—H          HBr
     |  |     |
     H  H     H
```

b) Write the overall equation for this reaction.

Q2 Hydrogen bromide reacts with but-1-ene to form either 1-bromobutane or 2-bromobutane. Explain why 2-bromobutane is the major product of the reaction. The structures of 1-bromobutane and 2-bromobutane are shown below.

```
     H  H  H  H              H  H  Br H
     |  |  |  |              |  |  |  |
  H—C—C—C—C—Br          H—C—C—C—C—H
     |  |  |  |              |  |  |  |
     H  H  H  H              H  H  H  H
```

Practice Questions — Fact Recall

Q1 What could you react with ethene in order to produce bromoethane?

Q2 Place the following carbocations in order of stability: primary, seconday and tertiary.

Learning Objectives:

- Know that the arrangement >C=C< is planar.
- Know that alkenes can exhibit E-Z stereoisomerism.
- Be able to draw the structures of E and Z isomers.
- Understand that E-Z isomers exist due to restricted rotation about the C=C bond.
- Know how addition polymers are formed from alkenes.
- Recognise that poly(alkenes), like alkanes, are unreactive.
- Be able to recognise the repeating unit in a poly(alkene).
- Know some typical uses of poly(ethene) and poly(propene) and know that poly(propene) is recycled.

Specification Reference 3.2.9

7. E/Z Isomers and Polymers

Time for a break from all those mechanisms. This topic contains a bit more on isomers (see pages 92-93) and a really interesting section on the formation of addition polymers. Enjoy.

Double bond rotation

Carbon atoms in a C=C double bond and the atoms bonded to these carbons all lie in the same plane (they're planar). Because of the way they're arranged, they're actually said to be trigonal planar — the atoms attached to each double-bond carbon are at the corners of an imaginary equilateral triangle.

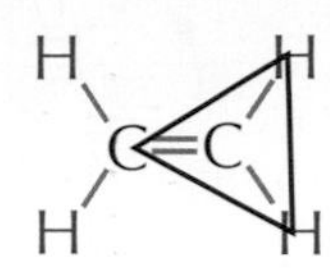

The bond angles in the planar unit are all 120°.

Ethene, C_2H_4 (like in the diagram above) is completely planar, but in larger alkenes, only the >C=C< unit is planar.

Example

This molecule is but-1-ene. The carbon-carbon double bond section of the molecule is planar and the carbon-carbon single bond section is non-planar.

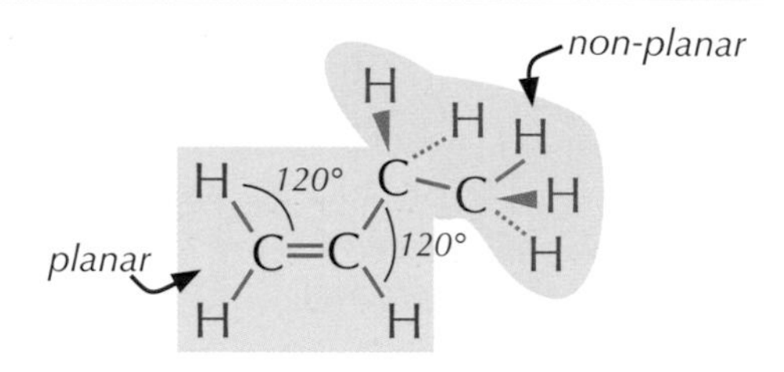

Another important thing about C=C double bonds is that atoms can't rotate around them like they can around single bonds. In fact, double bonds are fairly rigid — they don't bend much either. Even though atoms can't rotate about the double bond, things can still rotate about any single bonds in the molecule.

Example

In this molecule of but-1-ene the single C–C bond can rotate.

Tip: Don't get confused by all those crazy green lines on the diagram. The dotted ones mean that the bond is pointing in to the paper and the wedgy ones mean that the bond is pointing out of the paper. There's more on this on page 66.

The restricted rotation around the C=C double bond is what causes E/Z isomerism.

Stereoisomers

Stereoisomers have the same structural formula but a different arrangement in space. (Just bear with me for a moment... that will become clearer, I promise.) Because of the lack of rotation around the double bond, some alkenes can have stereoisomers. Stereoisomers happen when the two double-bonded carbon atoms each have different atoms or groups attached to them. Then you get an '**E-isomer**' and a '**Z-isomer**'.

The E-isomer is the one that has the highest priority groups across the double bond from each other. The Z-isomer is the one which has the highest priority groups both above or both below the double bond.

```
H       Y          H       H
 \     /            \     /
  C=C                C=C
 /     \            /     \
X       H          X       Y
```

E-isomer **Z-isomer**

In these diagrams X and Y are the largest groups.

> **Tip:** The group with the highest priority is the one that has the highest molecular mass.

Examples

The double-bonded carbon atoms in but-2-ene (C_4H_8) each have an H and a CH_3 group attached.

```
 H       CH3
  \     /
   C=C
  /     \
H3C      H
```

E-isomer

When the CH_3 groups are across the double bond then it's the E-isomer.

This molecule is E-but-2-ene.

```
H3C      CH3
   \    /
    C=C
   /    \
  H      H
```

Z-isomer

When the CH_3 groups are both above or both below the double bond then it's the Z-isomer.

This molecule is Z-but-2-ene.

> **Tip:** If all this isomer stuff is a bit confusing, try to get your hands on some molecular models and have a go making the isomers yourself — it should make everything a bit clearer.

In pent-2-ene (C_5H_{10}) one of the double bonded carbon atoms has an H and a CH_3 group attached to it. The other has an H and a CH_2CH_3 group attached.

```
     H       CH3
      \     /
       C=C
      /     \
H3CH2C       H
```

E-isomer

The high priority groups (CH_3 and CH_2CH_3) are across the double bond so it's the E-isomer.

This molecule is E-pent-2-ene.

```
     H       H
      \     /
       C=C
      /     \
H3CH2C       CH3
```

Z-isomer

The high priority groups are both below the double bond so it's the Z-isomer.

This molecule is Z-pent-2-ene.

> **Tip:** E stands for 'entgegen', a German word meaning 'opposite'. Z stands for 'zusammen', the German for 'together'.

Practice Questions — Application

Q1 State whether the following molecules are E-isomers or Z-isomers.

a)

```
     H       H
      \     /
       C=C
      /     \
H3CH2C       CH2CH3
```

b)

```
     H       CH2CH2CH3
      \     /
       C=C
      /     \
H3CH2C       CH3
```

Q2 Draw the two stereoisomers of 3,4-dimethylhex-3-ene and label which is the E-isomer and which is the Z-isomer.
The structure of 3,4-dimethylhex-3-ene is shown below.

```
   H  H  CH3   H  H
   |  |  |     |  |
H—C—C—C=C—C—C—H
   |  |     |  |  |
   H  H   H3C  H  H
```

Addition polymers

The double bonds in alkenes can open up and join together to make long chains called polymers. It's kind of like they're holding hands in a big line. The individual, small alkenes are called monomers. This is called **addition polymerisation**.

Example

Poly(ethene) is made by the addition polymerisation of ethene.

$$3\ \ H_2C{=}CH_2 \longrightarrow -\!CH_2\!-\!CH_2\!-\!CH_2\!-\!CH_2\!-\!CH_2\!-\!CH_2\!-$$

ethene monomers → *poly(ethene)*

Exam Tip
To pick up the marks in the exam you must show the trailing bonds at the end of the molecule. This shows that the polymer continues.

Addition polymerisation reactions can be written like this...

$$n\ H_2C{=}CH_2 \longrightarrow \left(\!-CH_2\!-\!CH_2-\!\right)_n$$

monomer → *polymer*

Tip: The bit in brackets is the 'repeating unit'.

...where the n stands for the number of repeating units (monomers) in the polymer.

To find the monomer used to form an addition polymer, take the repeating unit and add a double bond.

Example

To find the monomer used to make the polymer below you first need to look for the repeating unit.

$$-CH_2\!-\!CH(CH_3)\!-\!CH_2\!-\!CH(CH_3)\!-\!CH_2\!-\!CH(CH_3)- \longrightarrow -CH_2\!-\!CH(CH_3)-$$

polymer → *repeating unit*

Then replace the horizontal carbon-carbon bond with a double bond and remove the unnecessary side bonds to find the monomer.

$$-CH_2\!-\!CH(CH_3)- \longrightarrow H_2C{=}CH(CH_3)$$

repeating unit → *monomer — propene*

***Figure 1:** Polyvinyl chloride (PVC) fibres. PVC is an addition polymer.*

Because of the loss of the double bond, poly(alkenes), like alkanes, are unreactive. Different polymer structures have different properties, which means they're suited to different uses. Some typical uses of poly(ethene) and poly(propene) are shown in Figure 2.

	Properties	Uses
Low density poly(ethene)	Soft Flexible	Plastic bags Squeezy bottles
Poly(propene)	Tough Strong	Bottle crates Rope

Figure 2: *Typical uses of poly(ethene) and poly(propene).*

Figure 3: *Recycling poly(ethene).*

Many polymers are difficult to dispose of safely because they are non-biodegradable and can produce toxic fumes when they're burnt. Polymers are also made from non-renewable oil fractions, so it makes sense to recycle them. For example, poly(propene) is recycled — it can be melted and remoulded.

Practice Questions — Application

Q1 Write a reaction for the addition polymerisation of the monomer fluoroethene. The structure of fluoroethene is shown below.

```
F         H
 \       /
  C  =  C
 /       \
H         H
```

Q2 Find the monomer used to form the polymer shown below.

```
   H  Cl  H  Cl  H  Cl
   |  |   |  |   |  |
 — C — C — C — C — C — C —
   |  |   |  |   |  |
   H  H   H  H   H  H
```

Q3 Draw the repeating unit of the polymer shown below.

```
   H  Cl   H  Cl   H  Cl
   |  |    |  |    |  |
 — C — C — C — C — C — C —
   |  |    |  |    |  |
   H  CH3  H  CH3  H  CH3
```

Practice Questions — Fact Recall

Q1 What causes E/Z isomerism?

Q2 What is the name for the isomerism shown by E- and Z-isomers?

Q3 Briefly describe addition polymerisation.

Q4 Why are poly(alkenes) unreactive?

Q5 What properties does low density poly(ethene) have that makes it good for making plastic bags?

Q6 Give one use of poly(propene).

Q7 Explain why it makes sense to recycle polymers.

Learning Objectives:

- Be able to apply IUPAC rules for nomenclature to alcohols limited to chains with up to 6 carbon atoms.
- Understand that alcohols can be classified as primary, secondary or tertiary.
- Know how ethanol is produced industrially by fermentation.
- Know the conditions for this reaction and understand the economic and environmental advantages and disadvantages of this process compared with the industrial production from ethene.
- Understand the meaning of the term biofuel.
- Know that the term carbon neutral refers to 'an activity that has no net annual carbon (greenhouse gas) emissions to the atmosphere'.
- Appreciate the extent to which ethanol, produced by fermentation, can be considered to be a carbon-neutral biofuel.
- Know that alkenes can be formed from alcohols by acid catalysed elimination reactions.
- Appreciate that this method provides a possible route to polymers without using monomers derived from oil.

Specification Reference 3.2.10

8. Alcohols

This is a pretty important section — examiners love real life applications of chemistry and this topic is packed full of them. But before we get onto all that fun stuff here's a bit more nomenclature for you to learn.

Nomenclature of alcohols

The alcohol homologous series has the general formula $C_nH_{2n+1}OH$. Alcohols are named using the same IUPAC naming rules found on pages 95-99 but the suffix -ol is added in place of the -e on the end of the name. You also need to indicate which carbon atom the alcohol functional group is attached to — the carbon number(s) comes before the -ol suffix. If there are two –OH groups the molecule is a -diol and if there are three it's a -triol.

Examples

The longest continuous carbon chain is 2 carbon atoms, so the stem is ethane.

There's one –OH attached to the carbon chain so the suffix is -ol.

There's only one carbon atom it could be attached to (carbon atom 1) so there's no need to put a number.

So, the alcohol is called ethanol.

```
    H  H
    |  |
 H—C—C—OH
    |  |
    H  H
```

ethanol

```
    H  OH  H
    |  |   |
 H—C—C—C—H
    |  |   |
    H  CH3 H
```

2-methylpropan-2-ol

The longest continuous carbon chain is 3 carbon atoms, so the stem is propane.

There's one –OH attached to the carbon chain so the suffix is -ol.

It's attached to the second carbon so there's a 2 before the -ol.

There's also a methyl group attached to the second carbon so there's also a 2-methyl- prefix.

The alcohol is called 2-methylpropan-2-ol.

The longest continuous carbon chain is 2 carbon atoms, so the stem is ethane.

There are two –OH groups attached to the carbon chain so the suffix is -diol.

There's one –OH attached to each carbon atom so there's a 1,2-before the -diol.

So, the alcohol is called ethan-1,2-diol.

```
     H  H
     |  |
 HO—C—C—OH
     |  |
     H  H
```

ethan-1,2-diol

Primary, secondary and tertiary alcohols

An alcohol is primary, secondary or tertiary, depending on which carbon atom the hydroxyl group –OH is bonded to. **Primary alcohols** are given the notation 1° and the –OH group is attached to a carbon with one alkyl group attached (see Figure 1). **Secondary alcohols** are given the notation 2° and the –OH group is attached to a carbon with two alkyl groups attached. **Tertiary alcohols** are given the notation 3° (you can see where I'm going with this) and the –OH group is attached to a carbon with three alkyl groups attached.

```
       H                    R2                   R2
       |                    |                    |
  R1 — C — OH          R1 — C — OH          R1 — C — OH
       |                    |                    |
       H                    H                    R3
```

primary alcohol *secondary alcohol* *tertiary alcohol*

Figure 1: *Diagrams of 1°, 2° and 3° alcohols. R = alkyl group.*

Tip: Remember that an alkyl group is an alkane with a hydrogen removed, for example CH_3 or CH_3CH_2.

Examples

```
    H   H   H
    |   |   |
H — C — C — C — OH
    |   |   |
    H   H   H
```

propan-1-ol

Propan-1-ol is a primary (1°) alcohol because the carbon the –OH group is attached to is attached to one alkyl group (CH_3CH_2).

Propan-2-ol is a secondary (2°) alcohol because the carbon the –OH group is attached to is attached to two alkyl groups (CH_3 and CH_3).

```
    H   OH  H
    |   |   |
H — C — C — C — H
    |   |   |
    H   H   H
```

propan-2-ol

Industrial production of ethanol

At the moment most industrial ethanol is produced by steam hydration of ethene with a phosphoric acid catalyst (see page 174). The ethene comes from cracking heavy fractions of crude oil. But in the future, when crude oil supplies start running out, petrochemicals like ethene will be expensive — so producing ethanol by fermentation will become much more important...

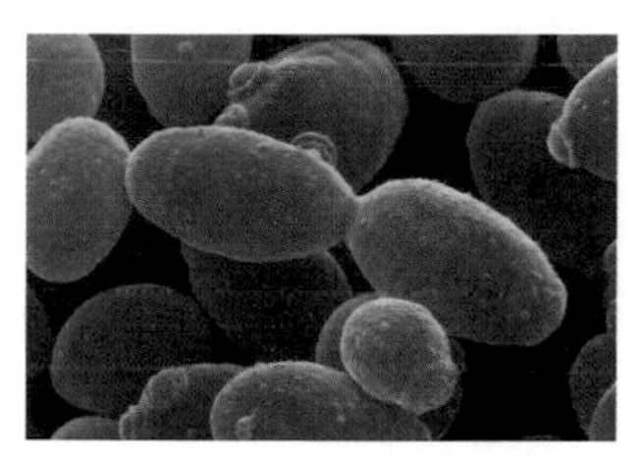

Figure 2: *A scanning electron micrograph (SEM) of yeast cells.*

Industrial production of ethanol by fermentation

Fermentation is an exothermic process, carried out by yeast in anaerobic conditions (without oxygen). Here's the equation for the reaction.

$$\underset{\text{glucose}}{C_6H_{12}O_{6(aq)}} \xrightarrow[\text{yeast}]{30\text{-}40°C} 2C_2H_5OH_{(aq)} + 2CO_{2(g)}$$

Exam Tip
When you're writing out this equation make sure you always include the conditions above and below the arrow.

Yeast produces enzymes which convert sugars, such as glucose, into ethanol and carbon dioxide. The enzyme works at an optimum (ideal) temperature of 30-40 °C. If it's too cold, the reaction is slow — if it's too hot, the enzyme is denatured (damaged). Figure 3 shows how the rate of reaction of fermentation is affected by temperature.

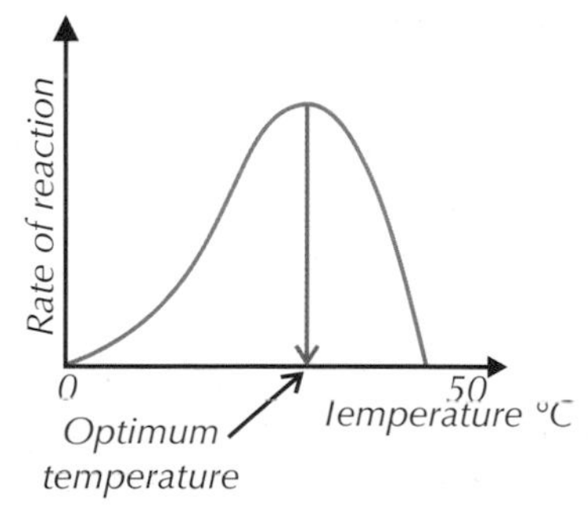

Figure 3: *Graph to show the effect of temperature on fermentation.*

When the solution reaches about 15% ethanol, the yeast dies. Fractional distillation is used to increase the concentration of ethanol. Fermentation is low-tech — it uses cheap equipment and renewable resources. The ethanol produced by this method has to be purified though.

Figure 4: *Vat for the fermentation of yeast.*

Tip: A batch process is a method of producing chemicals where you make one lot of a product, then take it all out and start making another lot of it.
A continuous process is happening all the time — you continually add reactants and remove products.

Comparison of ethanol production methods

Here's a quick summary of the advantages and disadvantages of the two methods of making ethanol.

	Hydration of Ethene	Fermentation
Rate of Reaction	Very fast	Very slow
Quality of Product	Pure	Very impure — needs further processing.
Raw Material	Ethene from oil — a finite resource.	Sugars — a renewable resource.
Process/Costs	Continuous process, so expensive equipment needed, but low labour costs.	Batch process, so cheap equipment needed, but high labour costs.

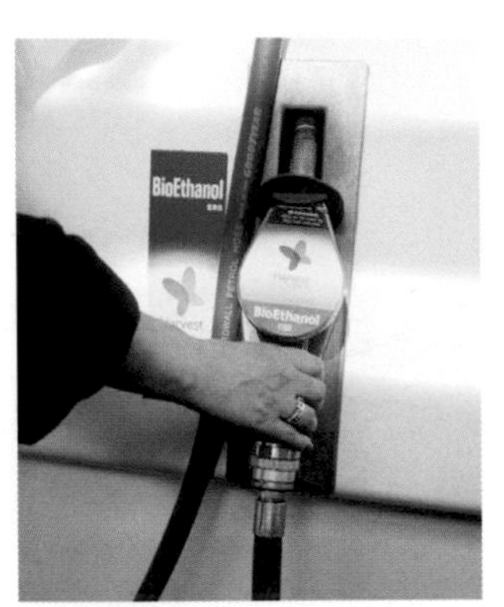

Figure 5: *A bioethanol fuel pump.*

Ethanol as a biofuel

Ethanol is also being used increasingly as a fuel, particularly in countries with few oil reserves. E.g. in Brazil, sugars from sugar cane are fermented to produce alcohol, which is added to petrol. Ethanol, made in this way, is a biofuel. A biofuel is a fuel that's made from biological material that's recently died. Ethanol is thought of as a carbon neutral fuel, because all the CO_2 released when the fuel is burned was removed by the crop as it grew. BUT — there are still carbon emissions if you consider the whole process. E.g. making the fertilisers and powering agricultural machinery will probably involve burning fossil fuels.

Dehydration of ethanol

You can make ethene by eliminating water from ethanol in a dehydration reaction (i.e. elimination of water).

$$C_2H_5OH \rightarrow CH_2{=}CH_2 + H_2O$$

Here's how you can go about it. You have to reflux ethanol with concentrated sulfuric acid. The reaction occurs in two stages:

$$C_2H_5OH + H_2SO_4 \rightarrow C_2H_5OSO_2OH + H_2O$$

$$C_2H_5OSO_2OH \rightarrow CH_2{=}CH_2 + H_2SO_4$$

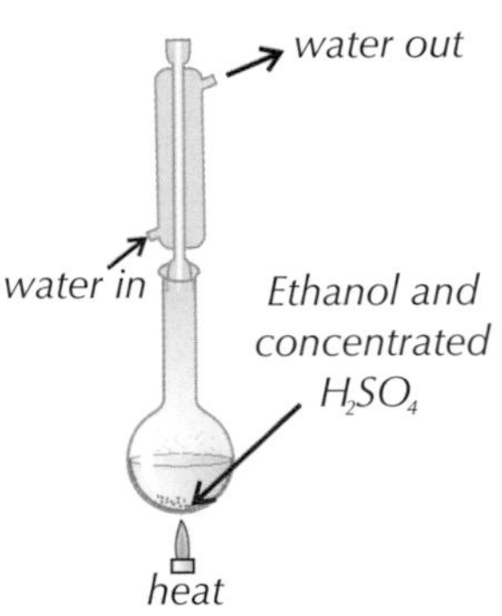

Figure 6: *Apparatus for refluxing ethanol. There's more on refluxing on page 190.*

The H_2SO_4 is unchanged at the end of the reaction, so it's acted as a catalyst. Phosphoric acid (H_3PO_4) can also be used as a catalyst for this reaction. This reaction allows you to produce alkenes from renewable resources (because you can produce ethanol by fermentation of glucose, which you can get from plants). This is important, because it means that you can produce polymers (poly(ethene), for example) without needing oil (see Figure 7).

Tip: The acid catalysed elimination of water from ethanol is the reverse of the acid catalysed hydration of ethene found on page 175.

Figure 7: *Producing alkenes from renewable resources.*

Practice Questions — Application

Q1 Name the following alcohols.

a)

```
    H  H  H  H  H
    |  |  |  |  |
 H—C—C—C—C—C—OH
    |  |  |  |  |
    H  H  H  H  H
```

b)

```
         OH
         |
       H—C—H
         |
   H3C—C—CH3
         |
        CH3
```

c)

```
    H  CH3 H  OH
    |  |   |  |
 H—C—C—C—C—H
    |  |   |  |
    H  H  CH3 H
```

d)

```
    H  H  H  CH3 H
    |  |  |  |   |
 H—C—C—C—C—C—H
    |  |  |  |   |
    H  H CH2 H   OH
          |
        CH2OH
```

Q2 State whether each of the alcohols above are primary (1°), secondary (2°) or tertiary (3°) alcohols.

Tip: Remember — name alcohols so that the names include the lowest numbers possible.

Practice Questions — Fact Recall

Q1 Give the general formula for the alcohol homologous series.

Q2 What is a secondary alcohol?

Q3 Write down the equation for the production of ethanol by fermentation.

Q4 Why is it necessary for the reaction to take place between 30°C and 40°C?

Q5 a) Explain why the ethanol produced by fermentation only has a concentration of 15%.

b) What can be done to increase the concentration of the ethanol?

Q6 What is a biofuel?

Q7 Write equations to show the two stage reaction for the dehydration of ethanol.

9. Oxidising Alcohols

Learning Objectives:

- Be able to apply IUPAC rules for nomenclature to aldehydes, ketones and carboxylic acids limited to chains with up to 6 carbon atoms.
- Understand that primary alcohols can be oxidised to aldehydes and carboxylic acids and that secondary alcohols can be oxidised to ketones by a suitable oxidising agent such as acidified potassium dichromate(VI) (equations showing [O] as oxidant are acceptable).
- Be able to use a simple chemical test to distinguish between aldehydes and ketones (e.g. Fehling's solution or Tollens' reagent).

Specification Reference 3.2.10

Oxidising an alcohol creates a carbon-oxygen double bond. Substances that contain these carbon-oxygen double bonds are known as carbonyl compounds — they're great fun. Honest.

The basics

The simple way to oxidise alcohols is to burn them. But you don't get the most exciting products by doing this. If you want to end up with something more interesting at the end, you need a more sophisticated way of oxidising. You can use the oxidising agent acidified potassium dichromate(VI) to mildly oxidise alcohols. In the reaction the orange dichromate(VI) ion is reduced to the green chromium(III) ion, Cr^{3+}. Primary alcohols are oxidised to aldehydes and then to carboxylic acids. Secondary alcohols are oxidised to ketones only. Tertiary alcohols aren't oxidised.

Aldehydes, ketones and carboxylic acids

Aldehydes and ketones are carbonyl compounds — they have the functional group C=O. Their general formula is $C_nH_{2n}O$. Aldehydes have a hydrogen and one alkyl group attached to the **carbonyl** carbon atom...

This is the aldehyde functional group.

Aldehydes have the suffix -al. You don't have to say which carbon the functional group is on — it's always on carbon-1. Naming aldehydes follows very similar rules to the naming of alcohols (see page 184).

Examples

propanal

The longest continuous carbon chain is 3 carbon atoms, so the stem is propane.

So, the aldehyde is called propanal.

The longest continuous carbon chain is 4 carbon atoms, so the stem is butane.

There's a methyl group attached to the second carbon atom so there's a 2-methyl- prefix.

So, the aldehyde is called 2-methylbutanal.

2-methylbutanal

Ketones have two alkyl groups attached to the carbonyl carbon atom.

This is the ketone functional group.

Tip: Remember that a suffix comes at the end of a name and a prefix comes at the beginning.

Tip: A molecule has to contain at least 3 carbon atoms for it to be a ketone.

The suffix for ketones is -one. For ketones with five or more carbons, you always have to say which carbon the functional group is on. (If there are other groups attached, such as methyl groups, you have to say it for four-carbon ketones too.)

Examples

```
   H  O  H
   |  ‖  |
H—C—C—C—H
   |     |
   H     H
```

propanone

The longest continuous carbon chain is 3 carbon atoms, so the stem is propane.

So, the ketone is called propanone.

The longest continuous carbon chain is 5 carbon atoms, so the stem is pentane.

The carbonyl is found on the second carbon atom.

So, the ketone is called pentan-2-one.

```
   H  H  H  O  H
   |  |  |  ‖  |
H—C—C—C—C—C—H
   |  |  |     |
   H  H  H     H
```

pentan-2-one

Figure 1: *The ketone propanone (also known as acetone) is commonly used as a nail varnish remover.*

Carboxylic acids have a COOH group at the end of their carbon chain.

```
   H  H  O
   |  |  ‖
H—C—C—C—OH
   |  |
   H  H
```

This is the carboxylic acid functional group. (the circled C(=O)—OH)

Tip: The carboxylic acid functional group is usually written COOH and not CO_2H to show that the two oxygens are different — one is part of a carbonyl group (CO) and the other is part of an OH group.

The suffix for carboxylic acids is -oic, you also add the word 'acid' to the end of the name.

Examples

```
   H  H  O
   |  |  ‖
H—C—C—C—OH
   |  |
   H  H
```

propanoic acid

The longest continuous carbon chain is 3 carbon atoms, so the stem is propane.

So, the carboxylic acid is called propanoic acid.

The longest continuous carbon chain is 3 carbon atoms, so the stem is propane.

There's a COOH group at each end of the carbon chain so it has a -dioic acid suffix.

So, the carboxylic acid is called propanedioic acid.

```
    O  H  O
    ‖  |  ‖
HO—C—C—C—OH
       |
       H
```

propanedioic acid

Exam Tip
Don't get all these functional groups mixed up in the exam — you could lose easy marks. The only way to learn them is practise, practise and more practise.

Oxidation of primary alcohols

A primary alcohol is first oxidised to an aldehyde, this aldehyde can then be oxidised to a carboxylic acid. You can use the notation [O] to represent an oxidising agent — this saves you having to write down acidified potassium dichromate(VI) every time you write out a reaction, which is handy.
This means you can write equations like this:

$$R{-}CH_2{-}OH + [O] \longrightarrow R{-}C({=}O){-}H + [O] \xrightarrow{\text{reflux}} R{-}C({=}O){-}OH$$

primary alcohol → *aldehyde* + H_2O → *carboxylic acid*

Figure 2: *Alcohol oxidation. The acidified potassium dichromate(VI) ion turns from orange to green when it oxidises an alcohol.*

You can control how far the alcohol is oxidised by controlling the reaction conditions.

Tip: Make sure you balance the oxidising agents when you're writing these equations.

Oxidising primary alcohols to aldehydes

Gently heating ethanol with potassium dichromate(VI) solution and sulfuric acid in a test tube should produce "apple" smelling ethanal (an aldehyde).

$$\begin{array}{c} \text{H}\ \ \text{H} \\ |\quad\ | \\ \text{H–C–C–OH} \\ |\quad\ | \\ \text{H}\ \ \text{H} \\ \textit{ethanol} \end{array} + [O] \xrightarrow[\text{distillation}]{H_2SO_4} \begin{array}{c} \text{H}\ \ \text{O} \\ |\quad\ \| \\ \text{H–C–C–H} \\ | \\ \text{H} \\ \textit{ethanal} \end{array} + H_2O$$

However, it's really tricky to control the amount of heat and the aldehyde is usually oxidised to form "vinegar" smelling ethanoic acid. To get just the aldehyde, you need to get it out of the oxidising solution as soon as it's formed. You can do this by gently heating excess alcohol with a controlled amount of oxidising agent in distillation apparatus (see Figures 3 and 4), so the aldehyde (which boils at a lower temperature than the alcohol) is distilled off immediately.

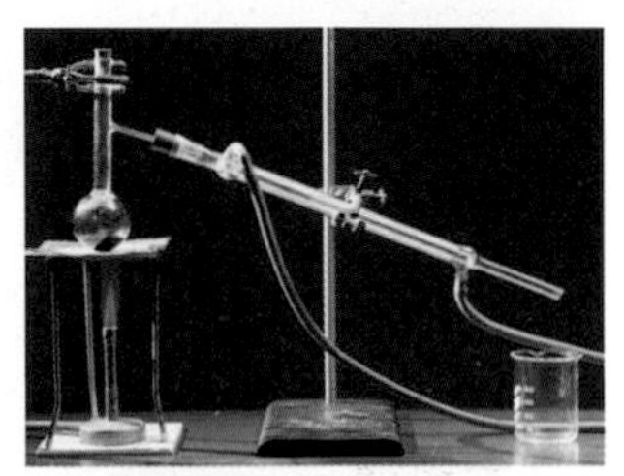

Figure 3: Distillation apparatus.

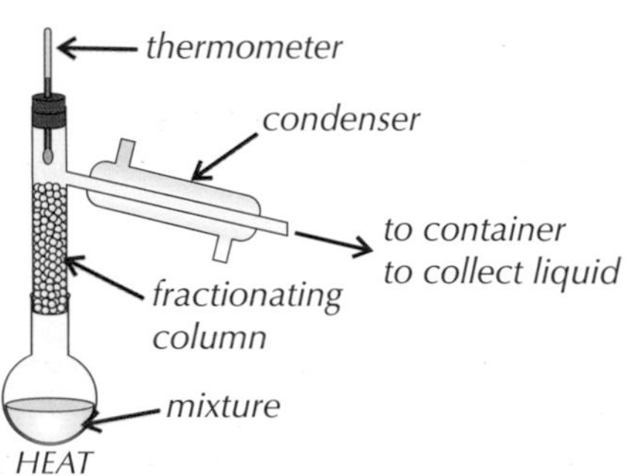

Figure 4: Distillation apparatus.

Exam Tip
It's really important that you learn the conditions required to produce both aldehydes and carboxylic acids. It can be pretty easy to mix them up but make sure you don't — you'll be expected to know them for the exam.

Oxidising primary alcohols to carboxylic acids

To produce the carboxylic acid, the alcohol has to be vigorously oxidised.

$$\begin{array}{c} \text{H}\ \ \text{H} \\ |\quad\ | \\ \text{H–C–C–OH} \\ |\quad\ | \\ \text{H}\ \ \text{H} \\ \textit{ethanol} \end{array} + 2[O] \xrightarrow{\text{reflux}} \begin{array}{c} \text{H}\ \ \text{O} \\ |\quad\ \| \\ \text{H–C–C–OH} \\ | \\ \text{H} \\ \textit{ethanoic acid} \end{array} + H_2O$$

The alcohol is mixed with excess oxidising agent and heated under reflux (see Figures 5 and 6). Heating under reflux means you can increase the temperature of an organic reaction to boiling without losing volatile solvents, reactants or products. Any vapourised compounds are cooled, condense and drip back into the reaction mixture. Handy, hey.

Figure 5: Refluxing apparatus.

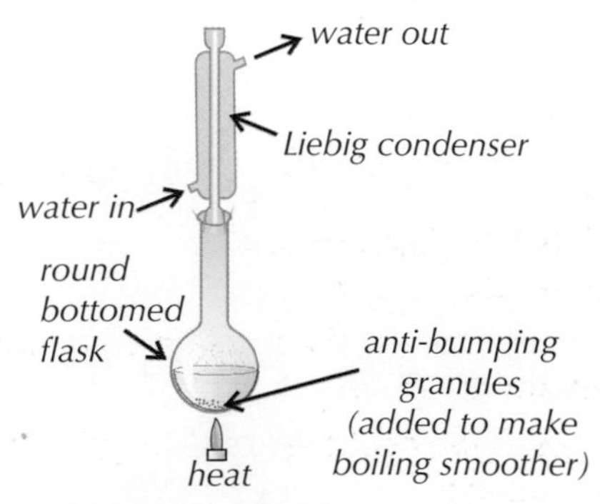

Figure 6: Refluxing apparatus.

Oxidation of secondary alcohols

Refluxing a secondary alcohol with acidified dichromate(VI) will produce a ketone.

$$R_1{-}C(R_2)(H){-}OH + [O] \xrightarrow[\text{acidic conditions}]{\text{reflux}} R_1{-}C(=O){-}R_2 + H_2O$$

secondary alcohol → *ketone*

Example

$$CH_3{-}CH(OH){-}CH_3 + [O] \xrightarrow[\text{acidic conditions}]{\text{reflux}} CH_3{-}C(=O){-}CH_3 + H_2O$$

propan-2-ol → *propanone*

Ketones can't be oxidised easily, so even prolonged refluxing won't produce anything more.

Oxidation of tertiary alcohols

Tertiary alcohols don't react with acidified potassium dichromate(VI) at all — the solution stays orange. The only way to oxidise tertiary alcohols is by burning them.

Testing for aldehydes and ketones

Aldehydes and ketones can be distinguished using oxidising agents — aldehydes are easily oxidised but ketones aren't. Fehling's solution and Benedict's solution are both deep blue Cu^{2+} complexes (alkaline solutions of copper(II) sulfate), which reduce to a brick-red Cu_2O precipitate when warmed with an aldehyde, but stay blue with a ketone (see Figure 7). Tollens' reagent is a colourless $[Ag(NH_3)_2]^+$ complex — it's reduced to silver when warmed with an aldehyde, but not with a ketone. The silver will coat the inside of the apparatus to form a silver mirror (see Figure 8).

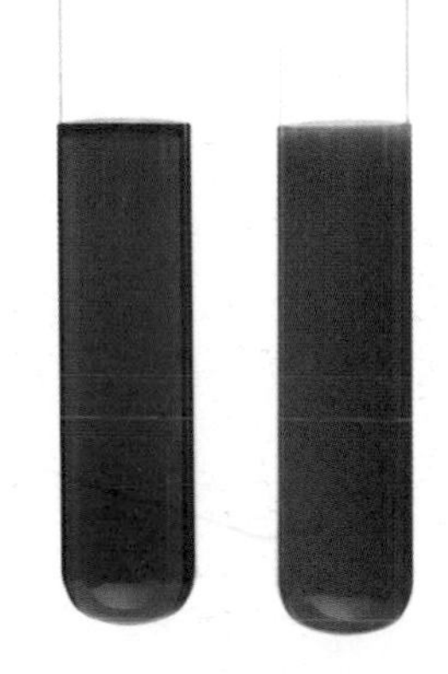

Figure 7: *Fehling's solution. The test-tube on the left shows the unreacted Fehling's solution. The test-tube on the right shows the result of the reaction of Fehling's solution with an aldehyde.*

Figure 8: *Tollens' reagent. The colourless solution in the test-tube on the left shows the unreacted Tollens' reagent. The test-tube on the right shows the result of a reaction with an aldehyde.*

Practice Question — Application

Q1 Draw the structures of the organic products of the following reactions.

a) A reaction between butan-2-ol and acidified potassium dichromate(VI) under reflux.

b) A reaction between butan-1-ol and acidified potassium dichromate(VI) using distillation apparatus.

c) A reaction between butan-1-ol and acidified potassium dichromate(VI) under reflux.

Practice Questions — Fact Recall

Q1 What are the functional groups of aldehydes, ketones and carboxylic acids?

Q2 Write a general equation for the reaction of a primary alcohol with an oxidising agent under reflux.

Q3 Name two reagents you could use to distinguish between an aldehyde and a ketone.

Learning Objective:

- Understand that high resolution mass spectrometry can be used to determine the molecular formula of a compound from the accurate mass of the molecular ion.

Specification Reference 3.2.11

10. Mass Spectrometry

An analytical technique is a method of analysing a substance to learn more about it. This topic deals with one specific analytic technique — mass spectrometry. Mass spectrometry uses the mass of a compound to identify it.

Finding relative molecular mass

You saw on pages 13-16 how mass spectrometry can be used to find relative isotopic masses, the abundance of different isotopes, and the relative molecular mass, M_r, of a compound. Remember — to find the relative molecular mass of a compound you look at the molecular ion peak (the M peak) on the spectrum. Molecular ions are formed when molecules have electrons knocked off. The mass/charge value of the molecular ion peak is the molecular mass (assuming the ion has 1+ charge, which it normally will have). For most organic compounds the M peak is the one with the second highest mass/charge ratio.

Tip: Mass spectrometers can have such a high resolution that they can determine the M_r of compounds to more than 4 d.p. precision. This means they can be used to distinguish between molecules with very similar M_rs.

Example

Here's the mass spectrum of pentane ($CH_3CH_2CH_2CH_2CH_3$).

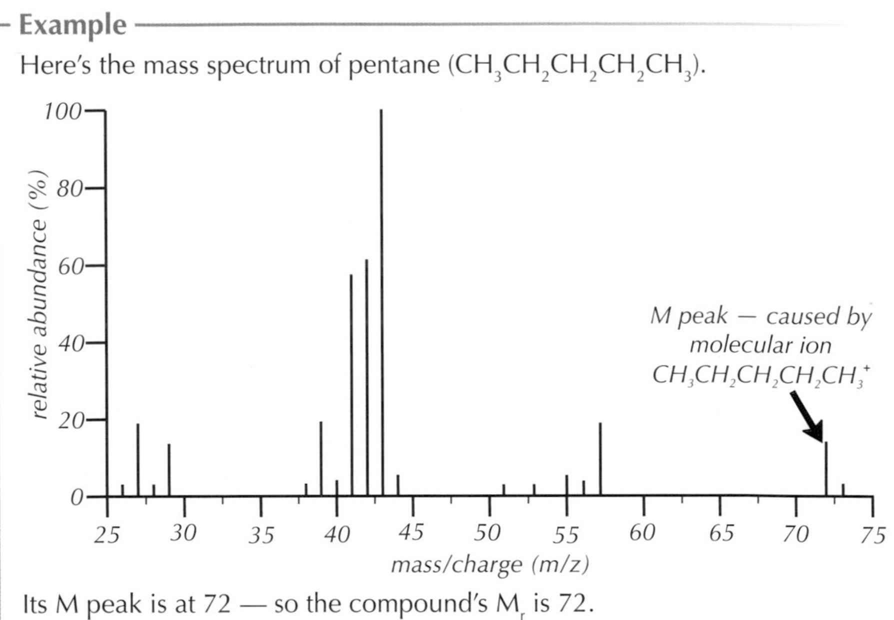

Its M peak is at 72 — so the compound's M_r is 72.

The smaller peak to the right of the M peak is called the M+1 peak — it's caused by the presence of the carbon isotope ^{13}C (you don't need to worry about this at AS).

Figure 1: Mass spectrometer.

Fragmentation

The bombarding electrons make some of the molecular ions break up into fragments. The fragments that are ions show up on the mass spectrum, making a fragmentation pattern. Fragmentation patterns are actually pretty cool because you can use them to identify molecules and even their structure.

Example

For propane ($CH_3CH_2CH_3$), the molecular ion is $CH_3CH_2CH_3^+$, and the fragments it breaks into include CH_3^+ (M_r = 15) and $CH_3CH_2^+$ (M_r = 29).

$$CH_3CH_2CH_3^+ \rightarrow CH_3CH_2\bullet \text{ (free radical)} + CH_3^+ \text{ (ion)}$$
$$CH_3CH_2CH_3^+ \rightarrow CH_3CH_2^+ \text{ (ion)} + CH_3\bullet \text{ (free radical)}$$

Tip: Make sure you understand that only the ions show up on the mass spectrum — the free radicals are 'lost' because they are uncharged.

To work out the structural formula, you've got to work out what ion could have made each peak from its m/z value. (You assume that the m/z value of a peak matches the mass of the ion that made it.)

Examples

The mass spectrum below is for a molecule with the molecular formula C_2H_6O. Use the mass spectrum to work out the structure of the molecule.

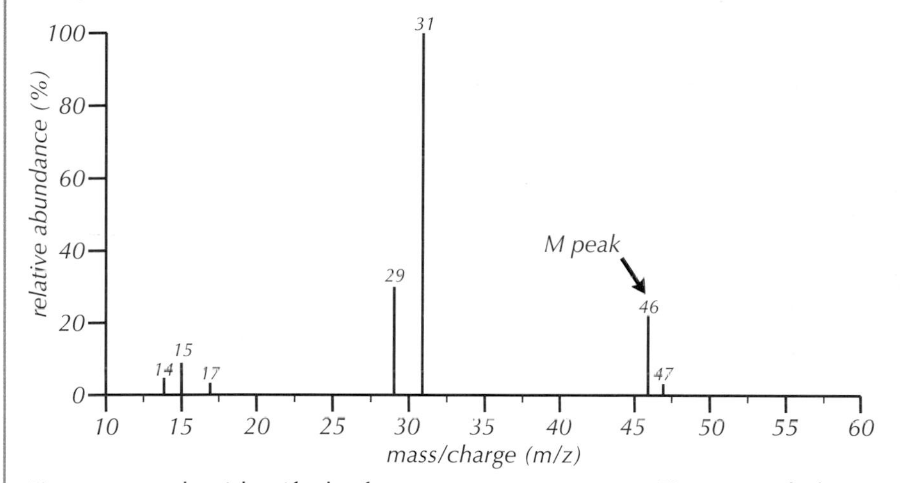

Exam Tip
For AS-Level, it's only the m/z values you're interested in — ignore the heights of the bars.

First you need to identify the fragments — you can use Figure 2 to help you identify some common ions.

- This molecule's got a peak at 15 m/z, so it's likely to have a CH_3 group.
- It's also got a peak at 17 m/z, so it's likely to have an OH group.
- To find the other fragments you just have to add combinations of 12 (the mass of carbon), 1 (the mass of hydrogen) and 16 (the mass of oxygen) until you come up with sensible fragment ions.

Other ions are matched to the peaks here:

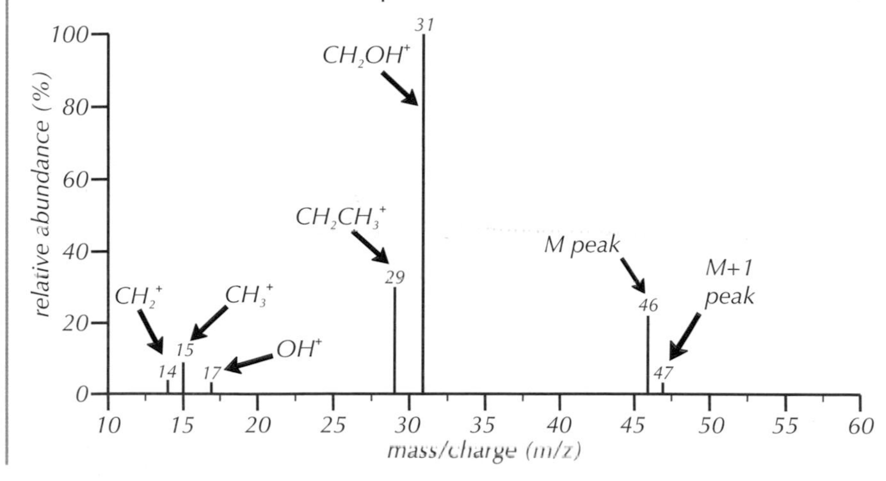

Fragment	m/z
CH_3^+	15
$CH_2CH_3^+$	29
$CH_2CH_2CH_3^+$	43
OH^+	17
$C{=}O^+$	28
$COCH_3^+$	43

Figure 2: Common fragment ions.

Exam Tip
You won't be given a common fragments table in the exam. But don't worry — if you can't remember an m/z value, you can work it out by finding the M_r of the ion (e.g. OH^+ = 16 + 1 = 17).

The next step is piecing them together to form a molecule with the correct M_r. Ethanol has all the fragments on this spectrum.

```
    H  H          H : H :
    |  |          | : | :
 H—C—C+  ←——  H—C—C—OH  ——→  +OH
    |  |          | : | :
    H  H          H : H :

  H                            H
  |                            |
H—C+            H            +C—OH
  |             |              |
  H             C+             H
                |
                H
```

Ethanol's formula is C_2H_6O, and its molecular mass is 46 — the same as the m/z value of the M peak. So, this is the mass spectrum of ethanol.

Exam Tip
Getting your head around these mass spectra is always difficult at first — get loads of practice in before the exam and you'll soon pick it up.

Here's another example:

The mass spectrum below is for a ketone.
Use the spectrum to work out the structure of the molecule.

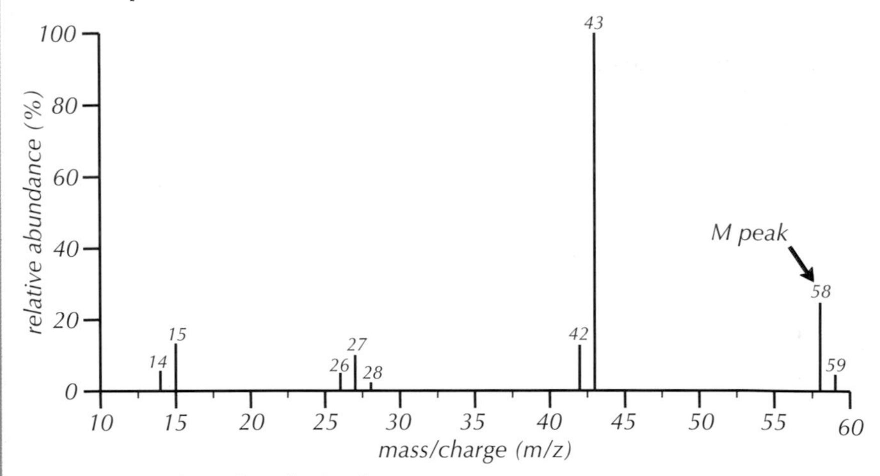

Exam Tip
Don't worry if you can't assign every line to a fragment — just make sure you assign most of them and that your final molecule makes sense.

First you need to identify the fragments:

- This molecule's got a peak at 15 m/z, so it's likely to have a CH_3 group.
- There's a peak at 28 m/z that (looking at Figure 2) could be a C=O group.
- Now let's try and identify that peak at 43 m/z. We know that there's a CH_3 from the peak at 15 m/z and a C=O at 28 m/z — 28 + 15 = 43 m/z. So the peak at 43 m/z could be $COCH_3$.
- The M peak for this molecule is at 58 m/z so let's see how much mass we haven't accounted for yet: 58 – 43 = 15 m/z. So, that could be another CH_3 group. That's all the mass accounted for — hurrah.

Tip: A $CH_2CH_2CH_3^+$ ion would also give a peak at m/z = 43. But there's no peak at m/z = 29 for a $CH_2CH_3^+$ ion, so this group can't be in the molecule.

Now let's see if the fragments fit together to make a molecule.

```
                                              H
  H              H : O : H                    |
  |              | : ‖ : |                  +C—H
H—C+  ←——    H—C—C—C—H   ——→              |
  |              | :   : |                    H
  H              H :   : H
                                           H  O
       O                                   |  ‖
       ‖                                 H—C—C+
       C+                                  |
                                           H
```

They all fit to make a propanone molecule, which has an M_r of 58 — this matches the m/z value of the M peak. So, this is the mass spectrum for propanone. Here's the spectrum with all the assigned fragments shown:

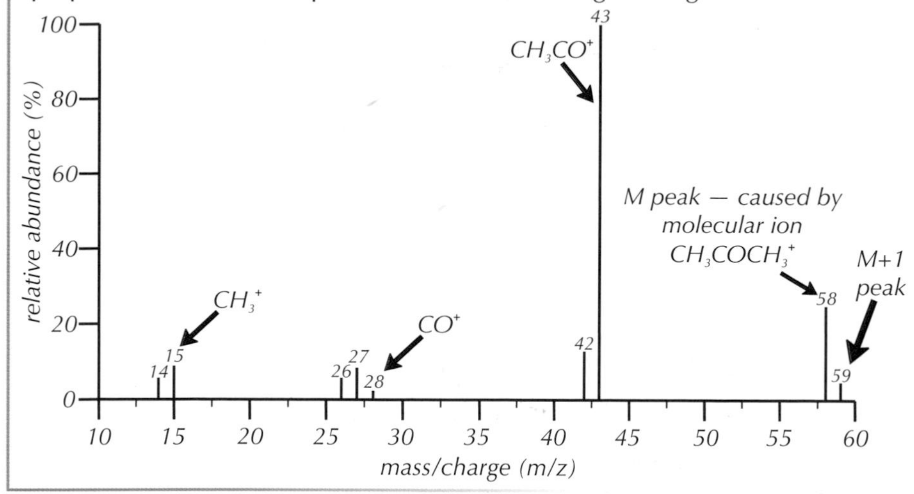

Practice Questions — Application

Q1 Write down some possible fragmentation ions of propan-1-ol. The structure of propan-1-ol is shown on the right.

```
   H  H  H
   |  |  |
H–C––C––C–OH
   |  |  |
   H  H  H
```

Q2 Use the mass spectrum below to work out the structure of the molecule. HINT: The molecule is a carboxylic acid.

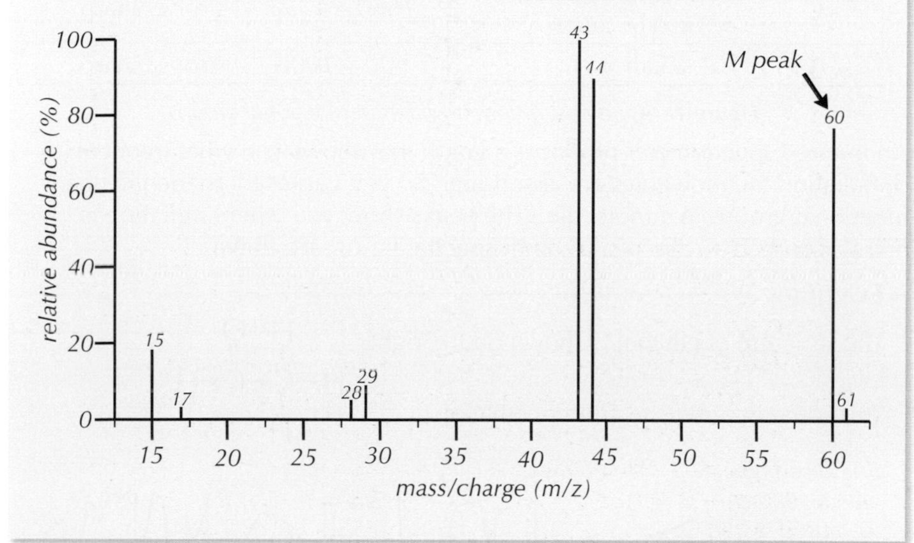

Tip: You can use the table on page 193 to help with this question if you like.

Practice Questions — Fact Recall

Q1 For most organic compounds, which peak is the M peak on a mass spectrum?

Q2 What information does the m/z value of the M peak give you?

Q3 If you have a peak at 15 m/z, what is the most likely fragment ion for an organic compound?

Learning Objectives:

- Understand that certain groups in a molecule absorb infrared radiation at characteristic frequencies.
- Understand that 'fingerprinting' allows identification of a molecule by comparison of spectra.
- Be able to use spectra to identify particular functional groups and to identify impurities, limited to data presented in wavenumber form.
- Understand the link between absorption of infrared radiation by bonds in CO_2, methane and water vapour and global warming.

Specification Reference 3.2.11

Tip: The 'type of absorption' column tells you what the peak on the infrared spectrum will look like.

Exam Tip
You'll get a table like the one in Figure 1 on the data sheet in your exam. So there's no need to memorise all those numbers — yay.

Tip: Most organic molecules will have loads of C–H bonds in them so the region at ~3000 cm^{-1} on an IR spectrum isn't always very useful.

11. Infrared Spectroscopy

Infrared spectroscopy is another analytical technique which can help you to identify a compound. The bonds of different functional groups absorb different frequencies of infrared light. This means we can use an infrared spectrum of a molecule to identify its functional groups.

The basics

In **infrared (IR) spectroscopy**, a beam of IR radiation is passed through a sample of a chemical. The IR radiation is absorbed by the covalent bonds in the molecules, increasing their vibrational energy. Bonds between different atoms absorb different frequencies of IR radiation. Bonds in different places in a molecule absorb different frequencies too — so the O–H group in an alcohol and the O–H in a carboxylic acid absorb different frequencies. Figure 1 shows what frequencies different bonds absorb — you don't need to learn this data, but you do need to understand how to use it. Wavenumber is the measure used for the frequency (it's just 1/wavelength).

Functional group	Where it's found	Frequency / Wavenumber (cm^{-1})	Type of absorption
C–H	most organic molecules	2800 – 3100	strong, sharp
O–H	alcohols	3200 – 3550	strong, broad
O–H	carboxylic acids	2500 – 3300	medium, broad
N–H	amines	3200 – 3500	strong, sharp
C=O	aldehydes, ketones, carboxylic acids	1680 – 1750	strong, sharp
C–X	haloalkanes	500 – 1000	strong, sharp

Figure 1: *Bond absorption for different functional groups.*

An infrared spectrometer produces a graph that shows you what frequencies of radiation the molecules are absorbing. So you can use it to identify the functional groups in a molecule. The peaks show you where radiation is being absorbed — the 'peaks' on IR spectra are upside-down.

Examples

The structure of ethanal is shown on the right:

This is the infrared spectrum of ethanal:

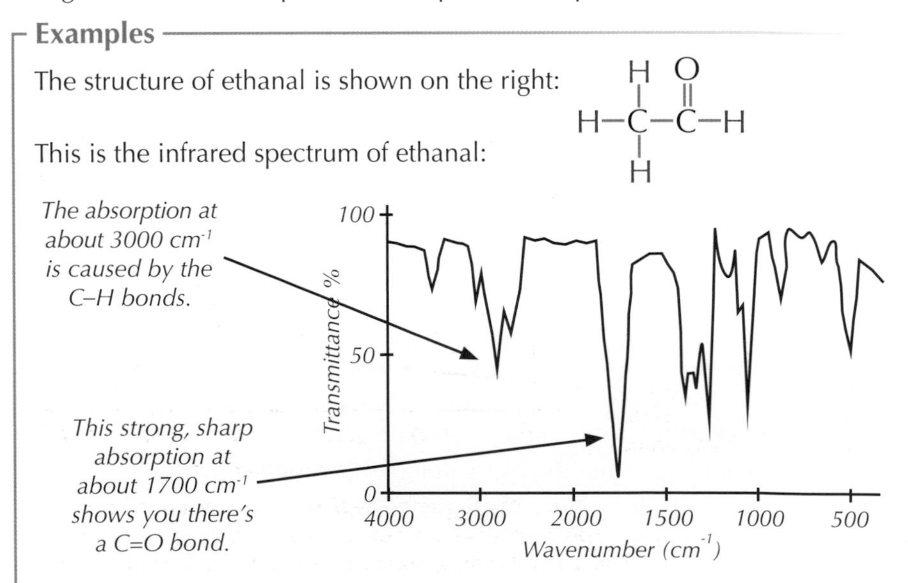

Here is the structure and infrared spectrum of ethylamine.

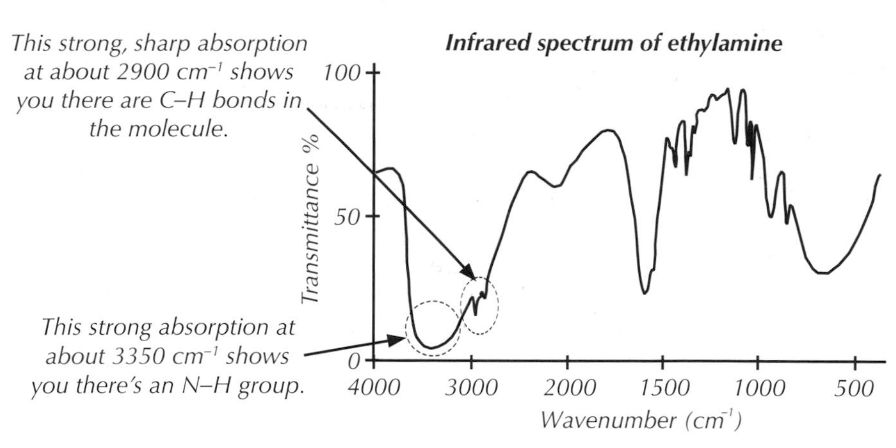

The fingerprint region

The region between 1000 cm^{-1} and 1550 cm^{-1} on the spectrum is called the **fingerprint region**. It's unique to a particular compound. You can check this region of an unknown compound's IR spectrum against those of known compounds. If it matches up with one of them, hey presto — you know what the molecule is.

Example

Here is the structure and the infrared spectrum of ethanoic acid.

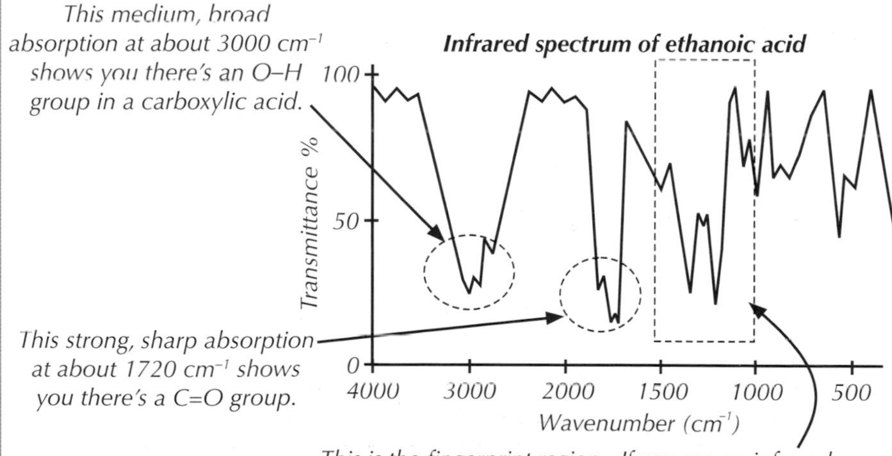

Tip: When you're reading an infrared spectrum, always double check the scale. The wavenumbers increase from right to left — don't get caught out.

Infrared spectroscopy can also be used to find out how pure a compound is, and identify any impurities. Impurities produce extra peaks in the fingerprint region.

Infrared absorption and global warming

Some of the electromagnetic radiation emitted by the Sun is in the form of infrared radiation. Molecules of greenhouse gases, like carbon dioxide, methane and water vapour, have bonds that are really good at absorbing infrared energy — so if the amounts of them in the atmosphere increase, it leads to global warming. There's lots more about how this happens on pages 103-104.

Figure 2: *The greenhouse effect.*

Tip: You can use the table on page 193 to help you out with these questions.

Practice Questions — Application

Q1 The spectrum below is the infrared spectrum of a carboxylic acid with $M_r = 74$.

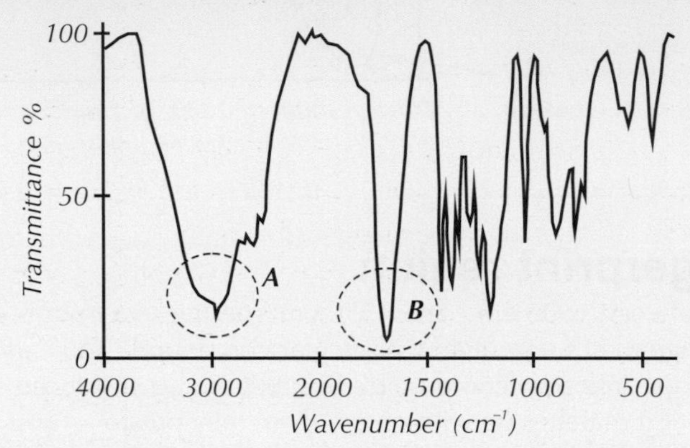

a) Identify the bonds that create the peaks marked **A** and **B** in the diagram.

b) Draw the displayed formula of the molecule.

Q2 The spectrum below shows the infrared spectrum for an unknown molecule. Use the spectrum to identify one important bond that can be found in the molecule.

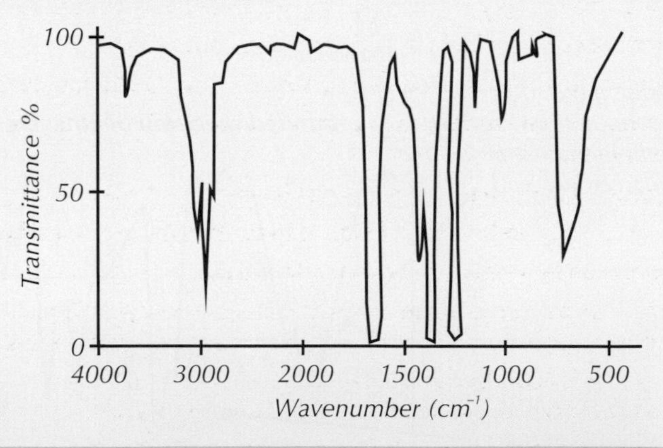

Practice Questions — Fact Recall

Q1 Give a brief explanation of how an infrared spectrum is created.

Q2 Over what frequency range is the fingerprint region of an IR spectrum found?

Section Summary

Make sure you know...

- The reaction mechanism of methane with chlorine as a free-radical substitution reaction.
- That chloroalkanes and chlorofluoroalkanes can be used as solvents.
- That ozone, which is formed naturally in the upper atmosphere, provides protection from the Sun's UV rays.
- How chlorine atoms catalyse the decomposition of ozone and have helped form a hole in the ozone layer.
- That chlorine atoms are formed in the upper atmosphere when energy from ultraviolet radiation causes C–Cl bonds in chlorofluorocarbons (CFCs) to break.
- That legislation to ban the use of CFCs was supported by chemists and that alternative chlorine-free compounds have been developed to replace CFCs.
- That haloalkanes contain polar bonds and are susceptible to nucleophilic attack by nucleophiles.
- The mechanism of nucleophilic substitution in primary haloalkanes.
- That the carbon–halogen bond enthalpy influences the rate of hydrolysis.
- That haloalkanes can undergo nucleophilic substitution and elimination reactions where the reagent can act as either a nucleophile or a base.
- That elimination and nucleophilic substitution reactions are very useful in organic synthesis.
- That alkenes are unsaturated hydrocarbons which contain a double covalent bond.
- That the double bond in an alkene is a centre of high electron density.
- The mechanism of electrophilic addition of alkenes with H_2SO_4 and Br_2.
- That bromine water can be used to test for alkenes.
- That alcohols are produced industrially by hydration of alkenes in the presence of an acid catalyst.
- The typical conditions for the industrial production of ethanol from ethene.
- The mechanism of electrophilic addition of alkenes with HBr.
- How to predict the products of addition to unsymmetrical alkenes.
- That the carbon–carbon double bond is planar and so alkenes can exhibit E/Z stereoisomerism.
- How to draw the structures of E and Z isomers.
- That E/Z isomerism exists due to restricted rotation about the C=C bond.
- How addition polymers are formed from alkenes.
- That poly(alkenes), like alkanes, are unreactive.
- How to recognise the repeating unit in a poly(alkene).
- Some typical uses of poly(ethene) and poly(propene) and that poly(propene) is recycled.
- How to name alcohols, aldehydes, ketones and carboxylic acids.
- How ethanol is produced industrially by fermentation, including the conditions for the reaction.
- The economic and environmental advantages and disadvantages of fermentation compared with the industrial production of ethanol from ethene.
- What a biofuel is and what carbon neutral means.
- That ethanol, produced by fermentation, can be thought of as a carbon-neutral biofuel.
- That alcohols can be primary, secondary or tertiary.
- That alkenes can be formed from alcohols by acid catalysed elimination reactions and that this method provides a possible route to polymers without using monomers derived from oil.
- That primary and secondary alcohols can be oxidised to aldehydes, carboxylic acids and ketones by using an oxidising agent such as acidified potassium dichromate(VI).
- How to use Fehling's solution or Tollens' reagent to distinguish between aldehydes and ketones.
- That high resolution mass spectrometry can be used to identify compounds.
- That certain functional groups absorb infrared radiation at characteristic frequencies.
- That the 'fingerprint region' of an infrared spectrum allows identification of a molecule by comparison of spectra.
- How to use infrared spectra to identify particular functional groups and to identify impurities.
- That greenhouse gases absorb infrared radiation and so increasing the amount of them can cause global warming.

Exam-style Questions

1 Ethanol is a simple alcohol that can be used as a fuel, in alcoholic beverages, as a solvent and also as a starting molecule for many organic synthesis reactions. Its structure is shown below.

```
   H  H
   |  |
H—C—C—OH
   |  |
   H  H
```

1 (a) Ethanol can be created by a nucleophilic substitution reaction of bromoethane with aqueous sodium hydroxide. Write the equation and draw the mechanism for this reaction.

Ethanol can also be produced by reaction of iodoethane with aqueous sodium hydroxide.

Which of the reactions would proceed more quickly? Explain your answer.

(5 marks)

1 (b) A fermentation reaction can be used to produce ethanol.

Write down the equation for this reaction and state the conditions needed for the reaction to occur.

Explain why production of ethanol by this method may be important in the future.

(4 marks)

1 (c) Industrially, ethanol is also produced by steam hydration.

Describe the conditions required for this reaction and explain how you could increase the yield of the reaction.

(3 marks)

1 (d) Ethanol can be used as a carbon neutral biofuel.

Define the term biofuel.

Explain why ethanol is thought of as carbon neutral and why this might not always be the case.

(4 marks)

2 A scientist has synthesised two molecules — molecule **A** and molecule **B**. Both of the molecules were synthesised by reacting 1-bromopropane with an ^{-}OH ion. The structure of 1-bromopropane is shown below.

```
    H  H  H
    |  |  |
Br—C—C—C—H
    |  |  |
    H  H  H
```

The infrared spectra of the molecules are shown below.

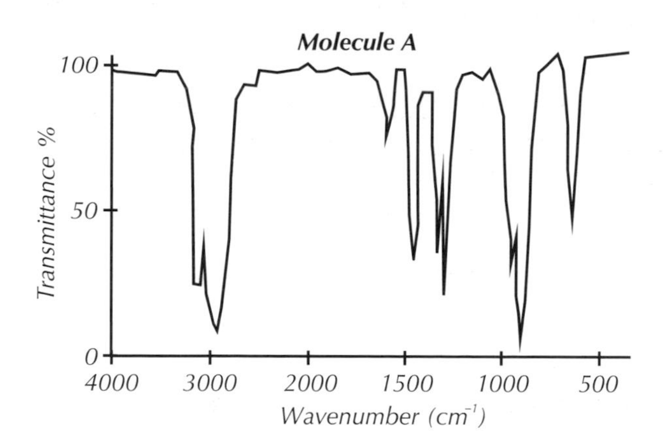

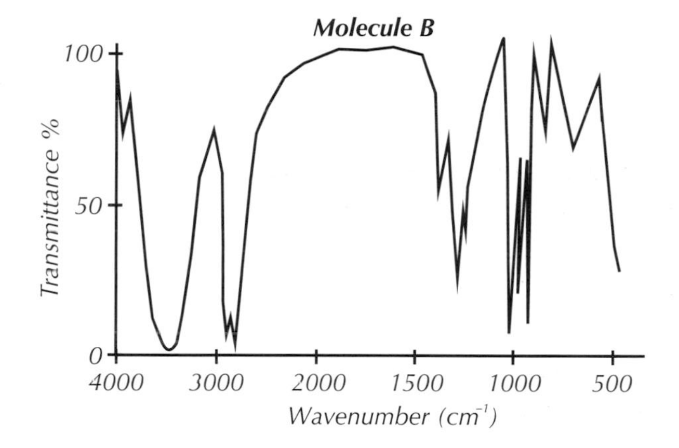

2 (a) Neither molecule **A** nor molecule **B** contains halogen atoms. Use the table on page 196 to predict the structures of molecule **A** and molecule **B.** Explain your reasoning.

(6 marks)

2 (b) Name molecule **A** and molecule **B**.

(2 marks)

2 (c) Give the reagents and conditions that are needed to produce each molecule from 1-bromopropane.

(2 marks)

3 A student has been given a sample of the alkene 3-methylpent-2-ene. The structure of 3-methylpent-2-ene is shown below.

```
   H  H     H  H
   |  |     |  |
H--C--C--C==C--C--H
   |  |  |     |
   H  H  CH3   H
```

3 (a) Describe how the student could prove that the sample is unsaturated.

(2 marks)

3 (b) 3-methylpent-2-ene has a number of different stereoisomers.

3 (b) (i) Define the term stereoisomer.

(1 mark)

3 (b) (ii) Draw two stereoisomers of 3-methylpent-2-ene.

(2 marks)

3 (b) (iii) Name the two stereoisomers you have drawn in **(b)** part **(ii)**.

(2 marks)

3 (c) The student reacts 3-methylpent-2-ene with hydrogen bromide (HBr).

3 (c) (i) Write the equation for the reaction.

(1 mark)

3 (c) (ii) Draw the structure of the major product of the reaction.

(1 mark)

3 (c) (iii) Use your knowledge of carbocation stability to explain why the structure given in **(c)** part **(ii)** is the major product of this reaction.

(3 marks)

3 (d) 3-methylpent-2-ene can be polymerised using an addition polymerisation reaction.

Write the equation for the addition polymerisation of 3-methylpent-2-ene.

(2 marks)

4 Analytical techniques are used to identify unknown compounds.

4 (a) Molecule **A** has the mass spectrum shown below.

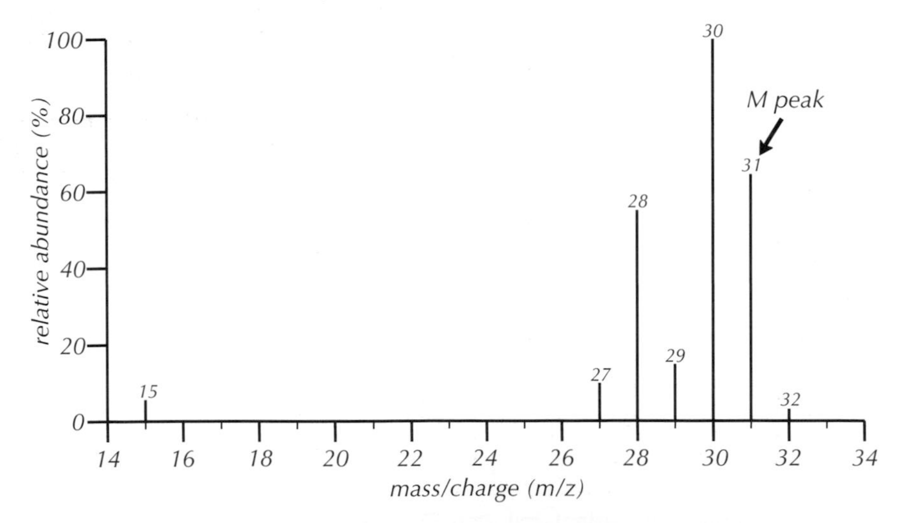

You can synthesise molecule **A** by reacting a haloalkane with ammonia.

Use your knowledge of organic chemistry and analytical techniques to identify the structure of molecule **A**. Explain your reasoning.

(4 marks)

4 (b) Molecule **B** contains only carbon, oxygen and hydrogen atoms.
It has the infrared spectrum shown below.

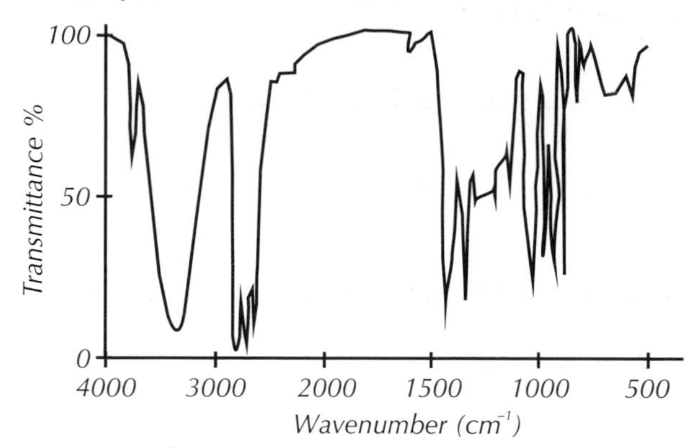

The mass spectrum of molecule **B** shows that the M_r of the molecule is 74.

If you react molecule **B** with acidified potassium dichromate(VI) you produce a ketone.

Use your knowledge of organic chemistry and analytical techniques along with the table on page 196 to identify the structure of molecule **B**. Explain your reasoning.

(4 marks)

4 (c) The infrared spectrum and mass spectrum of molecule **C** are shown below.

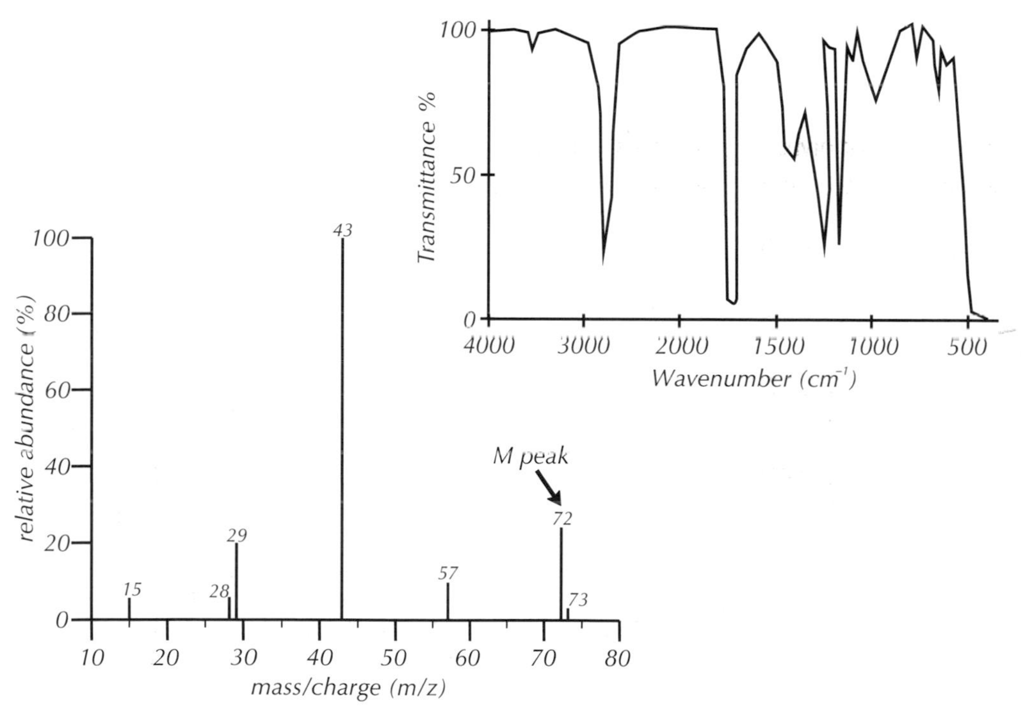

Molecule **C** will not react with Tollens' reagent.

Use your knowledge of organic chemistry and analytical techniques along with the table on page 196 to identify the structure of molecule **C**. Explain your reasoning.

(5 marks)

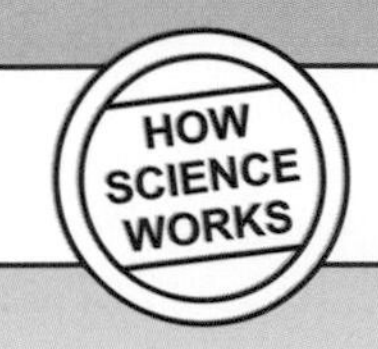

Investigative and Practical Skills

1. Variables and Data

When you're planning an experiment you need to think carefully about what things you're going to change, what things you're going to measure and how you're going to record your results.

Variables

You probably know this all off by heart but it's easy to get mixed up sometimes. So here's a quick recap. A **variable** is a quantity that has the potential to change, e.g. mass. There are two types of variable commonly referred to in experiments:

Tip: When drawing graphs, the dependent variable should go on the y-axis, the independent variable on the x-axis.

Independent variable — the thing that you change in an experiment.

Dependent variable — the thing that you measure in an experiment.

Example

You could investigate the effect of temperature on rate of reaction using the apparatus in Figure 1 below:

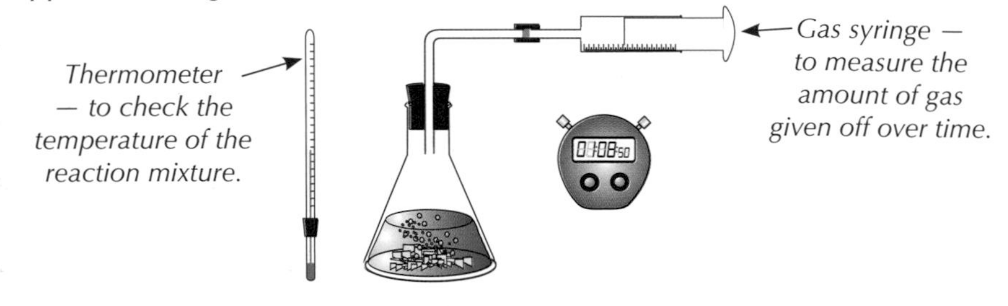

Figure 1: *Apparatus for measuring the rate of reaction.*

- The independent variable will be temperature.
- The dependent variable will be the amount of gas produced.
- All the other variables must be kept the same. These include the concentration and volume of solutions, mass of solids, pressure, the presence of a catalyst and the surface area of any solid reactants.

Types of data

Experiments always involve some sort of measurement to provide data. There are different types of data — and you need to know what they are.

1. Discrete data

You get discrete data by counting. E.g. the number of bubbles produced in a reaction would be discrete (see Figure 2). You can't have 1.25 bubbles. That'd be daft. Shoe size is another good example of a discrete variable.

Figure 2: *An acid-carbonate reaction. The number of bubbles produced is discrete data, but the volume of gas produced is continuous data.*

2. Continuous data

A continuous variable can have any value on a scale. For example, the volume of gas produced or the mass of products from a reaction. You can never measure the exact value of a continuous variable.

3. Categoric data

A categoric variable has values that can be sorted into categories. For example, the colours of solutions might be blue, red and green (see Figure 3). Or types of material might be wood, steel, glass.

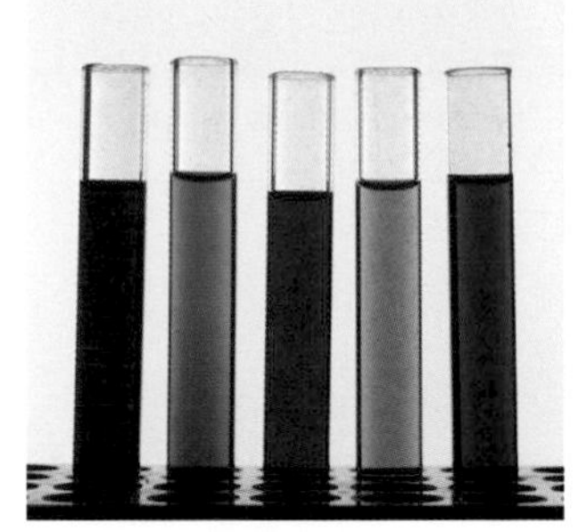

Figure 3: Different coloured solutions. Colour is a type of categoric data.

4. Ordered (ordinal) data

Ordered data is similar to categoric, but the categories can be put in order. For example, if you classify reactions as 'slow', 'fairly fast' and 'very fast' you'd have ordered data.

Tables of data

Before you start your experiment, make a table to write your results in. You'll need to **repeat** each test at least three times to check your results are reliable (see p.208 for more on reliable results). Figure 4 (below) is the sort of table you might end up with when you investigate the effect of temperature on reaction rate. (You'd then have to do the same for different temperatures.)

Temperature	Time (s)	Volume of gas evolved (cm^3) Run 1	Volume of gas evolved (cm^3) Run 2	Volume of gas evolved (cm^3) Run 3	Average volume of gas evolved (cm^3)
20 °C	10	8	7	8	**7.7**
	20	17	19	20	**18.7**
	30	28	20	30	**29**

***Figure 4:** Table of results showing the effect of temperature on the rate of reaction.*

Tip: To find the average of each set of repeated measurements you need to add them all up and divide by how many there are.

For example, for the average volume of gas evolved after 10 s, it's:

$8 + 7 + 8 \div 3 = 7.7$ cm^3

Watch out for **anomalous results**. These are ones that don't fit in with the other values and are likely to be wrong. They're usually due to random errors, such as making a mistake when measuring. You should ignore anomalous results when you calculate averages.

Example

Look at the table in Figure 4 again — the volume of gas evolved after 30 s in Run 2 looks like it might be an anomalous result. It's much lower than the values in the other two runs. It could have been caused by the syringe plunger getting stuck.

The anomalous result has been ignored when the average was calculated — that's why the average volume of gas evolved after 30 s is 29 cm^3 ($(28 + 30) \div 2 = 29$), rather than 26 cm^3 ($(28 + 20 + 30) \div 3 = 26$).

Tip: Just because you ignore anomalous results in your calculations you shouldn't ignore them in your write-up. Try to find an explanation for what went wrong so that it can be avoided in future experiments.

2. Graphs and Charts

You'll usually be expected to make a graph of your results. Graphs make your data easier to understand — so long as you choose the right type.

Types of graphs and charts

Tip: Use simple scales when you draw graphs — this'll make it easier to plot points.

Bar charts

You should use a bar chart when one of your data sets is categoric or ordered data, like in Figure 1.

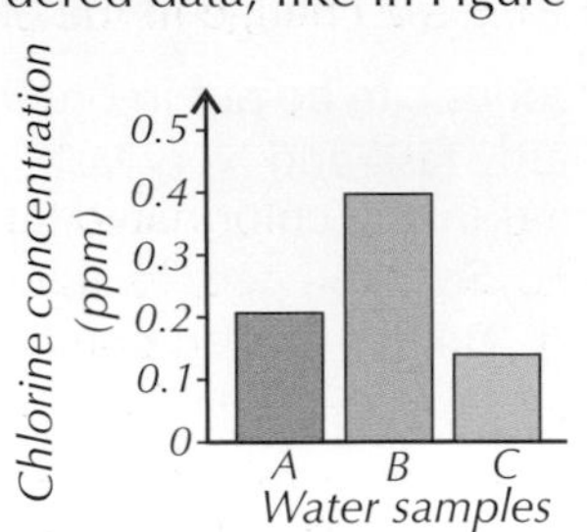

Figure 1: *Bar chart to show chlorine concentration in water samples.*

Pie charts

Pie charts are normally used to display categoric data, like in Figure 2.

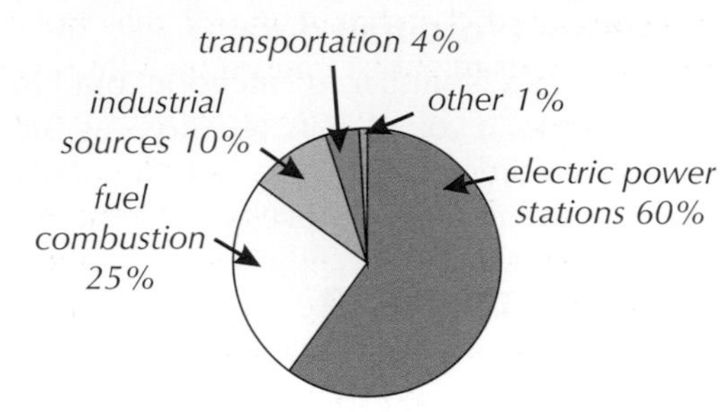

Figure 2: *Pie chart to show sources of a country's sulfur dioxide emissions.*

Tip: Whatever type of graph you make, you'll only get full marks if you:

1. Choose a sensible scale — don't do a tiny graph in the corner of the paper.
2. Label both axes — including units.
3. Plot your points accurately — using a sharp pencil.

Line Graphs

Line graphs are best when you have two sets of continuous data, like in Figure 3. Volume of gas and time are both continuous variables — you could get any value on the x or y-axis.

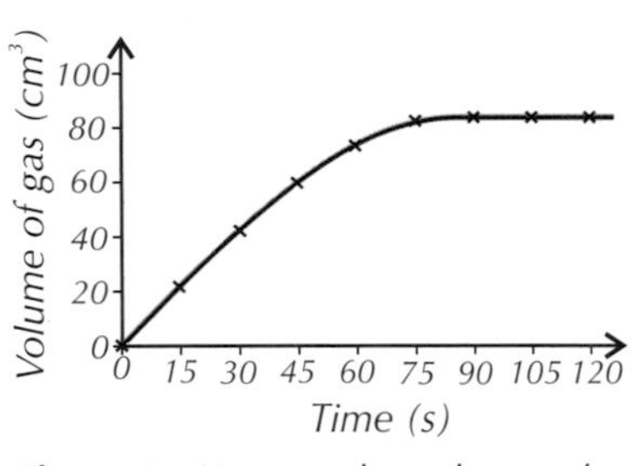

Figure 3: *Line graph to show volume of gas evolved against time.*

Scatter graphs

Scatter graphs, like Figure 4, are great for showing how two sets of data are related (or correlated — see below for more on correlation). Don't try to join all the points — draw a line of best fit to show the trend.

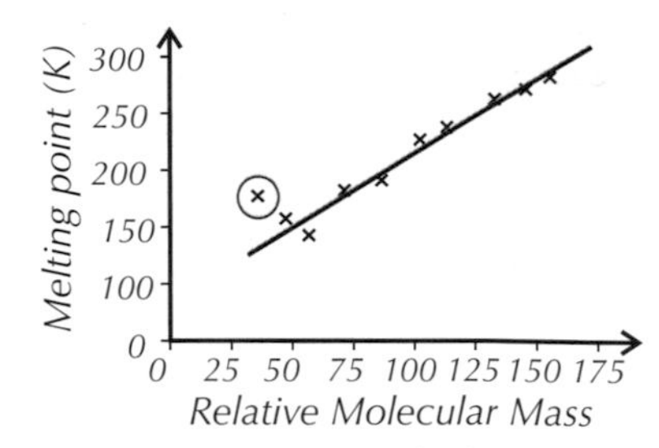

Figure 4: *Scatter graph showing the relationship between M_r and melting point of some alcohols.*

Tip: A line of best fit should have about half of the points above it and half of the points below. You can ignore any anomalous points like the one circled in Figure 4.

Scatter graphs and correlation

Correlation describes the relationship between two variables — usually the independent one and the dependent one. Data can show positive correlation, negative correlation or no correlation (see Figure 5).

Positive correlation
As one variable increases the other also increases.

Negative correlation
As one variable increases the other decreases.

No correlation
There is no relationship between the variables.

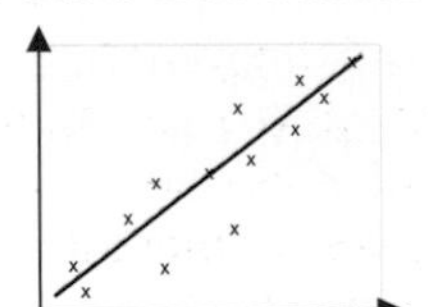

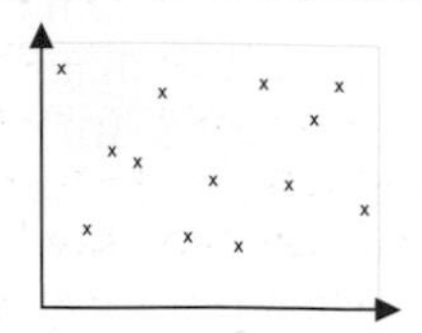

Figure 5: *Scatter graphs showing positive, negative and no correlation.*

Tip: Computers can make it a lot quicker to collect, record and analyse big sets of data from experiments — but you've still got to understand what all the numbers and graphs they churn out mean.

3. Conclusions and Evaluations

Once you've got your results nicely presented in graphical form you can start to draw a conclusion. But be careful — you may have a graph showing a lovely correlation, but that doesn't always tell you as much as you might think.

Correlation and cause

Ideally, only two quantities would ever change in any experiment — everything else would remain constant. But in experiments or studies outside the lab, you can't usually control all the variables. So even if two variables are correlated, the change in one may not be causing the change in the other. Both changes might be caused by a third variable.

Tip: If an experiment really does confirm that changing one variable causes another to change, we say there's a causal link between them.

Example

Some studies have found a correlation between drinking chlorinated tap water and the risk of developing certain cancers. So some people argue that this means water shouldn't have chlorine added. But it's hard to control all the variables between people who drink tap water and people who don't. It could be many lifestyle factors. Or, the cancer risk could be affected by something else in tap water — or by whatever the non-tap water drinkers drink instead.

Tip: Watch out for bias too — for instance, a bottled water company might point these studies out to people without mentioning any of the doubts.

Drawing conclusions

The data should always support the conclusion. This may sound obvious but it's easy to jump to conclusions. Conclusions have to be specific — not make sweeping generalisations.

Example

The rate of an enzyme-controlled reaction was measured at 10 °C, 20 °C, 30 °C, 40 °C, 50 °C and 60 °C. All other variables were kept constant, and the results are shown in Figure 1.

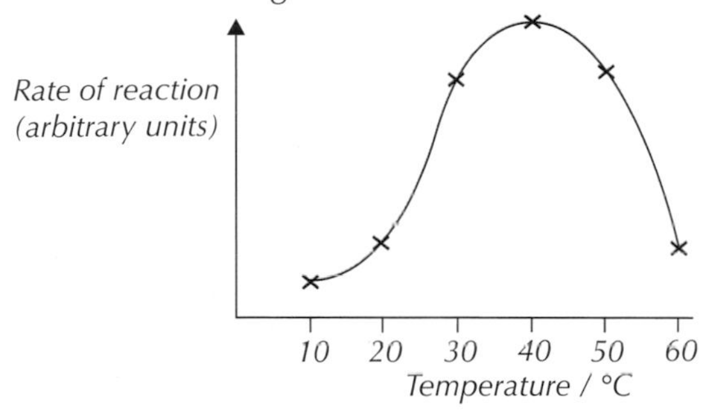

Figure 1: *Graph to show the effect of temperature on the rate of an enzyme-controlled reaction.*

A science magazine concluded from this data that enzyme X works best at 40 °C. The data doesn't support this. The enzyme could work best at 42 °C or 47 °C but you can't tell from the data because increases of 10 °C at a time were used. The rate of reaction at in-between temperatures wasn't measured. All you know is that it's faster at 40 °C than at any of the other temperatures tested.

Also, the experiment only gives information about this particular enzyme-controlled reaction. You can't conclude that all enzyme-controlled reactions happen faster at a particular temperature — only this one. And you can't say for sure that doing the experiment at, say, a different constant pressure, wouldn't give a different optimum temperature.

Tip: Whoever funded the research (e.g. a chemical manufacturer) may have some influence on what conclusions are drawn from the results, but scientists have a responsibility to make sure that the conclusions they draw are supported by the data.

Evaluations

There are a few terms that you need to understand. They'll be useful when you're evaluating how convincing your results are.

1. Valid results

Valid results answer the original question, using reliable data. For example, if you haven't controlled all the variables your results won't be valid, because you won't be testing just the thing you wanted to.

2. Accurate results

Accurate results are those that are really close to the true answer.

Tip: It's possible for results to be precise but not accurate, e.g. a balance that weighs to 1/1000th of a gram will give precise results, but if it's not calibrated properly the results won't be accurate.

3. Precise results

These are results taken using sensitive instruments that measure in small increments.

Example

A pH measured with a meter (pH 7.692) will be more precise than pH measured with paper (pH 7).

4. Reliable results

Reliable means the results can be consistently reproduced in independent experiments. And if the results are reproducible they're more likely to be true. If the data isn't reliable for whatever reason you can't draw a valid conclusion. For experiments, the more repeats you do, the more reliable the data. If you get the same result twice, it could be the correct answer. But if you get the same result 20 times, it'd be much more reliable. And it'd be even more reliable if everyone in the class got about the same results using different apparatus.

Tip: Part of the scientific process (see page 1) involves other scientists repeating your experiment too — then if they get the same results you can be more certain they're reliable.

5. Percentage error

You may have to calculate the percentage error of a measurement. If you know the precision that the measuring equipment is calibrated to, just divide this by the measurement taken and multiply by 100, as shown below.

Example

A balance is calibrated to within 0.1 g, and you measure a mass as 4 g.

The percentage error is: $(0.1 \div 4) \times 100 = 2.5\%$.

Using a larger quantity reduces the percentage error — a mass of 40 g has a percentage error of: $(0.1 \div 40) \times 100 = 0.25\%$.

Tip: You should always choose appropriate measuring equipment for the precision you need to work with.

Most measuring equipment has the precision it's calibrated to written on it. Where it doesn't, you can usually use the scale as a guide (e.g. if a measuring cylinder has a 1 ml scale, it is probably calibrated to within 0.5 ml).

Risks, hazards and ethical considerations

In any experiment you'll be expected to show that you've thought about the risks and hazards. It's generally a good thing to wear an apron and goggles, but you may need to take additional safety measures, depending on the experiment. For example, anything involving nasty gases will need to be done in a fume cupboard.

You need to make sure you're working ethically too. This is most important if there are other people or animals involved. You have to put their welfare first.

Figure 2: A scientist wearing protective clothing to handle hazardous chemicals.

Exam Help

1. Exam Structure and Technique

Passing exams isn't all about revision — it really helps if you know how the exam is structured and have got your exam technique nailed so that you pick up every mark you can.

Exam structure

For AQA AS-Level Chemistry you're gonna have to sit through two exams (Unit 1 and Unit 2) and complete an internal assessment (Unit 3).

Unit 1 — Foundation Chemistry

This paper will be 1 hour 15 minutes long and have 70 marks up for grabs. It's worth $33\frac{1}{3}\%$ of your total AS-Level and is split up into two sections.

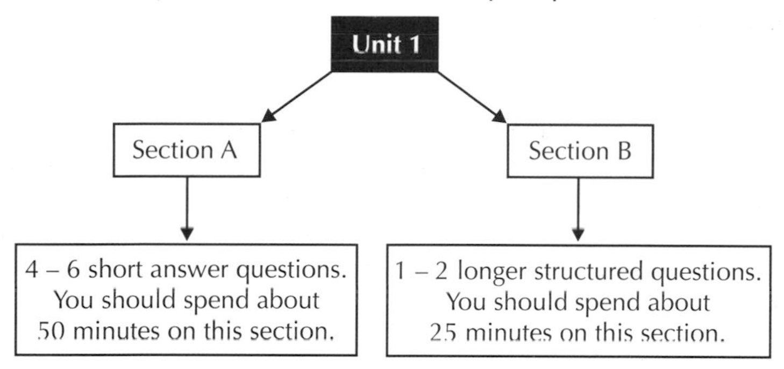

Unit 2 — Chemistry in Action

This paper will be 1 hour 45 minutes long and have 100 marks up for grabs. It's worth $46\frac{2}{3}\%$ of your total AS-Level and is also split up into two sections.

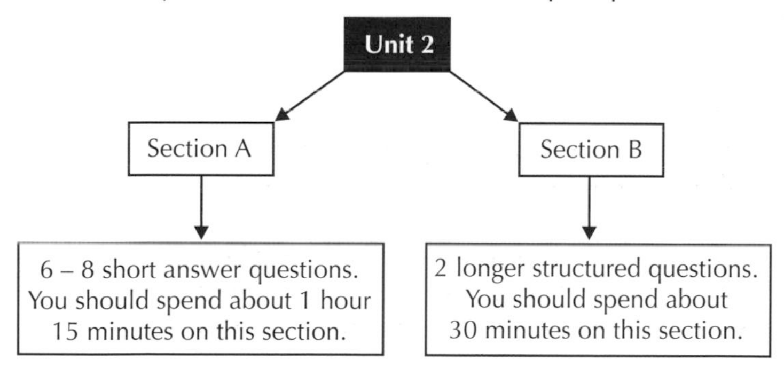

Unit 3 — Investigative and practical skills in AS Chemistry

You'll do this unit in school with your teacher. It'll test your understanding of chemistry and your ability to plan, carry out and evaluate experiments in the lab. It's worth 20% of your total AS-Level.

The assessments in Unit 3 test that you can use standard laboratory equipment, demonstrate safe and skilful practical techniques, plan a suitable experiment, take measurements with precision and accuracy, correctly record data and analyse and evaluate your experiment. This may sound a bit menacing but there's some stuff on pages 204-208 to help you out.

Exam Tip
Make sure you have a good read through of this exam structure. It might not seem important now but you don't want to get any nasty surprises just before an exam.

Exam Tip
Short answer questions are questions that are broken down into lots of different parts. They can still be worth lots of marks overall, it's just that you don't have to write that much for each individual part.

Figure 1: *Chemistry lesson — that guy at the back is totally checking out that girl.*

Quality of written communication (QWC)

All of the units you take for AS-Level Chemistry will have a quality of written communication element — this just means that the examiner will assess your ability to write properly. This may seem like a bit of a drag but you will lose marks if you don't do it. You need to make sure that:

- your scribble, sorry, writing is legible,
- your spelling, punctuation and grammar are accurate,
- your writing style is appropriate,
- you organise your answer clearly and coherently,
- you use specialist scientific vocabulary where it's appropriate.

In Section A of your Unit 1 and Unit 2 exam papers you're not specifically told that your quality of written communication will be assessed — but QWC will probably be tested here anyway. So... you must make sure you always write properly because you can never tell when those sneaky examiners are going to pop in some QWC marks. Section B of the exam papers require you to write in continuous prose when there's a long answer question — you will lose marks if you don't write in full sentences.

Exam Tip
You'll need to use black ink or a black ball-point pen to write your answers, so make sure that you've got a couple ready for the exam.

Exam Tip
Make sure that you write enough to get all the marks that are available. For example, if it's a four mark question a one sentence answer isn't likely to be enough.

Time management

This is one of the most important exam skills to have. How long you spend on each question is really important in an exam — it could make all the difference to your grade. Check out the exam timings suggested by AQA that can be found on the previous page and on the front of your exam paper. These timings give you about 1 minute per mark — try to stick to this to give yourself the best chance to pick up as many marks as possible.

Some questions will require lots of work for only a few marks but other questions will be much quicker. Don't spend ages struggling with questions that are only worth a couple of marks — move on. You can come back to them later when you've bagged loads of other marks elsewhere.

Examples

The questions below are both worth the same number of marks but require different amounts of work.

1 (a) Define the term 'standard enthalpy change of combustion'.

(2 marks)

2 (a) Draw a structural isomer of molecule **B** and state the type of structural isomerism it shows.

(2 marks)

Question 1 (a) only requires you to write down a definition — if you can remember it this shouldn't take you too long.

Question 2 (a) requires you to draw an isomer and then work out what type of isomer it is — this may take you a lot longer than writing down a definition, especially if you have to draw out a few structures before getting it right.

So, if you're running out of time it makes sense to do questions like 1(a) first and come back to 2 (a) if you've got time at the end.

Exam Tip
Everyone has their own method of getting through the exam. Some people find it easier to go through the paper question by question and some people like to do the questions they find easiest first. The most important thing is to find out the way that suits you best before the exam — that means doing all the practice exams you can before the big day.

Exam Tip
Don't forget to go back and do any questions that you left the first time round — you don't want to miss out on marks because you forgot to do the question.

Calculations

There's no getting away from those pesky calculation questions — they come up a lot in AS-Level Chemistry. The most important thing to remember is to show your working. You've probably heard it a million times before but it makes perfect sense. It only takes a few seconds more to write down what's in your head and it'll stop you from making silly errors and losing out on easy marks. You won't get a mark for a wrong answer but you could get marks for the method you used to work out the answer.

Exam Tip
It's so easy to mis-type numbers into a calculator when you're under pressure in an exam. Always double check your calculations and make sure the answer looks sensible.

Units

Make sure you always give the correct units for your answer (see page 215 for more on units).

Example

Here's an example of a question where you need to change the units so they match the answer the examiner wants.

1 A student measures the enthalpy change of reaction **A**. The temperature of the water increased by 2 °C during the reaction.

(a) Calculate the heat given out in the reaction in kJ.

(2 marks)

When you use $q = mc\Delta T$ to calculate the heat given out you'll get an answer in joules. Make sure you convert the units to kilojoules by dividing by 1000.

Exam Tip
You'll need to know what units your figures need to be in for different formulas — see page 214 for the units used in different formulas and pages 215-216 for how to convert between units.

Significant figures

Use the number of significant figures given in the question as a guide for how many to give in the answer. You should always give your answer to the lowest number of significant figures (s.f.) given in the question — if you're really unsure, write down the full answer and then round it to 3 s.f.. It always helps to write down the number of significant figures you've rounded to after your answer — it shows the examiner you really know what you're talking about.

Tip: The first significant figure of a number is the first digit that isn't a zero. The second, third and fourth significant figures follow on immediately after the first (even if they're zeros).

Examples

In this question the data given to you is a good indication of how many significant figures you should give your answer to.

1 (b) Calculate the enthalpy change measured by the student in kJ mol^{-1}. (The specific heat capacity of water is 4.18 J g^{-1} K^{-1}).

(2 marks)

The data in the question is given to 3 s.f. so it makes sense to give your answer to 3 s.f. too. But sometimes it isn't as clear as that.

3 (b) 13.5 cm^3 of a 0.51 M solution of sodium hydroxide reacts with 1.5 M hydrochloric acid. Calculate the volume of hydrochloric acid required to neutralise the sodium hydroxide.

(2 marks)

There are two types of data in this question, volume data and concentration data. The volume data is given to 3 s.f. and the concentration data is given to 2 s.f.. You should always give your answer to the lowest number of significant figures given — in this case that's to 2 s.f.. The answer in full is 4.59 cm^3 so the answer rounded correctly would be 4.6 cm^3 (2 s.f.).

Exam Tip
You might get told in the question how many significant figures or decimal places to give your answer to. If you are, make sure that you follow the instructions — you'll lose marks if you don't.

Standard form

You might be asked to give your answer in standard form. Standard form is used for writing very big or very small numbers in a more convenient way. Standard form must always look like this:

This number must always be between 1 and 10. → $A \times 10^n$ ← *This number is the number of places the decimal point moves.*

Examples

Here's how to write 3 500 000 in standard form.

- First write the non-zero digits with a decimal point after the first number and a '× 10' after it:

$$3.5 \times 10$$

- Then count how many places the decimal point has moved to the left. This number sits to the top right of the 10.

$$3\,5\,0\,0\,0\,0\,0 = 3.5 \times 10^6$$

(6 5 4 3 2 1)

- Et voilà... that's 3 500 000 written in standard form.

Here are some more examples.

- You can write 450 000 as 4.5×10^5.
- The number 0.000056 is 5.6×10^{-5} in standard form — the n is negative because the decimal point has moved to the right instead of the left.
- You can write 0.003456 as 3.456×10^{-3}.

Tip: Your calculator might give you your answer in standard form already — result.

Diagrams

When you're asked to draw diagrams or mechanisms in an exam it's important that you draw everything correctly.

Examples

Drawing organic reaction mechanisms

When you're drawing organic reaction mechanisms the curly arrows must come from either a lone pair of electrons or from a bond, like this:

The mechanisms below are all incorrect — you wouldn't get marks for them:

You won't get marks for showing a bond as a line with dots on either side like this... *or this...*

And you won't get marks if the curly arrows come from atoms, like this...

Tip: It's important that the curly arrows come from a lone pair or a bond because that's where the electrons are found. Remember, curly arrows are supposed to show the movement of electrons.

Drawing displayed formulas

If a question asks you for a displayed formula you have to show all of the bonds and all of the atoms in the molecule. That means you have to draw displayed formulas like this:

H
|
H–C–H
H | H
| | |
Cl–C–C–C–H
| | |
H H H

And not like this:

H CH_3
| |
Cl–C–C–CH_3
| |
H H

Some of the bonds between the carbon atoms and the hydrogen atoms haven't been shown, so it's not a displayed formula and you wouldn't get the marks.

If you're not asked specifically for a displayed formula then either of the diagrams above will do. Just make sure that the bonds are always drawn between the right atoms. For example, ethanol should be drawn like this:

H H
| |
H–C–C–OH
| |
H H

And not like this:

H H
| |
H–C–C–HO
| |
H H

It's the oxygen atom that's bonded to carbon, not the hydrogen atom, so drawing it like this is just plain wrong.

Drawing the shapes of molecules

You're probably going to have to draw diagrams to show the shapes of molecules. Make sure that you label all of the atoms and draw on all of the lone pairs. For example, this would be a good drawing of ammonia:

××
N
H *H* *H*
107°

The lone pair of electrons are shown and all of the atoms and bonds are included.

This would not:

N
107°

The lone pair of electrons are missing and the hydrogen atoms have not been included.

When you're drawing any diagram make sure it's really clear what you're drawing. A small scribble in the bottom corner of a page isn't going to show enough detail to get you the marks. Draw the diagrams nice and big, but make sure that you stay within the space given for that answer — you won't get marks for anything that's drawn in the margin.

Tip: A displayed formula shows how all the atoms are arranged and all the bonds between them. See page 89 for more on displayed formulas.

Exam Tip
If you've drawn a diagram incorrectly don't scribble part of it out and try to fix it — it'll look messy and be really hard for the examiner to figure out what you're trying to show. Cross the whole thing out and start again.

Tip: See pages 66-69 for more on shapes of molecules.

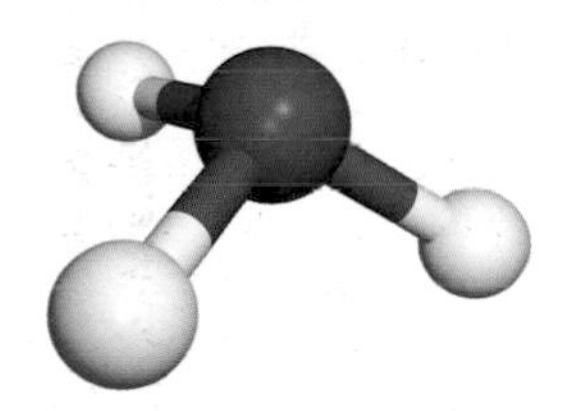

Figure 2: *An ammonia molecule. This is the 3D shape you are trying to represent when you draw the shape of ammonia.*

2. Formulas and Equations

There's quite a lot of mathsy type stuff in the exams, and a whole load of formulas that you need to learn to make sure that you get it all right. Luckily, here's a nice page with them all neatly summarised for you. Enjoy.

Unit 1 Formulas

First up is perhaps the most useful equation of all...

$$\text{Number of moles} = \frac{\text{Mass of substance}}{\text{Molar mass}} \qquad \text{also written as... } n = \frac{m}{M_r}$$

Tip: M_r is relative molecular mass (or relative formula mass). You work it out by adding up all the A_rs (atomic masses) of all the atoms in the compound.

You'll need these ones when you're dealing with solutions...

$$\text{Number of moles} = \frac{\text{Concentration} \times \text{Volume (in cm}^3)}{1000}$$

$$\text{Number of moles} = \text{Concentration} \times \text{Volume (in dm}^3)$$

...and these when you've got gases at room temperature and pressure.

$$\text{Number of moles} = \frac{\text{Volume (in dm}^3)}{24} \qquad \text{Number of moles} = \frac{\text{Volume (in cm}^3)}{24\,000}$$

Tip: In the formula for working out the number of moles of a gas, the "24" comes from the fact that at room temperature and pressure one mole of any gas occupies 24 dm³. See page 33 for more on this.

Here's the ideal gas equation.

$$pV = nRT$$

p (Pa), V (m^3), n (moles), R ($8.31\ J\ K^{-1}mol^{-1}$), T (K)

And finally...

$$\text{\% atom economy} = \frac{\text{Mass of desired product}}{\text{Total mass of reactants}} \times 100$$

$$\text{\% yield} = \frac{\text{Actual yield}}{\text{Theoretical yield}} \times 100$$

Exam Tip
All these formulas are really important — you have to learn them because they won't be given to you in the exam. Make sure you can rearrange them all and give the units of each formula too.

Unit 2 Formulas

There are two formulas you need to calculate enthalpy changes of a reaction. Here's one:

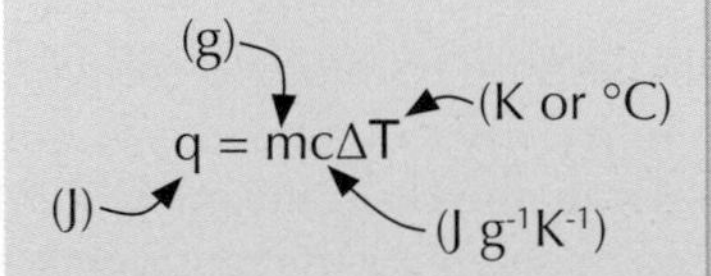

It doesn't matter whether the temperature is in K or °C — it's the change in temperature that goes into the formula, and that will be the same no matter what the units are.

And the slightly easier:

Enthalpy change of reaction = Total energy absorbed – Total energy released

3. Units

Units can trip you up if you're not sure which ones to use or how to convert between them. Here are the ones you're likely to have to deal with.

Volume

Volume can be measured in m^3, dm^3 and cm^3.

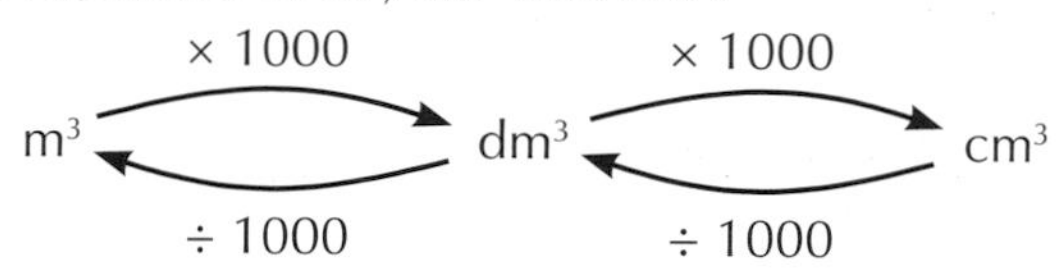

Exam Tip
You need to practice these conversions until you're sick of them. It'll save you loads of time in the exam if you're confident changing between units.

Examples

Write 6 dm^3 in m^3 and cm^3.

First, to convert 6 dm^3 into m^3 you need to divide by 1000.

$$6 \text{ dm}^3 \div 1000 = 0.006 \text{ m}^3 = 6 \times 10^{-3} \text{ m}^3$$

Then, to convert 6 dm^3 into cm^3 you need to multiply by 1000.

$$6 \text{ dm}^3 \times 1000 = 6000 \text{ cm}^3 = 6 \times 10^3 \text{ m}^3$$

Write 0.4 cm^3 in dm^3 and m^3.

First, to convert 0.4 cm^3 into dm^3 you need to divide by 1000.

$$0.4 \text{ cm}^3 \div 1000 = 0.0004 \text{ dm}^3 = 4 \times 10^{-4} \text{ dm}^3$$

Then, to convert 0.0004 dm^3 into m^3 you need to divide by 1000.

$$0.0004 \text{ dm}^3 \div 1000 = 0.0000004 \text{ m}^3 = 4 \times 10^{-7} \text{ m}^3$$

Tip: Standard form (that's showing numbers as, for example, 6×10^{-3}) is covered on page 212.

Temperature

Temperature can be measured in K and °C.

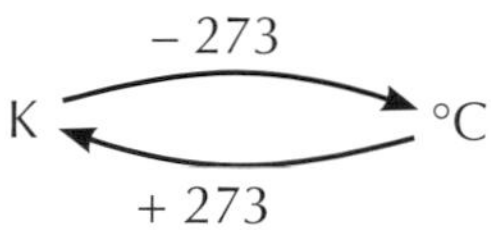

Examples

Write 21 °C in Kelvin.

To convert 21 °C into K you need to add 273: 21 °C + 273 = 294 K

Write 298 K in °C.

To convert 298 K into °C you need to subtract 273: 298 K – 273 = 25 °C

Pressure

Pressure can be measured in Pa and kPa.

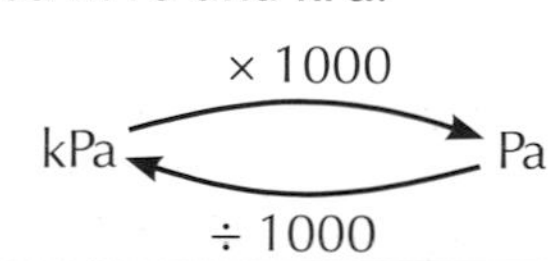

Example

Write 2100 Pa in kPa.

To convert 2100 Pa into kPa you need to divide by 1000.

$$2100 \text{ Pa} \div 1000 = 2.1 \text{ kPa}$$

***Figure 1:** A calculator. In an exam your brain can turn to mush and you can forget how to do the most simple maths. Don't be afraid to put every calculation into the calculator (even if it's just 2 × 10). If it stops you making mistakes then it's worth it.*

Mass

Mass can be measured in kg and g.

× 1000

kg → g

÷ 1000

Tip: If you're unsure about converting between units like these just think about a conversion you know and use that to help you. For example, if you know that 1 kg is 1000 g you know that to get from kg to g you must have to multiply by 1000 — simple.

Examples

Write 4.6 kg in g.

To convert 4.6 kg into g you need to multiply by 1000.

4.6 kg × 1000 = 4600 g

Write 320 g in kg.

To convert 320 g into kg you need to divide by 1000.

320 g ÷ 1000 = 0.32 kg

Energy

Energy can be measured in kJ and J.

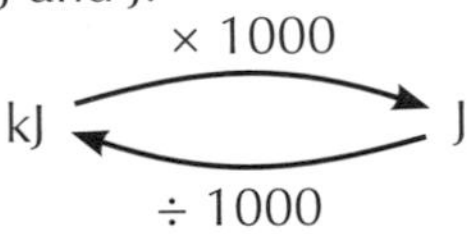

Tip: A kJ is bigger than a J, so you'd expect the number to get smaller when you convert from J to kJ — each unit is worth more so you'll have fewer of them.

Examples

Write 56 kJ in J.

To convert 56 kJ into J you need to multiply by 1000.

56 kJ × 1000 = 56 000 J = 5.6×10^4 J

Write 48 000 J in kJ.

To convert 48 000 J into kJ you need to divide by 1000.

48 000 J ÷ 1000 = 48 kJ

Concentration

Concentration can be measured in mol dm^{-3} (M) and mol cm^{-3}.

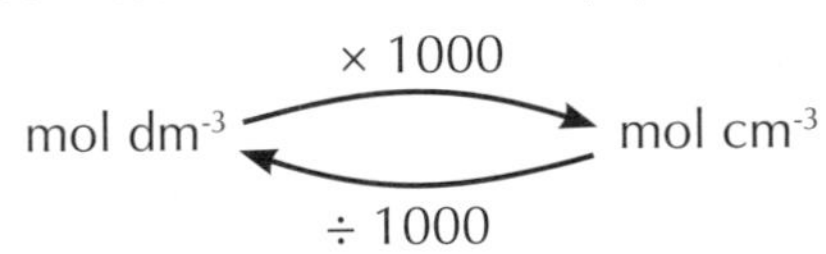

Exam Tip

Always, always, always give units with your answer. It's really important that the examiner knows what units you're working in — 10 g is very different from 10 kg.

Examples

Write 0.2 mol dm^{-3} in mol cm^{-3}.

To convert 0.2 mol dm^{-3} into mol cm^{-3} you need to multiply by 1000.

0.2 mol dm^{-3} × 1000 = 200 mol cm^{-3}

Write 34 mol cm^{-3} in mol dm^{-3}.

To convert 34 mol cm^{-3} into mol dm^{-3} you need to divide by 1000.

34 mol cm^{-3} ÷ 1000 = 0.034 mol dm^{-3}

Life gets a bit confusing if you have to do lots of calculations one after the other — sometimes it can be difficult to keep track of your units.
To avoid this, always write down the units you're using with each line of the calculation. Then when you get to the end you know what units to give with your answer.

4. The Periodic Table — Facts and Trends

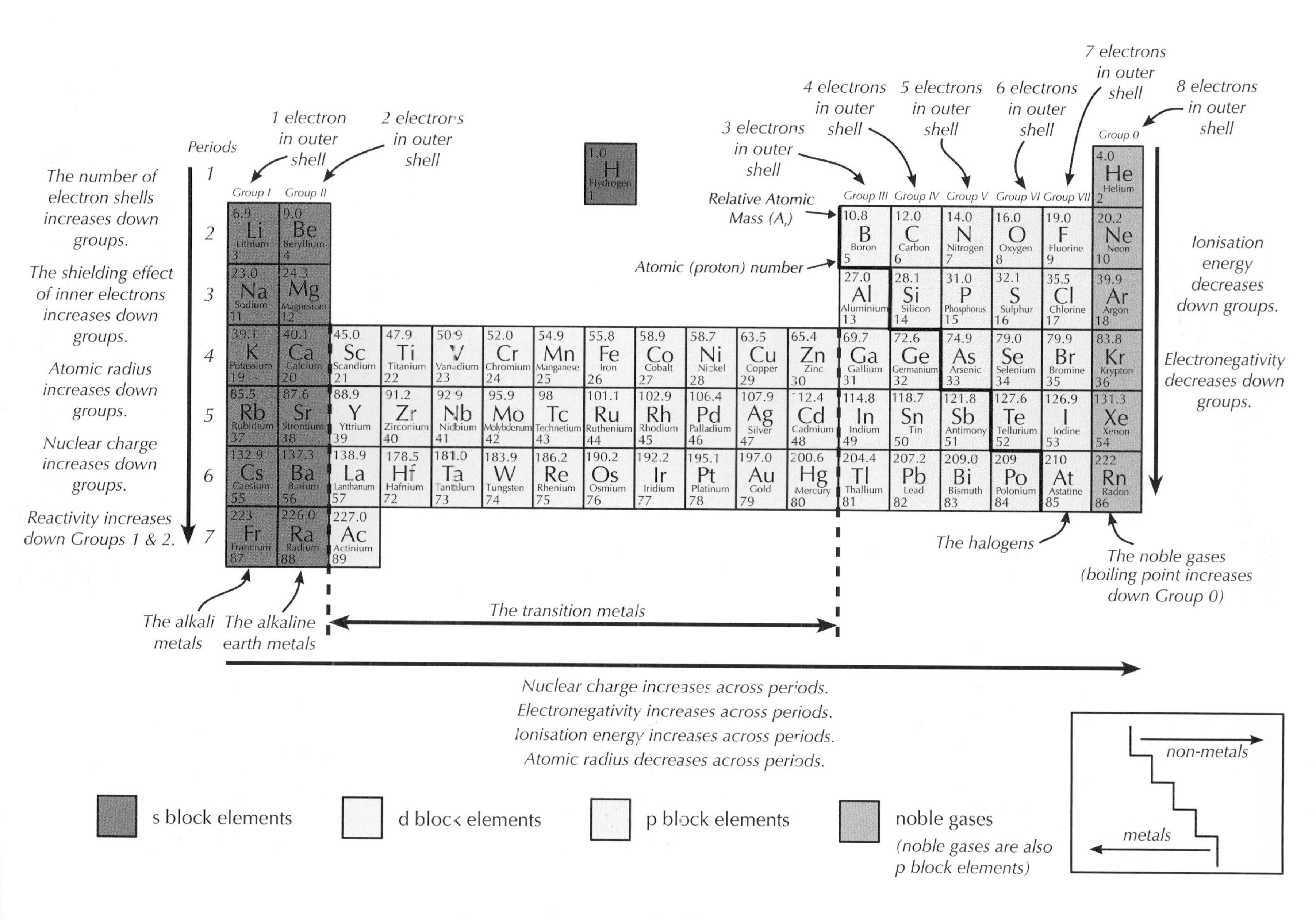

Answers

Unit 1

Section 1: Atomic Structure

1. The Atom

Page 7 — Application Questions

Q1 a) 13
b) 13
c) 27 – 13 = **14**

Q2 a) 19
b) 19 + 20 = **39**
c) $^{39}_{19}\mathrm{K}$
d) 19 – 1 = **18**

Q3 a) 20 – 2 = **18**
b) 40 – 20 = **20**

Q4 a) $^{93}_{41}\mathrm{A}$
(mass number = 41 + 52 = 93)
b) E.g. $^{94}_{41}\mathrm{A}$
The atomic number must be the same, the mass number must be different as an isotope will have a different number of neutrons.

Q5 a) A and C both have 10 electrons.
b) A and D both have 8 protons.
c) B and C both have 10 neutrons.
(17 – 7 = 10 and 20 – 10 = 10)
d) B and D both have 10 neutrons.
(17 – 7 = 10 and 18 – 8 = 10)
e) A and D are isotopes of each other because they have the same number of protons (8) but different numbers of neutrons.
(A has 16 – 8 = 8 and D has 18 – 8 = 10)

Page 7 — Fact Recall Questions

Q1 proton, neutron, electron
Q2 proton: 1, neutron: 1, electron: 1/2000
Q3 Protons and neutrons are found in the nucleus. Electrons are found in orbitals around the nucleus.
Q4 The total number of protons and neutrons in the nucleus of an atom.
Q5 The number of protons in the nucleus of an atom.
Q6 By subtracting the atomic number from the mass number.
Q7 Atoms with the same number of protons but different numbers of neutrons.
Q8 Chemical properties of an element are decided by the number and arrangement of electrons. Isotopes have the same configuration of electrons so have the same chemical properties.
Q9 Physical properties depend on the mass of an atom. Isotopes have different masses so can have different physical properties.

2. Atomic Models

Page 10 — Fact Recall Questions

Q1 Dalton described atoms as solid spheres.
J J Thomson suggested that atoms were not solid spheres — he thought they contained small negatively charged particles (electrons) in a positively charged "pudding".
Q2 the plum pudding model
Q3 Ernest Rutherford, Hans Geiger and Ernest Marsden.
Q4 If Thomson's model was correct the alpha particles fired at the sheet of gold should have been deflected very slightly by the positive "pudding" that made up most of the atom. Instead, most of the alpha particles passed straight through the gold atoms, and a very small number were deflected backwards. So the plum pudding model couldn't be right.
Q5 Rutherford's model has a tiny positively charged nucleus at the centre surrounded by a "cloud" of negative electrons. Most of the atom is empty space.
Q6 In Bohr's model the electrons only exist in fixed shells and not anywhere in between. Each shell has a fixed energy. When an electron moves between shells electromagnetic radiation is emitted or absorbed. Because the energy of the shells is fixed, the radiation will have a fixed frequency.
Q7 No

3. Relative Mass

Page 12 — Application Questions

Q1 a) 85.5
b) 200.6
c) 65.4

Q2 a) 14 + (3 × 1) = **17**
b) 12 + (16 × 2) = **44**
c) (12 × 2) + (1 × 4) + (16 × 6) + (14 × 2) = **152**

Q3 a) 40.1 + (35.5 × 2) = **111.1**
b) 24.3 + 32.1 + (16 × 4) = **120.4**
c) 23 + 16 + 1 = **40**

Q4 A_r = ((0.1 × 180) + (26.5 ×182) + (14.3 × 183) + (30.7 × 184) + (28.4 × 186)) ÷ 100 = 183.891 ≈ **183.9**

Q5 A_r = ((51.5 × 90) + (11.2 × 91) + (17.1 × 92) + (17.4 × 94) + (2.8 × 96)) ÷ 100 = 91.318 ≈ **91.3**

Page 12 — Fact Recall Questions

Q1 The average mass of an atom of an element on a scale where an atom of carbon-12 is exactly 12.
Q2 The average mass of a molecule on a scale where an atom of carbon-12 is exactly 12.
Q3 The average mass of a formula unit on a scale where an atom of carbon-12 is exactly 12.

4. Mass Spectrometry

Page 14 — Application Questions

Q1 a) 2
b) 63, 65
c) 69.0%, 30.9%

Q2 a) 3
b) 32, 33, 34
c) 91.5%, 0.5%, 8.0%

Pages 15-16 — Application Questions

Q1 $50.5 \times 79 = 3989.5$
$49.5 \times 81 = 4009.5$
$3989.5 + 4009.5 = 7999$
$7999 \div 100 =$ **79.99**

Q2 $20 \times 10 = 200$
$80 \times 11 = 880$
$200 + 880 = 1080$
$1080 \div 100 =$ **10.8**

Q3 $72 \times 85 = 6120$
$28 \times 87 = 2436$
$6120 + 2436 = 8556$
$8556 \div 100 =$ **85.56**

Q4 $8.0 \times 6 = 48$
$100 \times 7 = 700$
$700 + 48 = 748$
$748 \div (100 + 8) =$ **6.93**

Q5 $100 \times 69 = 6900$
$65.5 \times 71 = 4650.5$
$6900 + 4650.5 = 11550.5$
$11550.5 \div (100 + 65.5) =$ **69.79**

Page 17 — Application Questions

Q1 a) $CH_3CH_2COOH^+$
b) $C_3H_6O^+$
c) CH_3OH^+

Q2 74

Q3 58

Q4 32

Page 17 — Fact Recall Questions

Q1 vaporisation, ionisation, acceleration, deflection, detection

Q2 mass : charge

Q3 A molecular ion is formed when bombarding electrons in the mass spectrometer remove one electron from a molecule.

Q4 The relative molecular mass of the sample.

5. Electronic Structure

Page 20 — Application Questions

Q1 a) $1s^2\ 2s^1$
b) $1s^2\ 2s^2\ 2p^6\ 3s^2\ 3p^6\ 3d^2\ 4s^2$
c) $1s^2\ 2s^2\ 2p^6\ 3s^2\ 3p^6\ 3d^{10}\ 4s^2\ 4p^1$
d) $1s^2\ 2s^2\ 2p^3$

Q2 a)

1s	2s	2p	3s	3p	4s
↑↓	↑↓	↑↓ ↑↓ ↑↓	↑↓	↑↓ ↑↓ ↑↓	↑↓

b)

1s	2s	2p	3s	3p
↑↓	↑↓	↑↓ ↑↓ ↑↓	↑↓	↑↓ ↑↓ ↑↓

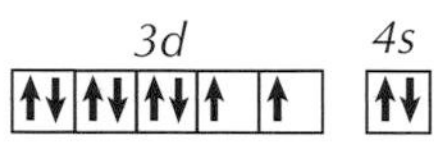

c)

1s	2s	2p	3s
↑↓	↑↓	↑↓ ↑↓ ↑↓	↑

d)

1s	2s	2p
↑↓	↑↓	↑↓ ↑ ↑

Q3 a)

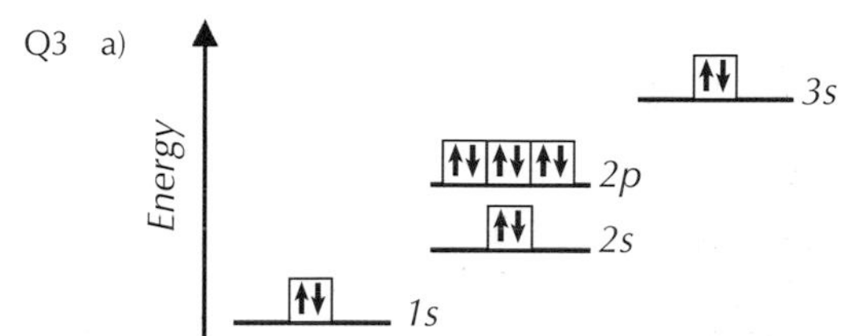

b)

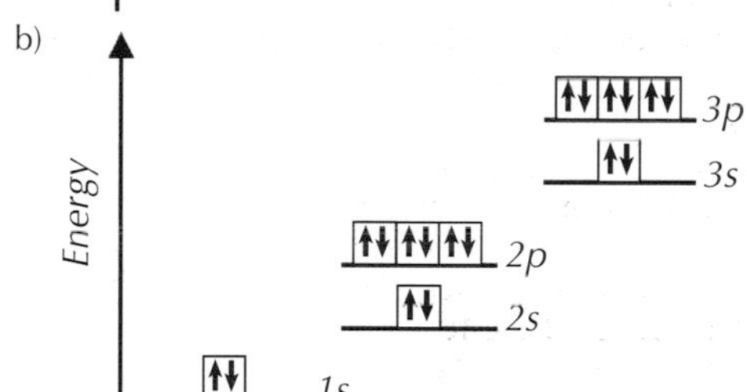

c)

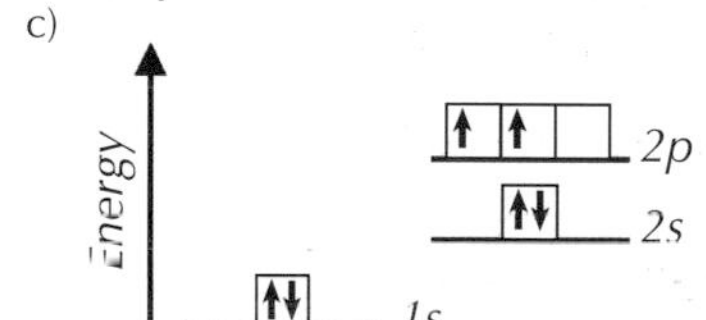

d)

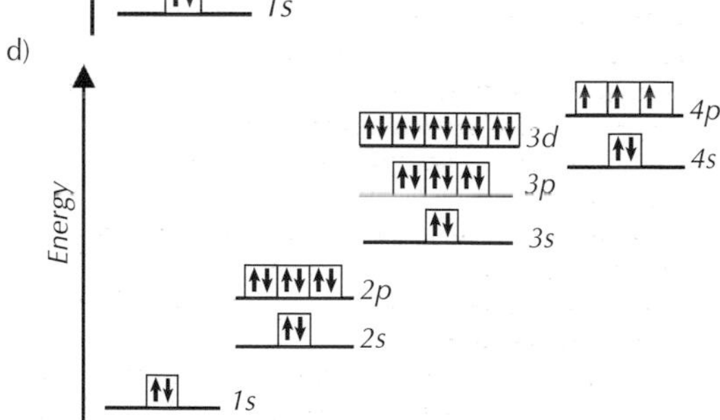

Q4 a) $1s^2\ 2s^2\ 2p^6$
b) $1s^2\ 2s^2\ 2p^6$
c) $1s^2\ 2s^2\ 2p^6$
d) $1s^2\ 2s^2\ 2p^6\ 3s^2\ 3p^6$

Q5 a) bromine
b) phosphorus
c) vanadium

Page 21 — Application Questions

Q1 $1s^2\ 2s^2\ 2p^6\ 3s^2\ 3p^6\ 3d^4$
Q2 $1s^2\ 2s^2\ 2p^6\ 3s^2\ 3p^6\ 3d^8$
Q3 $1s^2\ 2s^2\ 2p^6\ 3s^2\ 3p^6\ 3d^2$

Page 21 — Fact Recall Questions

Q1 3
Q2 6 (it can hold two electrons in each orbital)
Q3 18
Q4 The number of electrons that an atom or ion has and how they are arranged.
Q5 The shells with the lowest energy.
Q6 Electrons fill orbitals singly before they start sharing, so the electrons in the 2p sub-shell should be in separate orbitals.
Q7 $1s^2\ 2s^2\ 2p^6\ 3s^2\ 3p^6\ 3d^5\ 4s^1$
Q8 Copper donates one of its 4s electrons to the 3d sub-shell so that the 3d sub-shell is full, making it more stable.
Q9 They form negative ions with an inert gas configuration.

6. Ionisation Energies

Page 24 — Application Questions

Q1 $Cl(g) \rightarrow Cl^+(g) + e^-$
Q2

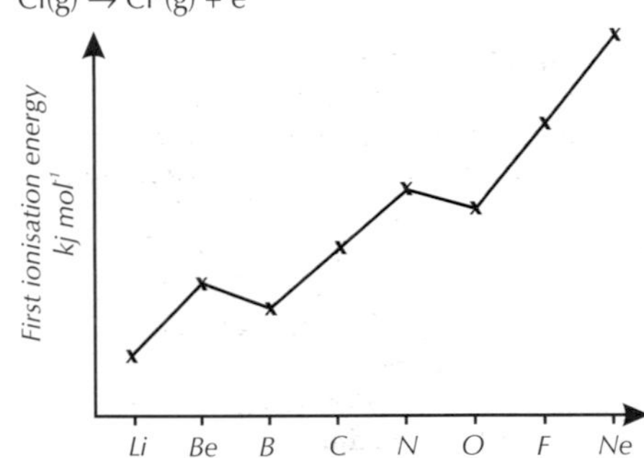

Q3 The electron being removed is in the same sub-shell and the shielding is identical in the two atoms. However, the electron being removed from oxygen is in an orbital where there are two electrons. The repulsion between these two electrons means that it's easier to remove the electron than it would be if it was unpaired (like in nitrogen), so the first ionisation energy of oxygen is lower than that of nitrogen.
Q4 Boron's outer electron is in a 2p orbital rather than a 2s (like beryllium's), which means it has a higher energy and is located further from the nucleus. The 2p orbital also has additional shielding provided by the 2s electrons. These two factors override the effect of the increased nuclear charge of the boron atom, and result in the first ionisation energy of beryllium being higher than the first ionisation energy of boron.

Page 24 — Fact Recall Questions

Q1 The first ionisation energy is the energy needed to remove 1 electron from each atom in 1 mole of gaseous atoms to form one mole of gaseous 1+ ions.
Q2 The more protons there are, the more positively charged the nucleus is, the stronger the attraction for the electrons and the higher the ionisation energy.
Q3 The distance between the outer electron and the nucleus, and the shielding effect of inner electrons.
Q4 It decreases.
Q5 The first ionisation energy increases.

Exam-style Questions — page 26

1 a) (i) silicon ***(1 mark)***
(ii) The p block ***(1 mark)***
b) (i) ionisation ***(1 mark)***
(ii) $Si(g) \rightarrow Si^+(g) + e^-$ or $Z(g) \rightarrow Z^+(g) + e^-$
(1 mark for correct equation, 1 mark for state symbols used correctly.)
(iii) [Ne] $3s^2\ 3p^1$ or $1s^2\ 2s^2\ 2p^6\ 3s^2\ 3p^1$ ***(1 mark)***
c) The magnetic field alters the ions' path by deflecting them ***(1 mark)***. Lighter ions are deflected more than heavier ions ***(1 mark)***. So by increasing the field strength different ions can reach the detector ***(1 mark)***.
d) (i) three ***(1 mark)***
(ii) $^{28}_{14}\mathrm{Si}$
(2 marks for correct nuclear symbol, otherwise 1 mark for correct mass number of 28.)
(iii) The isotopes would have the same chemical properties ***(1 mark)*** as they have the same electron arrangement and it's the electron arrangement that determines the chemical properties of an element ***(1 mark)***.

2 a) (i) The first ionisation energy increases across Period 3 ***(1 mark)***.
(ii) Magnesium's outer electron is in a 3s orbital and aluminium's outer electron is in a 3p orbital ***(1 mark)***. The 3p orbital has a higher energy than the 3s orbital so the electron is further from the nucleus ***(1 mark)***. The 3p orbital also has additional shielding provided by the $3s^2$ electrons ***(1 mark)***. These factors mean that less energy is needed to remove the outer electron and so the first ionisation energy is lower.
Both these factors mean that the attraction between the nucleus and the outer electron is less in aluminium than in magnesium.
b) (i) Any answer between 650 kJ mol^{-1} and 950 kJ mol^{-1} ***(1 mark)***.
(ii) The shielding effect and the distance between the nucleus and the outer electron is very similar in aluminium, silicon and phosphorus ***(1 mark)***. But the nuclear charge of silicon is higher than aluminium and lower than phosphorus ***(1 mark)***. So the attraction between the nucleus and the outer electron in silicon is greater than it is in aluminium and lower than it is in phosphorus ***(1 mark)***.
c) (i) Any answer between the value suggested for the first ionisation energy of silicon in (b) part (i) and 1000 kJ mol^{-1} (the value for phosphorus) ***(1 mark)***.
(ii) In phosphorus, the electron is being removed from a singly-occupied orbital, but in sulfur the electron is being removed from an orbital containing two electrons ***(1 mark)***. The repulsion between the two electrons means that electrons are easier to remove from shared orbitals and so the first ionisation energy of sulfur is lower than that of phosphorus ***(1 mark)***.

3 a) (i) [Ar] $3d^3\ 4s^2$ or $1s^2\ 2s^2\ 2p^6\ 3s^2\ 3p^6\ 3d^3\ 4s^2$ ***(1 mark)***.
(ii) V^{2+}: [Ar] $3d^3$ or $1s^2\ 2s^2\ 2p^6\ 3s^2\ 3p^6\ 3d^3$ ***(1 mark)***.
V^{3+}: [Ar] $3d^2$ or $1s^2\ 2s^2\ 2p^6\ 3s^2\ 3p^6\ 3d^2$ ***(1 mark)***.
b) (i) [Ar] $3d^{10}\ 4s^1$ or $1s^2\ 2s^2\ 2p^6\ 3s^2\ 3p^6\ 3d^{10}\ 4s^1$ ***(1 mark)***.
Copper donates one of its 4s electrons to the 3d sub-shell to make a more stable full 3d sub-shell ***(1 mark)***.
(ii) e.g. chromium ***(1 mark)***
c) iron ***(1 mark)***
d) manganese ***(1 mark)***

4 a) $((20 \times 90.48) + (21 \times 0.27) + (22 \times 9.25)) \div (90.48 + 0.27 + 9.25) = 20.1877 \approx$ **20.2** ***(1 mark for correct calculation, 1 mark for correct answer.)***
Element X is neon ***(1 mark)***.
^{20}X has 10 protons, 10 electrons and $20 - 10 =$ **10** neutrons ***(1 mark)***. ^{21}X has 10 protons, 10 electrons and $21 - 10 =$ **11** neutrons ***(1 mark)***. ^{22}X has 10 protons, 10 electrons and $22 - 10 =$ **12** neutrons ***(1 mark)***.

b) The mass number of an atom is the total number of protons and neutrons in the nucleus of the atom ***(1 mark)***.
The proton number of an atom is the number of protons in the nucleus of the atom ***(1 mark)***.
The mass number ***(1 mark)***. Physical properties of elements depend more on the mass of the atom ***(1 mark)***.

c) The first ionisation energy is the energy needed to remove 1 electron from each atom in 1 mole of gaseous atoms ***(1 mark)*** to form 1 mole of gaseous 1+ ions ***(1 mark)***.
The first ionisation energy of element A would be lower than the first ionisation energy of element Z ***(1 mark)***. Element A has more electrons than element Z so the distance between the outer electrons and the nucleus is greater ***(1 mark)***. The shielding effect of the inner electrons is greater in element A than in element Z, so the first ionisation energy of element A would be lower ***(1 mark)***.

Section 2: Amount of Substance

1. The Mole

Page 30 — Application Questions

Q1 4 moles of Na react with 1 mole of O_2 to give 2 moles of Na_2O. So 6 moles of Na must react with 1.5 moles of oxygen to give **3 moles** of Na_2O.

Q2 a) $M_r = 19 + 19 = 38$
$M =$ **38 g mol⁻¹**
b) $M_r = 40.1 + (35.5 \times 2) = 111.1$
$M =$ **111.1 g mol⁻¹**
c) $M_r = 24.3 + 32.1 + (4 \times 16) = 120.4$
$M =$ **120.4 g mol⁻¹**

Q3 $M = 23 + 14 + (16 \times 3) = 85$ g mol^{-1}
number of moles $= 212.5 \div 85 =$ **2.5 moles**

Q4 $M = 65.4 + (35.5 \times 2) = 136.4$ g mol^{-1}
number of moles $= 15.5 \div 136.4 =$ **0.114 moles**

Q5 $M = 23 + 35.5 = 58.5$ g mol^{-1}
Mass $= 58.5 \times 2 =$ **117 g**

Q6 $M = 52 + (35.5 \times 3) = 158.5$ g mol^{-1}
Mass $= 158.5 \times 0.6 =$ **95.1 g**

Q7 $M = 24.3 + 12 + (3 \times 16) = 84.3$ g mol^{-1}
Mass $= 84.3 \times 0.25 =$ **21.1 g**

Q8 $M = 66 \div 1.5 =$ **44 g mol⁻¹**

Page 32 — Application Questions

Q1 Number of moles $= (2 \times 50) \div 1000 =$ **0.1 moles**

Q2 Number of moles $= 0.08 \times 0.5 =$ **0.04 moles**

Q3 Number of moles $= (0.7 \times 30) \div 1000 =$ **0.021 moles**

Q4 Concentration $= 0.25 \div 0.5 =$ **0.5 mol dm⁻³**

Q5 Concentration $= 0.08 \div 0.75 =$ **0.11 mol dm⁻³**

Q6 Concentration $= 0.1 \div (36 \div 1000) =$ **2.8 mol dm⁻³**
Dividing a volume in cm³ by 1000 converts it to dm³. Then you can stick it into the equation concentration = number of moles ÷ volume (dm³).

Q7 Volume $= 0.46 \div 1.8 =$ **0.26 dm³**

Q8 Volume $= 0.01 \div 0.55 =$ **0.02 dm³**

Q9 Number of moles = concentration × volume (dm³)
$= 0.8 \times (75 \div 1000) = 0.06$
M of $Na_2O = (23 \times 2) + 16 = 62$ g mol^{-1}
Mass = moles × molar mass $= 0.06 \times 62 =$ **3.72 g**

Q10 Number of moles = concentration × volume (dm³)
$= 0.5 \times (30 \div 1000) = 0.015$
M of $CoBr_2 = 58.9 + (79.9 \times 2) = 218.7$ g mol^{-1}
Mass = number of moles × molar mass
$= 0.015 \times 218.7 =$ **3.3 g**

Q11 Number of moles = concentration × volume (dm³)
$= 1.2 \times (100 \div 1000) = 0.12$
molar mass = mass ÷ number of moles
$= 4.08 \div 0.12 =$ **34 g mol⁻¹**

Page 32 — Fact Recall Questions

Q1 a) 6×10^{23}
b) Avogadro's constant

Q2 The mass of one mole of the chemical.

Q3 Number of moles = mass of substance ÷ molar mass

Q4 1000

Q5 E.g. mol dm⁻³ and M.

Q6 Number of moles $= \dfrac{\text{concentration} \times \text{volume (in cm}^3)}{1000}$
Number of moles = concentration × volume (dm³)

2. Gases and the Mole

Page 33 — Application Questions

Q1 Number of moles = 2.4 ÷ 24 = **0.1 moles**
Q2 Number of moles = 0.65 ÷ 24 = **0.027 moles**
Q3 Number of moles = 3120 ÷ 24 000 = **0.13 moles**
Q4 Number of moles = 250 ÷ 24 000 = **0.010 moles**
Q5 Volume = 0.21 × 24 = **5.04 dm^3**
Q6 Volume = 1.1 × 24 = **26.4 dm^3**
Q7 Volume = 0.028 × 24000 = **672 cm^3**
Q8 Volume = 0.072 × 24000 = **1728 cm^3**

Page 35 — Application Questions

Q1 n = pV ÷ RT
= (70 000 × 0.04) ÷ (8.31 × 350) = **0.96 moles**

Q2 V = nRT ÷ p
= (0.65 × 8.31 × 280) ÷ 100 000 = **0.015 m^3**

Q3 0.55 dm^3 = 0.55 × 10^{-3} m^3 35 °C = 308 K
n = pV ÷ RT
= (90 000 × (0.55 × 10^{-3})) ÷ (8.31 × 308)
= **0.019 moles**

Q4 1200 cm^3 = 1200 × 10^{-6} m^3 = 1.2 × 10^{-3} m^3
T = pV ÷ nR
= (110 000 × (1.2 × 10^{-3})) ÷ (0.05 × 8.31) = 317.7 K
317.7 K = (317.7 – 273) °C = **44.7 °C**

Q5 75 kPa = 75 000 Pa 22 °C = 295 K
V = nRT ÷ p
= (0.75 × 8.31 × 295) ÷ 75 000 = **0.025 m^3**

Q6 80 kPa = 80 000 Pa 1.5 dm^3 = 1.5 × 10^{-3} m^3
n = pV ÷ RT
= (80 000 × (1.5 × 10^{-3})) ÷ (8.31 × 300)
= 0.048 moles
Molar mass = mass ÷ moles = 2.6 ÷ 0.048 = 54 g mol^{-1}
So the relative molecular mass is **54**.

Q7 44 °C = 317 K 100 kPa = 100 000 Pa
n = pV ÷ RT
= (100 000 × 0.003) ÷ (8.31 × 317)
= 0.114 moles
Molar mass of neon = 20.2
mass = number of moles × molar mass
= 0.114 × 20.2 = **2.30 g**

Page 35 — Fact Recall Questions

Q1 number of moles = volume in dm^3 ÷ 24
Q2 number of moles = volume in cm^3 ÷ 24 000
Q3 pV = nRT
p = pressure measured in Pascals (Pa)
V = volume measured in m^3
n = number of moles
R = 8.31 J $K^{-1}mol^{-1}$. R is the gas constant.
T = temperature measured in Kelvin (K)

3. Balancing Equations

Page 37 — Application Questions

Q1 a) $Mg + \mathbf{2}HCl \rightarrow MgCl_2 + H_2$
b) $S_8 + \mathbf{24}F_2 \rightarrow \mathbf{8}SF_6$
c) $Ca(OH)_2 + H_2SO_4 \rightarrow CaSO_4 + \mathbf{2}H_2O$
d) $Na_2CO_3 + \mathbf{2}HCl \rightarrow \mathbf{2}NaCl + CO_2 + H_2O$
e) $C_4H_{10} + \mathbf{6\tfrac{1}{2}}O_2 \rightarrow \mathbf{4}CO_2 + \mathbf{5}H_2O$
If you wanted to double the numbers to get rid of the half in this equation that would be fine too (making it $2C_4H_{10} + 13O_2 \rightarrow 8CO_2 + 10H_2O$).

Q2 a) $Ag \rightarrow Ag^{2+}$ **+ 2e⁻**
b) Br_2 **+ 2e⁻** $\rightarrow 2Br^-$
c) CrO_4^{2-} **+ 2H₂O + 3e⁻** $\rightarrow CrO_2^- +$ **4**OH^-
d) MnO_4^- **+ 8**H^+ **+ 5e⁻** $\rightarrow Mn^{2+} +$ **4**H_2O

4. Equations and Calculations

Page 39 — Application Questions

Q1 a) $Zn + 2HCl \rightarrow ZnCl_2 + H_2$
b) M_r of Zn = 65.4
number of moles = mass ÷ M_r = 3.3 ÷ 65.4 = **0.05 moles**
c) The molar ratio of Zn : $ZnCl_2$ is 1 : 1. So 0.05 moles of Zn will give **0.05 moles** of $ZnCl_2$.
d) M_r of $ZnCl_2$ = 65.4 + (2 × 35.5) = 136.4
mass = number of moles × M_r = 0.05 × 136.4 = **6.82 g**

Q2 a) $C_2H_4 + 3O_2 \rightarrow 2CO_2 + 2H_2O$
b) M_r of H_2O = (2 × 1) + 16 = 18
number of moles = mass ÷ M_r = 15 ÷ 18 = **0.83 moles**
c) The molar ratio of H_2O : C_2H_4 is 2 : 1.
So 0.83 moles of H_2O must be made from (0.83 ÷ 2) = **0.42 moles** of C_2H_4.
d) M_r of C_2H_4 = (2 × 12) + (4 × 1) = 28
mass = number of moles × M_r = 0.42 × 28 = **11.7 g**

Q3 $Na_2CO_3 + BaCl_2 \rightarrow 2NaCl + BaCO_3$
M_r of $BaCl_2$ = 137.3 + (2 × 35.5) = 208.3
number of moles = mass ÷ M_r = 4.68 ÷ 208.3 = 0.022 moles
The molar ratio of $BaCl_2$: $BaCO_3$ is 1 : 1.
So 0.022 moles of $BaCO_3$ must be made from 0.022 moles of $BaCl_2$.
M_r of $BaCO_3$ = 137.3 + 12 + (16 × 3) = 197.3
mass = number of moles × M_r = 0.022 × 197.3 = **4.34 g**

Page 40 — Application Questions

Q1 a) aq
b) s
c) l
d) aq
e) g
f) s

Q2 a) $2H_2O_{(l)} \rightarrow 2H_{2(g)} + O_{2(g)}$
b) M_r of H_2O = (2 × 1) + 16 = 18
number of moles = mass ÷ M_r = 9 ÷ 18 = **0.5 moles**
c) The molar ratio of H_2O to O_2 is 2 : 1.
So 0.5 moles of H_2O will produce (0.5 ÷ 2) = **0.25 moles** of O_2.
d) At room temperature and pressure 1 mole of gas takes up 24 dm^3.
Volume in dm^3 = number of moles × 24
Volume of O_2 = 0.25 × 24 = **6 dm^3**

Q3 a) $ZnS_{(s)} + 1\tfrac{1}{2}O_{2(g)} \rightarrow ZnO_{(s)} + SO_{2(g)}$
b) M_r of ZnS = 65.4 + 32.1 = 97.5
number of moles = mass ÷ M_r = 7 ÷ 97.5 = **0.07 moles**
c) The molar ratio of ZnS to SO_2 is 1 : 1.
So 0.07 moles of ZnS will give **0.07 moles** of SO_2.
d) At room temperature and pressure 1 mole of gas takes up 24 dm^3.
Volume in dm^3 = number of moles × 24
Volume of SO_2 = 0.07 × 24 = **1.7 dm^3**

Q4 a) $C_6H_{14\,(g)} \rightarrow C_4H_{10\,(g)} + C_2H_{4\,(g)}$

b) M_r of $C_4H_{10} = (4 \times 12) + (10 \times 1) = 58$
number of moles = mass ÷ M_r = 3 ÷ 58 = **0.05 moles**

c) The molar ratio of C_4H_{10} to C_6H_{14} is 1 : 1.
So 0.05 moles of C_4H_{10} must be made from **0.05 moles** of C_6H_{14}

d) Using the ideal gas equation:
V = nRT ÷ p
= (0.05 × 8.31 × 308) ÷ 100 000
= 0.0013 m^3

Q5 $2Mg_{(s)} + 2H_2O_{(g)} \rightarrow 2MgO_{(s)} + 2H_{2\,(g)}$
M_r of MgO = 24.3 + 16.0 = 40.3
number of moles = mass ÷ M_r = 10 ÷ 40.3 = 0.25 moles
The molar ratio of MgO : H_2O is 1 : 1.
So 0.25 moles of MgO is made from 0.25 moles of H_2O.
Using the ideal gas equation:
V = nRT ÷ p
= (0.25 × 8.31 × (100 + 273)) ÷ 101 325
= **0.0076 m³**

5. Titrations

Page 43 — Application Questions

Q1 a) $HCl_{(aq)} + KOH_{(aq)} \rightarrow KCl_{(aq)} + H_2O_{(l)}$

b) moles HCl = (conc. × volume (cm³)) ÷ 1000
= (0.75 × 28) ÷ 1000 = **0.021 moles**

c) 1 mole of HCl reacts with 1 mole of KOH.
So 0.021 moles of HCl must react with **0.021 moles** of KOH.

d) concentration = (moles KOH × 1000) ÷ vol. (cm³)
= (0.021 × 1000) ÷ 40 = **0.525 M**

Q2 a) $NaOH_{(aq)} + HNO_{3\,(aq)} \rightarrow NaNO_{3\,(aq)} + H_2O_{(l)}$

b) moles NaOH = (conc. × volume (cm³)) ÷ 1000
= (1.5 × 15.3) ÷ 1000 = **0.023 moles**

c) 1 mole of NaOH reacts with 1 mole of HNO_3.
So 0.023 moles of NaOH must react with **0.023 moles** of HNO_3.

d) concentration = (moles HNO_3 × 1000) ÷ vol. (cm³)
= (0.023 × 1000) ÷ 35 = **0.66 M**

Q3 $LiOH_{(aq)} + HCl_{(aq)} \rightarrow LiCl_{(aq)} + H_2O_{(l)}$
moles HCl = (conc. × volume (cm³)) ÷ 1000
= (0.5 × 12) ÷ 1000 = 0.006 moles
1 mole of HCl reacts with 1 mole of LiOH, so 0.006 moles of HCl must react with 0.006 moles of LiOH.
concentration = (moles LiOH × 1000) ÷ vol. (cm³)
= (0.006 × 1000) ÷ 24 = **0.25 M**

Page 44 — Application Questions

Q1 a) $HNO_3 + LiOH \rightarrow LiNO_3 + H_2O$

b) moles HNO_3 = (conc. × volume (cm³)) ÷ 1000
= (0.2 × 18.8) ÷ 1000 = **0.0038 moles**

c) 1 mole of HNO_3 reacts with 1 mole of LiOH.
So 0.0038 moles of HNO_3 must react with **0.0038 moles** of LiOH.

d) volume = (moles LiOH × 1000) ÷ concentration
= (0.0038 × 1000) ÷ 0.45 = **8.4 cm³**

Q2 a) $KOH + CH_3COOH \rightarrow CH_3COOK + H_2O$

b) moles KOH = (conc. × volume (cm³)) ÷ 1000
= (0.42 × 37.3) ÷ 1000 = **0.016 moles**

c) 1 mole of KOH reacts with 1 mole of CH_3COOH.
So 0.016 moles of KOH must react with **0.016 moles** of CH_3COOH.

d) volume = (moles CH_3COOH × 1000) ÷ conc.
= (0.016 × 1000) ÷ 1.1 = **14.5 cm³**

Q3 $NaOH + HCl \rightarrow NaCl + H_2O$
moles of NaOH = (conc. × volume (cm³)) ÷ 1000
= (14 × 1) ÷ 1000 = 0.014 moles
1 mole of NaCl reacts with 1 mole of HCl. So, 0.014 moles of NaOH must react with 0.014 moles of HCl.
volume = (moles HCl × 1000) ÷ conc. = (0.014 × 1000) ÷ 0.5
= **28 cm³**

Page 44 — Fact Recall Questions

Q1 pipette
Q2 burette
Q3 To make sure that the acid and the alkali are properly mixed.
Q4 The exact point at which the indicator changes colour (at this point the amount of acid added is just enough to neutralise the alkali).

6. Formulas

Page 46 — Application Questions

Q1 empirical mass = (4 × 12) + (9 × 1) = 57 g
molecular mass = 171 g, so there are (171 ÷ 57) = 3 empirical units in the molecule.
molecular formula = $\mathbf{C_{12}H_{27}}$

Q2 empirical mass = (3 × 12) + (5 × 1) + (2 × 16) = 73 g
M_r = 146, so there are (146 ÷ 73) = 2 empirical units in the molecule.
molecular formula = $\mathbf{C_6H_{10}O_4}$

Q3 empirical mass = (2 × 12) + (6 × 1) + (1 × 16) = 46 g
molecular mass = 46 g, so there is (46 ÷ 46) = 1 empirical unit in the molecule.
molecular formula = $\mathbf{C_2H_6O}$

Q4 empirical mass = (4 × 12) + (6 × 1) + (2 × 35.5) + (1 × 16) = 141 g
M_r = 423, so there are (423 ÷ 141) = 3 empirical units in the molecule.
molecular formula = $\mathbf{C_{12}H_{18}Cl_6O_3}$

Page 47 — Application Questions

Q1 Mass of each element:
H = 5.9 g O = 94.1 g
Moles of each element:
H = (5.9 ÷ 1) = 5.9 moles
O = (94.1 ÷ 16) = 5.9 moles
Divide each by 5.9:
H = (5.9 ÷ 5.9) = 1 O = (5.9 ÷ 5.9) = 1
The ratio of H : O is 1 : 1.
So the empirical formula is **HO**.

Q2 Mass of each element:
Al = 20.2 g Cl = 79.8 g
Moles of each element:
Al = (20.2 ÷ 27) = 0.75 moles
Cl = (79.8 ÷ 35.5) = 2.25 moles
Divide each by 0.75:
Al = (0.75 ÷ 0.75) = 1 Cl = (2.25 ÷ 0.75) = 3
The ratio of Al : Cl is 1 : 3.
So the empirical formula is $\mathbf{AlCl_3}$.

Q3 Mass of each element:
C = 8.5 g H = 1.4 g I = 90.1 g
Moles of each element:
C = (8.5 ÷ 12) = 0.7 moles
H= (1.4 ÷ 1) = 1.4 moles
I = (90.1 ÷ 126.9) = 0.7 moles
Divide each by 0.7:
C = (0.7 ÷ 0.7) = 1
H = (1.4 ÷ 0.7) = 2
I = (0.7 ÷ 0.7) = 1
The ratio of C : H : I is 1 : 2 : 1.
So the empirical formula is $\mathbf{CH_2I}$.

Q4 Mass of each element:
Cu = 50.1 g P = 16.3 g O = 33.6 g
Moles of each element:
Cu = (50.1 ÷ 63.5) = 0.79 moles
P = (16.3 ÷ 31) = 0.53 moles
O = (33.6 ÷ 16) = 2.1 moles
Divide each by 0.53:
Cu = (0.79 ÷ 0.53) = 1.5
P = (0.53 ÷ 0.53) = 1
O = (2.1 ÷ 0.53) = 4
The ratio of Cu : P : O is 1.5 : 1 : 4.
Multiply by 2 — 2 × (1.5 : 1 : 4) = 3 : 2 : 8.
So the empirical formula is $\mathbf{Cu_3P_2O_8}$.

Q5 % V = 32.3 % Cl = 100 – 32.3 = 67.7
Mass of each element:
V = 32.3 g Cl = 67.7 g
Moles of each element:
V = (32.3 ÷ 50.9) = 0.63 moles
Cl = (67.7 ÷ 35.5) = 1.91 moles
Divide each by 0.63:
V = (0.63 ÷ 0.63) = 1 Cl = (1.91 ÷ 0.63) = 3
The ratio of V : Cl is 1 : 3.
So the empirical formula is $\mathbf{VCl_3}$.

Q6 % O = 31.58 % Cr = 100 – 31.58 = 68.42
Mass of each element:
O = 31.58 g Cr = 68.42 g
Moles of each element:
O = (31.58 ÷ 16) = 1.97 moles
Cr = (68.42 ÷ 52) = 1.32 moles
Divide each by 1.32:
O = (1.97 ÷ 1.32) = 1.5 Cr = (1.32 ÷ 1.32) = 1
The ratio of Cr : O is 1 : 1.5.
Multiply by 2... 2 × (1 : 1.5) = 2 : 3.
So the empirical formula is $\mathbf{Cr_2O_3}$.

Page 47 — Fact Recall Questions

Q1 The empirical formula gives the smallest whole number ratio of atoms in a compound.

Q2 The molecular formula gives the actual numbers of atoms in a molecule.

7. Chemical Yield

Page 49 — Application Questions

Q1 % yield = (actual yield ÷ theoretical yield) × 100
= (1.76 ÷ 3.24) × 100 = **54.3%**

Q2 % yield = (actual yield ÷ theoretical yield) × 100
= (3.7 ÷ 6.1) × 100 = **61%**

Q3 a) Molar mass of Fe = 55.8 g mol^{-1}
Number of moles Fe = mass ÷ molar mass
= 3 ÷ 55.8 = **0.054 moles**

b) From the equation: 4 moles of Fe produces 2 moles of Fe_2O_3, so 0.054 moles of Fe will produce (0.054 ÷ 2) = 0.027 moles of Fe_2O_3.
molar mass of Fe_2O_3 = 159.6 g mol^{-1}
theoretical yield = moles Fe_2O_3 × molar mass
= 0.027 × 159.6 = **4.3 g**

c) % yield = (actual yield ÷ theoretical yield) × 100
= (3.6 ÷ 4.3) × 100 = **84%**

Q4 Molar mass of Al_2O_3 = 102 g mol^{-1}
Number of moles Al_2O_3 = mass ÷ molar mass
= 1000 ÷ 102 = 9.8 moles
From the equation: 2 moles of Al_2O_3 produce 4 moles of Al, so 9.8 moles of Al_2O_3 will produce (9.8 × 2) = 19.6 moles of Al.
molar mass of Al = 27 g mol^{-1}
theoretical yield = moles Al × molar mass
= 19.6 × 27 = **529 g**

Q5 Molar mass of NaOH = 40 g mol^{-1}
Number of moles NaOH = mass ÷ molar mass
= 4.70 ÷ 40 = 0.118 moles
From the equation: 2 moles of NaOH produce 1 mole of Na_2SO_4, so 0.118 moles of NaOH will produce (0.118 ÷ 2) = 0.059 moles of Na_2SO_4.
molar mass of Na_2SO_4 = 142.1 g mol^{-1}
theoretical yield = moles Na_2SO_4 × molar mass
= 0.059 × 142.1 = 8.4 g
% yield = (actual yield ÷ theoretical yield) × 100
= (6.04 ÷ 8.4) × 100 = **72%**

Page 49 — Fact Recall Questions

Q1 The theoretical yield is the mass of product that should be formed in a chemical reaction.

Q2 $$\text{percentage yield} = \frac{\text{actual yield}}{\text{theoretical yield}} \times 100$$

8. Atom Economy

Page 51 — Application Questions

Q1 a) mass of reactants = (12 + (4 × 1)) + (2 × 35.5) = **87**

b) mass of CH_3Cl = 12 + (3 × 1) + 35.5 = **50.5**

c) $\% \text{ atom economy} = \frac{\text{mass of desired product}}{\text{total mass of reactants}} \times 100$

= (50.5 ÷ 87) × 100 = **58%**

d) E.g. sell the HCl so it can be used in other chemical reactions / use the HCl as a reactant in another reaction.

Q2 mass of reactants = (2 × 27) + (3 × (2 × 35.5)) = 267

mass of $2AlCl_3$ = 2 × (27 + (3 × 35.5)) = 267

$\% \text{ atom economy} = \frac{\text{mass of desired product}}{\text{total mass of reactants}} \times 100$

= (267 ÷ 267) × 100 = **100%**

Award yourself an extra chocolate biscuit if you spotted that this reaction has 100% atom economy before you did the calculations — any reaction where there's only one product will have 100% atom economy.

Q3 mass of reactants = (2 × ((2 × 55.8) + (3 × 16))) + (3 × 12) = 355.2

mass of 4Fe = 4 × 55.8 = 223.2

$\% \text{ atom economy} = \frac{\text{mass of desired product}}{\text{total mass of reactants}} \times 100$

= (223.2 ÷ 355.2) × 100 = **63%**

Q4 a) Reaction 1:

mass of reactants = (2 × 14) + (3 × (2 × 1)) = 34

mass of $2NH_3$ = 2 × (14 + (3 × 1)) = 34

$\% \text{ atom economy} = \frac{\text{mass of desired product}}{\text{total mass of reactants}} \times 100$

= (34 ÷ 34) × 100 = **100%**

Reaction 2:

mass of reactants = (2 × (14 + (4 × 1) + 35.5)) + (40.1 + ((16 + 1) × 2)) = 107 + 74.1 = 181.1

mass of $2NH_3$ = 2 × (14 + (3 × 1)) = 34

$\% \text{ atom economy} = \frac{\text{mass of desired product}}{\text{total mass of reactants}} \times 100$

= (34 ÷ 181.1) × 100 = **18.8%**

b) E.g. reaction 1 has a much higher atom economy / produces no waste.

Page 51 — Fact Recall Questions

Q1 Atom economy is a measure of the proportion of reactant atoms that become part of the desired product (rather than by-products) in the balanced chemical equation.

Q2 $\% \text{ atom economy} = \frac{\text{mass of desired product}}{\text{total mass of reactants}} \times 100$

Exam-style Questions — page 53

1 a) (i) M_r = 23 + 35.5 = 58.5

Number of moles = 20.0 ÷ 58.5 = **0.342 moles**

(2 marks for correct answer, otherwise 1 mark for correct M_r of NaCl)

(ii) Number of moles = 0.342 ÷ 2 = **0.171**

(1 mark)

Even if you got part (i) wrong you can still get the marks for part (ii) as long as you've used the correct method. This will happen for all of the calculation questions.

b) 98 kPa = 98 000 Pa

pV = nRT

V = nRT ÷ p

= (0.65 × 8.31 × 330) ÷ 98 000 = **0.018 m³**

(3 marks for correct answer, otherwise 1 mark for converting 98 kPa into Pa and 1 mark for correctly rearranging the equation to find V.)

c) (i) mass of reactants = (2 × (23 + 35.5)) + (2 × ((2 × 1) + 16)) = 153

mass of Cl_2 = 2 × 35.5 = 71

% atom economy = (71 ÷ 153) × 100 = **46.4%**

(2 marks for correct answer, otherwise 1 mark for correct formula.)

(ii) E.g. the other products (H_2 and NaOH) are useful starting chemicals for other reactions/can be sold to make money ***(1 mark)***.

2 a) $C_8H_{18\,(l)} + 12\frac{1}{2}O_{2\,(g)} \rightarrow 8CO_{2\,(g)} + 9H_2O_{(l)}$

(1 mark for balanced equation, 1 mark for state symbols. Allow any correct multiple of the balanced equation. Allow (g) as the state symbol for water.)

b) (i) pV = nRT

n = pV ÷ RT

= (101 000 × 0.02) ÷ (8.31 × 308) = **0.79 moles**

(2 marks for correct answer, otherwise 1 mark for correctly rearranging the equation to find n.)

(ii) Number of moles = 0.79 ÷ 8 = 0.099 ***(1 mark)***

From the balanced equation you wrote in part a) you know that the molar ratio of CO_2 : C_8H_{18} is 8 : 1. So, to find how many moles of octane were burnt, you can divide the number of moles of CO_2 by 8.

c) C = 85.7 H = 100 – 85.7 = 14.3 ***(1 mark)***

Moles of each element:

C = (85.7 ÷ 12) = 7.14 moles

H = (14.3 ÷ 1) = 14.3 moles

Divide each by 7.14:

C = (7.14 ÷ 7.14) = 1 H = (14.3 ÷ 7.14) = 2

The ratio of C : H is 1 : 2 ***(1 mark)***.

So the empirical formula is $\mathbf{CH_2}$ ***(1 mark)***.

3 a) (i) O = 43.6 P = 100 – 43.6 = 56.4 ***(1 mark)***

Moles of each element:

P = (56.4 ÷ 31) = 1.82 moles

O = (43.6 ÷ 16) = 2.73 moles

Divide each by 1.82:

P = (1.82 ÷ 1.82) = 1 O = (2.73 ÷ 1.82) = 1.5

The ratio of P : O is 1 : 1.5 ***(1 mark)***.

Multiply by 2: 2 × (1 : 1.5) = 2 : 3.

So the empirical formula is $\mathbf{P_2O_3}$ ***(1 mark)***.

All the numbers in an empirical formula must be whole numbers — that's why you need to multiply the ratio by two here.

(ii) empirical mass = (2 × 31) + (3 × 16) = 110 g
molecular mass = 220 g
(220 ÷ 110) = 2 empirical units in the molecular formula ***(1 mark)***
Molecular formula = $\mathbf{P_4O_6}$ ***(1 mark)***

b) (i) M_r of NH_3 = 14 + (3 × 1) = 17 ***(1 mark)***
number of moles = mass ÷ M_r
= 2.5 ÷ 17 = **0.15** ***(1 mark)***

(ii) Number of moles = 0.15 ÷ 2 = **0.075** ***(1 mark)***

The equation tells you that the molar ratio of $NH_3 : (NH_4)_2HPO_4$ is 2 : 1. So to find the number of moles of $(NH_4)_2HPO_4$ you divide the number of moles of NH_3 by 2.

(iii) M_r of $(NH_4)_2HPO_4$ = (2 × (14 + (4 × 1))) + 1 + 31 + (4 × 16)
= 132 ***(1 mark)***
mass = number of moles × M_r
= 0.075 × 132 = **9.9 g** ***(1 mark)***

4 a) The atom economy is 100% ***(1 mark)*** because the reaction only has one product ***(1 mark)***.

If the reaction only has one product, all of the reactants end up in the desired product.

b) (i) M_r of Ca = 40.1 ***(1 mark)***
number of moles = mass ÷ M_r
= 3.4 ÷ 40.1 = **0.085** ***(1 mark)***

(ii) Number of moles = **0.085** ***(1 mark)***

You can see from the equation that the molar ratio of Ca : CaO is 2 : 2. So the number of moles of CaO must be the same as the number of moles of Ca.

(iii) M_r of CaO = 40.1 + 16 = 56.1 ***(1 mark)***
mass = number of moles × M_r
= 0.085 × 56.1 = **4.8 g** ***(1 mark)***

(iv) % yield = (actual yield ÷ theoretical yield) × 100
= (3.7 ÷ 4.8) × 100 = **77%** ***(1 mark)***

5 a) moles KOH = concentration × volume (dm^3)
= 0.5 × (150 ÷ 1000) = 0.075 ***(1 mark)***
M_r of KOH = 39.1 + 16 + 1 = 56.1 ***(1 mark)***
Mass = number of moles × M_r
= 0.075 × 56.1 = **4.2 g** ***(1 mark)***

b) Average titre = (26.00 + 26.05 + 26.00 + 26.00) ÷ 4
= 26.01 cm^3 ***(1 mark)***
moles KOH = concentration × volume (dm^3)
= 0.5 × (26.01 ÷ 1000) = 0.013 ***(1 mark)***
moles HCl = 0.013 ***(1 mark)***
concentration of HCl = moles ÷ volume (dm^3)
= 0.013 ÷ (20 ÷ 1000)
= **0.65 mol dm^{-3}** ***(1 mark)***

c) moles HX = concentration × volume (dm^3)
= 0.12 × 0.20 ***(1 mark)***
= 0.024 ***(1 mark)***
M_r of HX = mass ÷ number of moles
= 3.07 ÷ 0.024 ***(1 mark)***
= 127.9 ***(1 mark)***
A_r of X = M_r of HX – A_r of H
= 127.9 – 1 = 126.9 ***(1 mark)***
So the mystery halogen, X, is iodine (I) ***(1 mark)***.

Section 3: Bonding and Periodicity

1. Ionic Bonding

Page 59 — Application Questions

Q1 a) 1–
b) 1+
c) 2+

Q2 a) $S + 2e^- \rightarrow S^{2-}$
b)

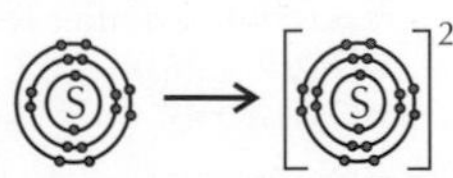

Q3 a) 2+
b) 1–
c) CaI_2

Q4 a) LiF
b) A lithium atom (Li) loses 1 electron to form a lithium ion (Li^+). The fluorine atom (F) gains 1 electron to form a fluoride ion (F^-). Electrostatic attraction holds the positive and negative ions together — this is an ionic bond.

Page 59 — Fact Recall Questions

Q1 It holds positive and negative ions together.
Q2 A regular structure made up of ions.
Q3

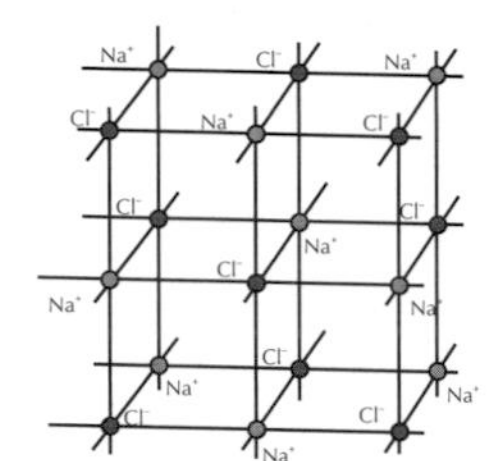

Q4 The ions in a liquid are free to move (and they carry a charge).
Q5 It will have a high melting point. It will dissolve in water.

2. Covalent Bonding

Page 62 — Fact Recall Questions

Q1 It forms when two atoms share electrons so that they've both got full outer shells of electrons.
Q2

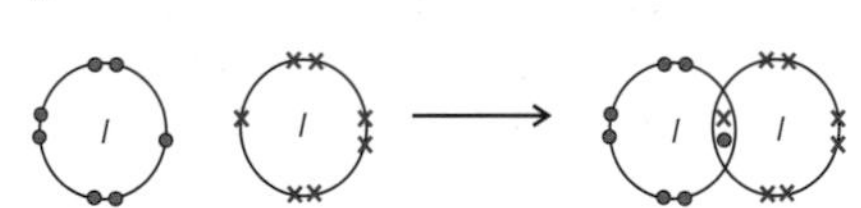

Q3 It is a covalent bond formed when two atoms share three pairs of electrons.
Q4 a) The weak forces between the molecules are easily broken.
b) No — chlorine wouldn't conduct electricity because there are no free ions to carry the charge.
Q5 The weak bonds between layers are easily broken, so the sheets can slide over each other.
Q6 Diamond is a giant covalent structure made up of carbon atoms. Each carbon atom is covalently bonded to four other carbon atoms and the atoms arrange themselves in a tetrahedral shape.

3. Dative Covalent Bonding

Page 64 — Application Questions

Q1 a) 5
b) 8
c) P
d)

Don't forget to include the charge on PH_4^+.

Q2

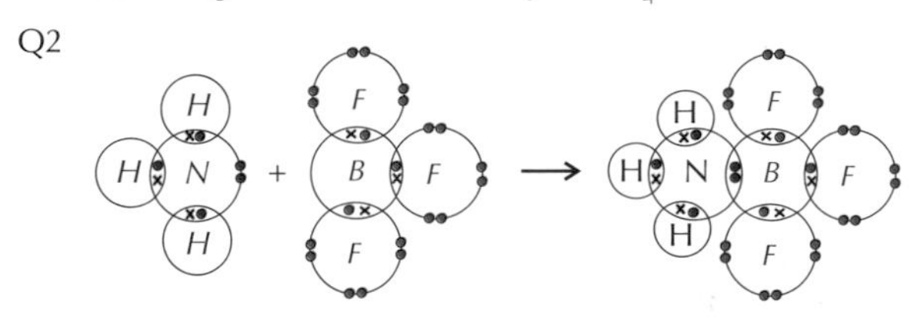

Page 64 — Fact Recall Questions

Q1 A bond formed between two atoms where one of the atoms provides both of the shared electrons.
Q2 Co-ordinate bonding.
Q3 The arrow shows a pair of electrons from one atom shared between 2 atoms in a dative bond. The direction of the arrow shows which atom is the donor atom.

4. Charge Clouds

Page 65 — Fact Recall Questions

Q1 Electrons in an atom that are unshared.
Q2 A charge cloud is an area where you have a really big chance of finding an electron pair.
Q3 Lone-pair charge clouds repel more than bonding-pair charge clouds. So, the greatest angles are between lone pairs of electrons, and bond angles between bonding pairs are often reduced because they are pushed together by lone-pair repulsion.

5. Shapes of Molecules

Page 69 — Application Questions

Q1 a) Sulfur has 6 outer electrons and 2 hydrogen atoms donate one electron each. So there are 8 electrons on the S atom, which is **4** electron pairs.
b) 2 electron pairs are involved in bonding, so there are **2** lone pairs.
c)

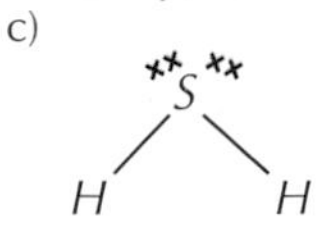

d) non-linear/bent
e) 104.5°

Q2 a) Oxygen has 6 outer electrons and 3 hydrogen atoms donate one electron each. It's a positive ion so one electron has been removed. So there are 8 electrons on the O atom, which is **4** electron pairs.
b) 3 electron pairs are involved in bonding, so there is **1** lone pair.
c)

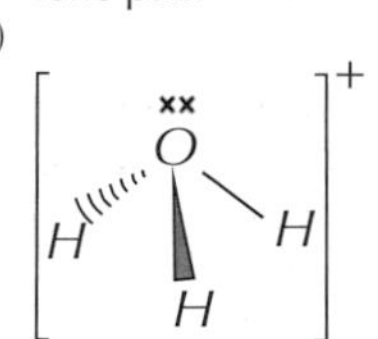

The shape is trigonal pyramidal.
d) 107°

Q3 a)

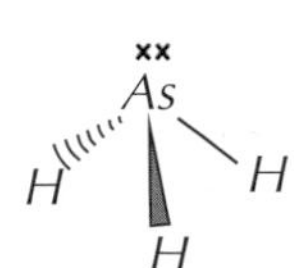

The shape is trigonal pyramidal.
Arsenic has 5 outer electrons and 3 hydrogen atoms donate one electron each. So there are 8 electrons on the As atom, which is 4 electron pairs. 3 electron pairs are involved in bonding, so there is 1 lone pair.
b) 107°

Q4

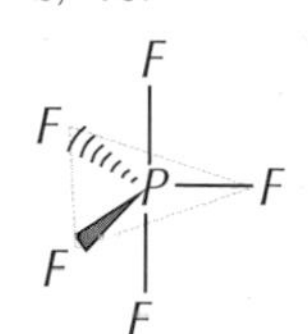

The shape is trigonal bipyramidal.
Phosphorus has 5 outer electrons and 5 fluorine atoms donate one electron each. So there are 10 electrons on the P atom, which is 5 electron pairs. All the electron pairs are involved in bonding.

Q5

The shape is tetrahedral.
Carbon has 4 outer electrons and 2 chlorine and 2 fluorine atoms donate one electron each. So there are 8 electrons on the C atom, which is 4 electron pairs. All the electron pairs are involved in bonding.

Page 69 — Fact Recall Questions

Q1 120°
Q2 four
Q3 octahedral

6. Polarisation

Page 70 — Fact Recall Questions

Q1 Electronegativity is the ability to attract the bonding electrons in a covalent bond. So a chlorine atom is better able to attract the electrons than a hydrogen atom.

Q2 Fluorine is more electronegative than hydrogen so attracts the electrons in the H—F covalent bond more than hydrogen. The bonding electrons are pulled towards the fluorine atom. This makes the bond polar.

Q3 A dipole is a difference in charge between two atoms caused by a shift in the electron density in the bond between them.

7. Intermolecular Forces

Page 74 — Application Questions

Q1 van der Waals forces / induced dipole-dipole forces

Q2 a) Oxygen is more electronegative than chlorine so it has a greater ability to pull the bonding electrons away from hydrogen atoms. So the bonds are more polarised in H_2O than in HCl, which means that hydrogen bonds form in H_2O but not in HCl.

b) fluorine/F

c) permanent dipole-dipole forces

d) carbon/C

Q3 a) NH_3 has hydrogen bonds between molecules whereas PH_3 only has van der Waals forces, as the electronegativity values of P and H are very similar. It takes less energy to break van der Waals forces than hydrogen bonds so the boiling point of PH_3 is lower.

b) lower

Page 74 — Fact Recall Questions

Q1 van der Waals forces / induced dipole-dipole forces

Q2 There are covalent bonds within iodine molecules and van der Waals forces between iodine molecules.

Q3 Permanent dipole-dipole forces are weak electrostatic forces of attraction between polar molecules.

Q4 a) hydrogen bonding

b)

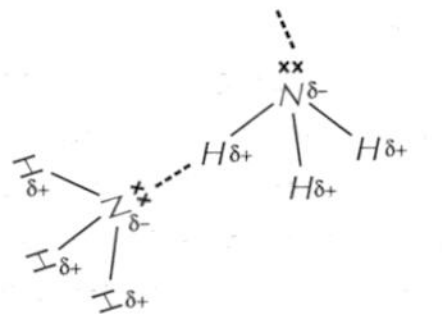

Q5 hydrogen bonding

Q6 Ice has more hydrogen bonds than liquid water, and hydrogen bonds are relatively long. So the H_2O molecules in ice are further apart on average, making ice less dense than liquid water.

8. Metallic Bonding

Page 75 — Fact Recall Questions

Q1 Magnesium exists as a giant metallic lattice structure. The outermost shell of electrons of a magnesium atom is delocalised — the electrons are free to move about the metal. This leaves positive metal ions, Mg^{2+}, which are attracted to the delocalised negative electrons. They form a lattice of closely packed positive ions in a sea of delocalised electrons.

Q2 metallic bonding

Q3 a) As there are no bonds holding specific ions together, the copper ions can slide over each other when the structure is pulled, so it can be drawn into a wire.

b) Copper has delocalised electrons which can pass kinetic energy to each other, making copper a good thermal conductor.

9. Properties of Structures

Page 77 — Application Questions

Q1 Iodine has more electrons than bromine so there are stronger van der Waals forces between the molecules. This means more energy is needed to break the forces and turn it from a liquid to a gas.

Q2 a) Decane contains more atoms than methane, therefore it has more electrons and stronger van der Waals forces between the molecules. This means more energy is needed to break the forces between the molecules.

b) Silicon dioxide has a giant covalent structure. It has a high melting point because the strong covalent forces between all the atoms have to be broken to turn silicon dioxide from a solid to a liquid. This takes a lot of energy.

Page 77 — Fact Recall Questions

Q1 The particles go from vibrating about a fixed point and being unable to move about freely, to being able to move about freely and randomly.

Q2 In a gas the particles move about freely and diffuse to fill the container.

Q3 To melt a simple covalent compound you only have to overcome the intermolecular forces that hold the molecules together. To melt a giant molecular structure you need to break the much stronger covalent bonds that hold the structure together. This takes a lot more energy, so the melting points of giant molecular structures are higher.

Q4 Most bonds aren't purely ionic or purely covalent but are somewhere in between. This is down to bond polarisation and means that most compounds end up with a mixture of ionic and covalent properties.

10. The Periodic Table

Page 80 — Application Questions

Q1 a) 3
b) 2
c) 4
d) 2
e) 5

Q2 a) 6
b) 1
c) 7
d) 3
e) 2

Q3 a) $1s^2\ 2s^2\ 2p^6\ 3s^1$
b) $1s^2\ 2s^2\ 2p^6\ 3s^2\ 3p^6\ 4s^2$
c) $1s^2\ 2s^2\ 2p^6\ 3s^2\ 3p^5$
d) $1s^2\ 2s^2\ 2p^6\ 3s^2\ 3p^6\ 3d^{10}\ 4s^2\ 4p^3$
e) $1s^2\ 2s^2\ 2p^6\ 3s^2\ 3p^6\ 3d^3\ 4s^2$
f) $1s^2\ 2s^2\ 2p^6\ 3s^2\ 3p^6\ 3d^1\ 4s^2$

Page 80 — Fact Recall Questions

Q1 The periodic table is arranged into periods (rows) and groups (columns) by atomic (proton) number.

Q2 a) Z
b) Y
c) X and W

11. Periodicity

Page 83 — Application Questions

Q1 a) Aluminium has 13 protons and sulfur has 16 protons. So the positive charge of the nucleus of sulfur is greater. This means electrons are pulled closer to the nucleus, making the atomic radius of sulfur smaller than the atomic radius of aluminium.
b) sodium/magnesium

Q2 Aluminium is a metal so it has strong metallic bonds holding all the atoms together. Sulfur is a molecular substance with only van der Waals forces between the molecules. It takes much less energy to break van der Waals forces than metallic bonds, so the boiling point of aluminium is much higher than the boiling point of sulfur.

Q3 a) Silicon is macromolecular so has strong covalent bonds linking all its atoms together. Phosphorus is a molecular substance with van der Waals forces between its molecules. It takes much less energy to break van der Waals forces than covalent bonds so the melting point of phosphorus is much lower than the melting point of silicon.
b) chlorine / argon

Page 83 — Fact Recall Questions

Q1 The atomic radius decreases across Period 3.

Q2 The melting and boiling points generally increase from sodium to silicon, but then decrease from silicon to argon.

Q3 There's a general increase in the first ionisation energy as you go across Period 3.

Exam-style Questions — page 85

1 a) (i) $1s^2\ 2s^2\ 2p^6\ 3s^2\ 3p^6\ 3d^{10}\ 4s^2\ 4p^2$ ***(1 mark)***
(ii) Covalent bonding ***(1 mark)***. A germanium atom and a hydrogen atom share a pair of electrons, with each atom donating one electron ***(1 mark)***.
(iii)

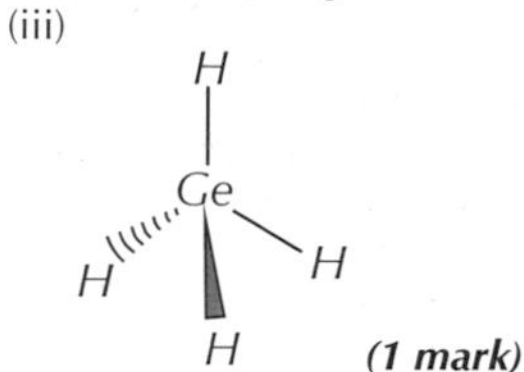

(1 mark)

The shape is tetrahedral ***(1 mark)***.

Ge has 4 electrons in its outer shell and each H atom donates 1 electron, so there are 8 electrons on the Ge atom, which is 4 electron pairs. 4 pairs are involved in bonding so there are no lone pairs.

(iv) 109.5° ***(1 mark)***
(v) It will not conduct electricity ***(1 mark)*** as there are no free ions to carry the charge ***(1 mark)***.

b) (i)

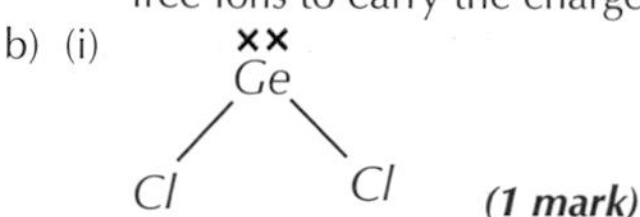

(1 mark)

The shape is non-linear/bent ***(1 mark)***

Ge has 4 outer electrons and each Cl atom donates 1 electron, so there are 6 outer electrons on the Ge atom, which is 3 electron pairs. 2 pairs are involved in bonding, so there is one lone pair.

(ii) Accept 112°-119° ***(1 mark)***
There are 3 pairs of electrons on the central atom, but lone pair/bonding pair repulsion is greater than bonding pair/bonding pair repulsion, so the bond angle will be less than 120° ***(1 mark)***.

2 a) (i) Sodium has a giant metallic lattice structure ***(1 mark)***. It is made up of Na^+ ions surrounded by delocalised electrons ***(1 mark)***.
(ii) metallic bonding ***(1 mark)***
(iii) As there are no bonds holding specific ions together, the sodium ions can slide over each other when the structure is pulled ***(1 mark)***.

b) The number of protons in chlorine is higher than in sodium so the positive charge on the nucleus is higher ***(1 mark)***. Both atoms have the same number of electron shells so they have the same amount of shielding ***(1 mark)***. This means that the outer electrons are pulled closer to the nucleus in chlorine ***(1 mark)***.

c) Oppositely charged ions held together by electrostatic attraction ***(1 mark)***.

d) $Na + \frac{1}{2}Cl_2 \rightarrow NaCl$ ***(1 mark)***

The question asks for the equation to make one mole of NaCl, so you need to balance the equation so there's only one mole on the right hand side of the arrow.

e) Sodium chloride is a giant ionic lattice ***(1 mark)*** with a cube shape made up of alternating sodium and chloride ions ***(1 mark)***.

3 a) The p block *(1 mark)*.

b) (i) As you go down Group 5 the atoms have more electrons in them ***(1 mark)*** so the van der Waals forces between the molecules increase ***(1 mark)***. It takes more energy to break stronger van der Waals forces so the boiling points increase from PH_3 to SbH_3 ***(1 mark)***.

(ii) The melting point would increase from PH_3 to AsH_3 to SbH_3 ***(1 mark)***.

c) hydrogen bonding ***(1 mark)***

d) (i) It is a dative/co-ordinate bond ***(1 mark)***. The ammonia molecule has a lone pair of electrons ***(1 mark)*** which it donates to the hydrogen ion to form a dative bond ***(1 mark)***.

(ii) NH_3 has one lone pair of electrons and three bonding pairs whereas NH_4^+ has four bonding pairs ***(1 mark)***. As lone-pair/bonding pair repulsion is greater than bonding-pair/bonding-pair repulsion ***(1 mark)***, the bond angle is pushed smaller in the NH_3 molecule than in NH_4^+ ***(1 mark)***.

4 a) Electronegativity is the ability to attract the bonding electrons ***(1 mark)*** in a covalent bond ***(1 mark)***. If there's a difference in the electronegativities of two covalently bonded atoms ***(1 mark)*** there's a shift in the electron density towards the more electronegative atom, making the bond polar ***(1 mark)***. This creates a dipole and causes weak electrostatic forces of attraction between molecules ***(1 mark)***.

b) HCl: permanent dipole-dipole forces ***(1 mark)***
CH_4: van der Waals forces / induced dipole-dipole forces ***(1 mark)***
HF: hydrogen bonds ***(1 mark)***

$\delta+$ H—F $\delta-$ ··· $\delta+$ H—F $\delta-$

(3 marks, otherwise 1 mark for showing all lone pairs, 1 mark for showing the partial charges and 1 mark for showing the hydrogen bond going from a lone pair on an F atom to an H atom.)
The Cl atoms in Cl_2 have equal electronegativities so the covalent bond is non-polar ***(1 mark)***.

5 a) (i) Giant covalent/macromolecular ***(1 mark)***

(ii) Graphite consists of flat sheets of carbon atoms ***(1 mark)*** covalently bonded to three other carbon atoms and arranged in hexagons ***(1 mark)***. The sheets of hexagons are bonded together by weak van der Waals forces ***(1 mark)***. Each carbon atom in diamond is covalently bonded to four other carbon atoms ***(1 mark)***. The atoms arrange themselves in a tetrahedral shape ***(1 mark)***.

(iii) The delocalised electrons in graphite are free to move along the sheets, so an electric current can flow ***(1 mark)***. Diamond doesn't have any free electrons ***(1 mark)***.

b) Van der Waals forces / induced dipole-dipole forces ***(1 mark)***
The forces between the C_3H_8 molecules would be stronger ***(1 mark)*** because each molecule contains more atoms so has larger electron clouds ***(1 mark)***.
For diamond to boil the covalent bonds between carbon atoms have to be broken ***(1 mark)***. This would need a lot more energy than breaking the van der Waals forces between methane molecules ***(1 mark)***.

Section 4: Alkanes and Organic Chemistry

1. Formulas

Page 91 — Application Questions

Q1
```
  H Br H
  |  |  |
H-C--C--C-H
  |  |  |
  H  H  H
```
It doesn't matter if you draw the bromine atom above or below the carbon atom — it means the same thing.

Q2 C_8H_{18}

Q3 a) CH_2
b) C_4H_7Br
c) $C_9H_{17}Cl_3$

Q4 a) C_4H_8
b) Heptene contains 14 H atoms.

Q5 a) $C_3H_6Br_2$
b)
```
  H Br H
  |  |  |
H-C--C--C-H
  |  |  |
  H  H  Br
```
c) $C_3H_6Br_2$
For this molecule the empirical formula is the same as the molecular formula because you can't cancel the atoms down and still have whole numbers.

Q6 a) C_5H_{10}
b) $CH_3CH_2CH_2CHCH_2$
c) CH_2

Page 91 — Fact Recall Questions

Q1 A molecular formula is the actual number of atoms of each element in a molecule.

Q2 A displayed formula shows how all the atoms are arranged, and all the bonds between them.

Q3 To find the empirical formula you have to divide the molecular formula by the smallest number of atoms for a given element in the molecule.

Q4 A homologous series is a bunch of organic compounds which have the same general formula and similar chemical properties.

2. Isomers

Page 94 — Application Questions

Q1
```
   H CH3
   |  |
Cl-C--C-CH3
   |  |
   H  H
```
You could draw the chlorine atom attached to any other carbon atom apart from the one it was on originally.

Q2 There are three chain isomers of C_5H_{12}.
```
  H  H  H  H  H
  |  |  |  |  |
H-C--C--C--C--C-H
  |  |  |  |  |
  H  H  H  H  H

  H CH3 H  H
  |  |  |  |
H-C--C--C--C-H
  |  |  |  |
  H  H  H  H
```

```
      CH3
      |
H3C — C — CH3
      |
      CH3
```

Q3

```
    H  O  H
    |  ‖  |
H — C — C — C — H
    |     |
    H     H
```

Q4 a) A and B
b) chain isomerism

Page 94 — Fact Recall Questions

Q1 A chain isomer is a molecule that has the same molecular formula but a different arrangement of the carbon skeleton to another molecule. Some are straight chains and others branched in different ways.

Q2 A positional isomer has the same skeleton and the same atoms or groups of atoms attached as another molecule. The difference is that the atom or group of atoms is attached to a different carbon atom.

Q3 A functional group isomer has the same atoms as another molecule but the atoms are arranged into different functional groups.

3. Alkanes and Nomenclature

Page 97 — Application Questions

Q1 butane

Q2 a) 3-methylpentane
b) 3-ethyl-3-methylpentane
c) 3,3-diethylhexane
d) 3,3-diethyl-2-methylhexane

Page 97 — Fact Recall Questions

Q1 C_nH_{2n+2}

Q2 A cycloalkane is a ring of carbon atoms with two hydrogens attached to each carbon.

Q3 hex-

Q4 ethyl-

Q5 di-

4. More Nomenclature

Page 99 — Application Questions

Q1 a) 1,4-dibromobutane
b) 1,3-dichloropropane
c) 2-chloro-2-methylpropane
d) 2-iodopropane

Q2 a) hex-1-ene
b) hexa-1,3-diene or 1,3-hexadiene
c) 3,4-dichlorohex-1-ene

Page 99 — Fact Recall Questions

Q1 An alkane where one or more hydrogens have been swapped for a halogen.

Q2 iodo-

Q3 A molecule with at least one double bond between carbon atoms in its carbon chain.

Q4 diene

5. Petroleum

Page 101 — Fact Recall Questions

Q1 A mixture that consists mainly of alkane hydrocarbons.

Q2 They are separated by boiling point.

Q3 Cracking is breaking long-chain alkanes into smaller hydrocarbons.

Q4 There is more demand for lighter petroleum fractions so, to meet the demand, the heavier fractions are cracked into lighter fractions.

Q5 Using a catalyst cuts costs, because the reaction can be done at a lower temperature and pressure.

6. Alkanes as Fuels

Page 104 — Application Questions

Q1 $C_5H_{12} + 8O_2 \rightarrow 5CO_2 + 6H_2O$

Q2 $C_5H_{12} + 5\frac{1}{2}O_2 \rightarrow 5CO + 6H_2O$

Page 104 — Fact Recall Questions

Q1 NO_x

Q2 E.g. $2NO_{(g)} \rightarrow N_{2(g)} + O_{2(g)}$ or
$2NO_{(g)} + 2CO_{(g)} \rightarrow N_{2(g)} + 2CO_{2(g)}$

Q3 The sulfur burns to produce sulfur dioxide gas which then enters the atmosphere, dissolves in the moisture, and is converted into sulfuric acid.

Q4 E.g. water vapour, carbon dioxide, methane.

Q5 Some of the electromagnetic radiation from the Sun reaches the Earth and is absorbed. The Earth then re-emits it as infrared radiation. Various gases in the troposphere absorb some of this infrared radiation and re-emit it in all directions — including back towards Earth, keeping us warm.

Exam-style Questions — page 106

Q1 a) C_nH_{2n+2} ***(1 mark)***

b) E.g.

```
    H   H   H   H   H
    |   |   |   |   |
H — C — C — C — C — C — H
    |   |   |   |   |
    H   H  CH2  H   H
            |
           CH3
```

(1 mark)

There are loads of possible answers for this question. As long as you've drawn a molecule with seven carbon atoms, sixteen hydrogen atoms and have arranged the carbon skeleton so there is at least one branch from the main carbon chain you'll pick up the mark.

c) (i) E.g. $C_7H_{16(g)} + 7\frac{1}{2}O_{2(g)} \rightarrow 7CO_{(g)} + 8H_2O_{(g)}$
(1 mark for the correct products and 1 mark for a correctly balanced equation)

There are quite a few correct answers for this. You'll get both marks if you've shown carbon monoxide as one of the products (the only other products are water, carbon and carbon dioxide) and your equation is balanced.

(ii) It can be dangerous because carbon monoxide gas is poisonous ***(1 mark)***. Carbon monoxide molecules bind to the same sites on haemoglobin molecules in red blood cells as oxygen molecules ***(1 mark)***. So oxygen can't be carried around the body ***(1 mark)***.

d) (i) There is more demand for light fractions ***(1 mark)***.
(ii) E.g. $C_7H_{16} \rightarrow C_4H_8 + C_3H_8$ ***(1 mark)***

Any answer where heptane is broken into smaller molecules and the equation is balanced will get a mark.

(iii) Using a catalyst cuts costs, because the reaction can be done at a lower temperature and pressure ***(1 mark)***. The catalyst also speeds up the rate of reaction ***(1 mark)***.

e) (i) pentane
(ii) 2,3-dimethylbutane

Q2 a) (i) 3,4-dichlorohex-1-ene ***(1 mark)***
(ii) $C_6H_{10}Cl_2$ ***(1 mark)***
(iii) C_3H_5Cl ***(1 mark)***

b) (i) functional group isomer
(ii) E.g.

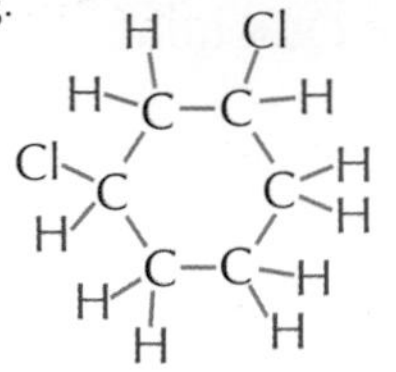

(1 mark)

Any positional isomer where the two chlorine atoms aren't on adjacent carbons and the carbon skeleton is the same as the other isomer will get the marks.

c) (i) positional isomer
(ii) 3,5-dichlorohex-1-ene

Q3 a) (i) A homologous series is a bunch of organic compounds which have the same general formula ***(1 mark)*** and similar chemical properties ***(1 mark)***. Each member differs by $-CH_2-$ ***(1 mark)***.
(ii) Propane, C_3H_8 ***(1 mark)***.

b) (i) Because boiling points of alkanes increase as the molecules get bigger, each fraction condenses at a different temperature ***(1 mark)***. As the crude oil vapour goes up the fractionating column, it gets cooler ***(1 mark)***. So the fractions are drawn off at different levels in the column ***(1 mark)***.
(ii) E.g. Liquefied Petroleum Gas (LPG) / camping gas ***(1 mark)***.

c) (i) The two types of cracking are thermal cracking and catalytic cracking ***(1 mark)***.
(ii) Thermal cracking takes place at high temperature (up to 1000 °C) and high pressure (up to 70 atm) ***(1 mark)***. It produces a lot of alkenes ***(1 mark)***. Catalytic cracking uses a zeolite catalyst, at a slight pressure and high temperature (about 450 °C) ***(1 mark)***. It makes mostly motor fuels and aromatic hydrocarbons ***(1 mark)***.

d) (i) Methane's produced by rubbish rotting in landfill sites ***(1 mark)*** and by cows ***(1 mark)***. The human population is increasing so more landfill is produced and more cows are needed for food ***(1 mark)***.
(ii) Methane absorbs IR radiation (heat) from the Earth and re-emits it in all directions — including back towards the Earth ***(1 mark)***. As the amount of methane in the atmosphere increases, more heat is absorbed and re-emitted back to Earth ***(1 mark)***. This increases the average global temperature of the Earth — this is global warming ***(1 mark)***.

Unit 2

Section 1: Energetics

1. Enthalpy

Page 109 — Fact Recall Questions

Q1 ΔH°_{298}

Q2 Exothermic reactions give out energy, and endothermic reactions absorb energy. For exothermic reactions, the enthalpy change (ΔH) is negative. For endothermic reactions it is positive.

2. Bond Enthalpies

Page 112 — Application Questions

Q1 a) Bonds broken = (1 × C=C) + (1 × H–H)
So total energy absorbed = 612 + 436
= 1048 kJ mol^{-1}.
Bonds formed = (2 × C–H) + (1 × C–C)
So total energy released = (2 × 413) + 347
= 1173 kJ mol^{-1}.
Enthalpy change of reaction
= total energy absorbed – total energy released
= 1048 – 1173 = **–125 kJ mol^{-1}**.

b) Bonds broken = (1 × C–O) + (1 × H–Cl)
So total energy absorbed = 358 + 432
= 790 kJ mol^{-1}.
Bonds formed = (1 × C–Cl) + (1 × O–H)
So total energy released = 346 + 460
= 806 kJ mol^{-1}.
Enthalpy change of reaction
= total energy absorbed – total energy released
= 790 – 806 = **–16 kJ mol^{-1}**.

c) Bonds broken =
(2 × C–C) + (8 × C–H) + (5 × O=O)
So total energy absorbed =
(2 × 347) + (8 × 413) + (5 × 498) = 6488 kJ mol^{-1}.
Bonds formed = (6 × C=O) + (8 × O–H)
So total energy released = (6 × 805) + (8 × 460)
= 8510 kJ mol^{-1}.
Enthalpy change of reaction/combustion
= total energy absorbed – total energy released
= 6488 – 8510 = **–2022 kJ mol^{-1}**.

It really helps if you've drawn a sketch for this question.

d) Bonds broken = (1 × C–Cl) + (1 × N–H)
So total energy absorbed = 346 + 391
= 737 kJ mol^{-1}.
Bonds formed = (1 × C–N) + (1 × H–Cl)
So total energy released = 286 + 432
= 718 kJ mol^{-1}.
Enthalpy change of reaction
= total energy absorbed – total energy released
= 737 – 718 = **+19 kJ mol^{-1}**.

Q2 The balanced equation for the combustion of ethene is:
$C_2H_4 + 3O_2 \rightarrow 2CO_2 + 2H_2O$.
Bonds broken =
(1 × C=C) + (4 × C–H) + (3 × O=O)
So total energy absorbed =
(1 × 612) + (4 × 413) + (3 × 498) = 3758 kJ mol^{-1}.
Bonds formed = (4 × C=O) + (4 × O–H)
So total energy released = (4 × 805) + (4 × 460)
= 5060 kJ mol^{-1}.
Enthalpy change of combustion
= total energy absorbed – total energy released
= 3758 – 5060 = **–1302 kJ mol^{-1}**.

Q3 The balanced equation for the formation of 1 mole of HCl is: $\frac{1}{2}H_2 + \frac{1}{2}Cl_2 \rightarrow HCl$.

The enthalpy change of formation is the enthalpy change when 1 mole of a compound is formed, so your equation needs to have 1 mole of HCl on the RHS, which means you need half a mole of H_2 and half a mole of Cl_2 on the LHS of the equation.

Bonds broken = ½(1 × H–H) + ½(1 × Cl–Cl)
So total energy absorbed = (½ × 436) + (½ × 243.4)
= 339.7 kJ mol^{-1}.
Bonds formed = 1 × H–Cl
So total energy released = 432 kJ mol^{-1}.
Enthalpy change of formation
= total energy absorbed – total energy released
= 339.7 – 432 = **–92.3 kJ mol^{-1}**.

Q4 Call the unknown bond enthalpy between N and O 'X'.
Bonds broken = 2 × X
So total energy absorbed = $2X$ kJ mol^{-1}.
Bonds formed = (1 × N≡N) + (1 × O=O)
So total energy released = 945 + 498
= 1443 kJ mol^{-1}.
Enthalpy change of reaction = –181 kJ mol^{-1}
= total energy absorbed – total energy released.
So: –181= $2X$ – 1443
$2X$ = –181 + 1443 = 1262
X = 1262 ÷ 2 = **+631 kJ mol^{-1}**.

Page 112 — Fact Recall Questions

Q1 a) ΔH_f°
b) ΔH_c°

Q2 Standard enthalpy change of reaction, ΔH_r°, is the enthalpy change when a reaction occurs in the molar quantities shown in the chemical equation, under standard conditions with all reactants and products in their standard states.

3. Measuring Enthalpy Changes

Page 115 — Application Questions

Q1 $q = mc\Delta T = 220 \times 4.18 \times (301 - 298) = 2758.8$ J
= 2.7588 kJ

$$\Delta H = \frac{q}{n} = -\frac{2.7588 \text{ kJ}}{0.05 \text{ mol}} = \mathbf{-55.2 \text{ kJ mol}^{-1}} \text{ (to 3 s.f.)}.$$

Don't forget — the enthalpy change must be negative because it's an exothermic reaction (you can tell because the temperature increased).

Q2 a) $q = mc\Delta T = 200 \times 4.18 \times 29 = 24244$ J
= 24.244 kJ

$$n = \frac{\text{mass}}{M} = \frac{0.5 \text{ g}}{72 \text{ g mol}^{-1}} = 0.00694 \text{ moles of fuel}$$

$$\Delta H = \frac{q}{n} = -\frac{24.244 \text{ kJ}}{0.00694 \text{ mol}}$$

= **–3490 kJ mol^{-1}** (to 3 s.f.).

b) E.g. some heat from the combustion will be transferred to the surroundings and not the water. / The combustion may not be complete combustion. / The combustion may not have taken place under standard conditions. / There could be inaccuracies due to the measuring equipment.

3 $q = mc\Delta T = 300 \times 4.18 \times 55 = 68970$ J
= 68.97 kJ

$$\Delta H_c^\circ \text{ octane} = -5512 \text{ kJ mol}^{-1} = \frac{q}{n}$$

$$n = \frac{q}{\Delta H} = \frac{68.97 \text{ kJ}}{5512 \text{ kJ mol}^{-1}} = 0.0125... \text{ mol.}$$

$$n = \frac{\text{mass}}{M}, \text{ so mass} = n \times M = 0.0125... \times 114$$

= **1.43 g** of octane (to 3 s.f.).

Page 115 — Fact Recall Questions

Q1 The temperature change due to the reaction, and the mass of the reactant (which is used to calculate the number of moles that has reacted).

Q2 E.g.

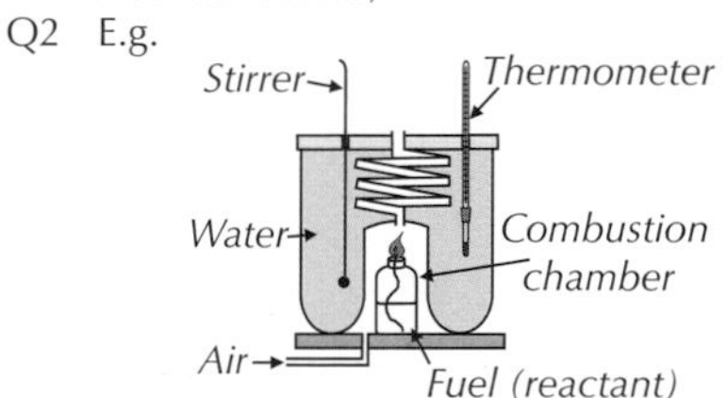

Q3 a) q is the heat lost or gained during a reaction.
b) joules (J)

Q4 The reaction needs to be performed at a constant pressure of 100 kPa, with all reactants and products in their standard states.

Q5 Find the number of moles of that reactant that react in the balanced chemical equation, then calculate ΔH_r° using:

$$\Delta H_r^\circ = \frac{q}{n} \times \text{number of moles reacting in balanced chemical equation}$$

4. Hess's Law

Pages 119-120 — Application Questions

Q1 a) First draw out a reaction scheme with an alternative reaction route that includes balanced equations for the formation of each compound:

Reactants: $2Na_{(s)} + 2H_2O_{(l)}$ —ΔH_r° (Route 1)→ Products: $2NaOH_{(aq)} + H_{2(g)}$

$\Delta H_{f(reactants)}^\circ$ ← Elements: $2Na_{(s)} + 2H_{2(g)} + O_{2(g)}$ → $\Delta H_{f(products)}^\circ$ (Route 2)

$\Delta H_{f\,(reactants)}^\circ = (2 \times \Delta H_{f\,[Na]}^\circ) + (2 \times \Delta H_{f\,[H_2O]}^\circ)$
$\Delta H_{f\,(reactants)}^\circ = (2 \times 0) + (2 \times -286) = -572$ kJ mol^{-1}.
$\Delta H_{f\,(products)}^\circ = (2 \times \Delta H_{f\,[NaOH]}^\circ) + \Delta H_{f\,[H_2]}^\circ$
$\Delta H_{f\,(products)}^\circ = (2 \times -469) + 0 = -938$ kJ mol^{-1}.

Remember that the enthalpy change of formation of Na and H_2 is zero because they're elements.

Using Hess's Law: Route 1 = Route 2, so:
$\Delta H_{f\,(reactants)}^\circ + \Delta H_r^\circ = \Delta H_{f\,(products)}^\circ$
$-572 + \Delta H_r^\circ = -938$
$\Delta H_r^\circ = -938 + 572 =$ **–366 kJ mol^{-1}**.

b)

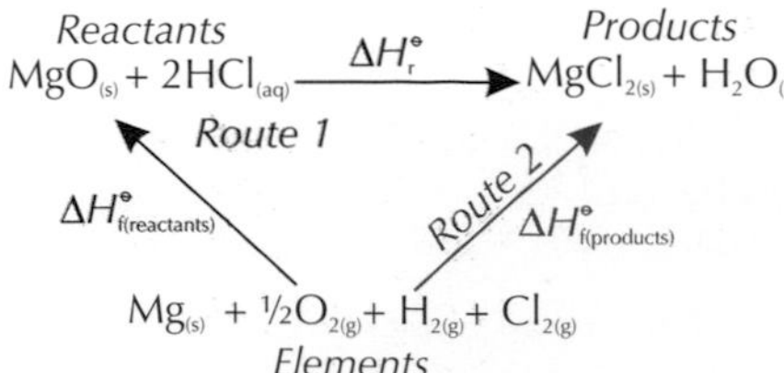

$\Delta H^\circ_{f\ (reactants)} = \Delta H^\circ_{f\ [MgO]} + (2 \times \Delta H^\circ_{f\ [HCl]})$
$\Delta H^\circ_{f\ (reactants)} = -602 + (2 \times -167) = -936\ kJ\ mol^{-1}$.
$\Delta H^\circ_{f\ (products)} = \Delta H^\circ_{f\ [MgCl]} + \Delta H^\circ_{f\ [H_2O]}$
$\Delta H^\circ_{f\ (products)} = -641 + (-286) = -927\ kJ\ mol^{-1}$.
Using Hess's Law: Route 1 = Route 2, so:
$\Delta H^\circ_{f\ (reactants)} + \Delta H^\circ_r = \Delta H^\circ_{f\ (products)}$
$-936 + \Delta H^\circ_r = -927$
$\Delta H^\circ_r = -927 + 936 = \mathbf{+9\ kJ\ mol^{-1}}$.

c)

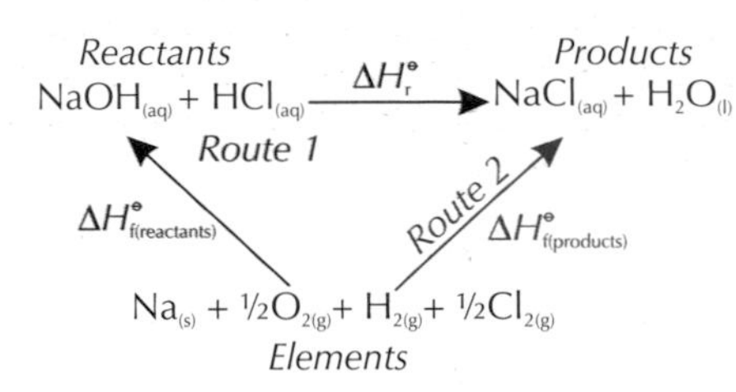

$\Delta H^\circ_{f\ (reactants)} = \Delta H^\circ_{f\ [NaOH]} + \Delta H^\circ_{f\ [HCl]}$
$\Delta H^\circ_{f\ (reactants)} = -469 + (-167) = -636\ kJ\ mol^{-1}$.
$\Delta H^\circ_{f\ (products)} = \Delta H^\circ_{f\ [NaCl]} + \Delta H^\circ_{f\ [H_2O]}$
$\Delta H^\circ_{f\ (products)} = -407 + (-286) = -693\ kJ\ mol^{-1}$.
Using Hess's Law: Route 1 = Route 2, so:
$\Delta H^\circ_{f\ (reactants)} + \Delta H^\circ_r = \Delta H^\circ_{f\ (products)}$
$-636 + \Delta H^\circ_r = -693$
$\Delta H^\circ_r = -693 + 636 = \mathbf{-57\ kJ\ mol^{-1}}$.

Q2 a) First draw out balanced reactions for the formation of the compound, and the combustion of the reactants and product:

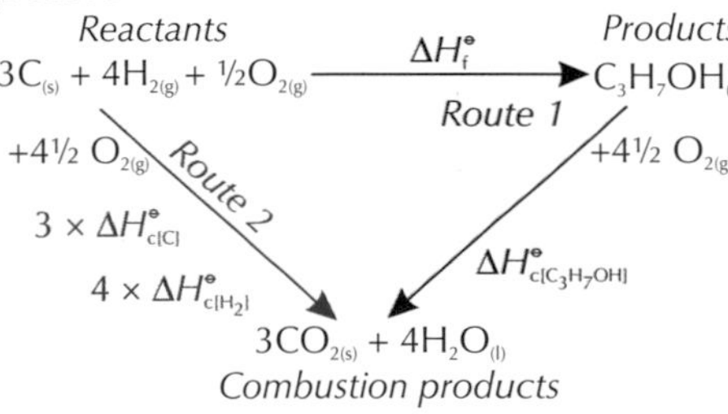

Using Hess's Law: Route 1 = Route 2, so:
$\Delta H^\circ_f + \Delta H^\circ_{c\ [C_3H_7OH]} = (3 \times \Delta H^\circ_{c\ [C]}) + (4 \times \Delta H^\circ_{c\ [H_2]})$
$\Delta H^\circ_f + (-2021) = (3 \times -394) + (4 \times -286)$
$\Delta H^\circ_f = -1182 - 1144 + 2021 = \mathbf{-305\ kJ\ mol^{-1}}$.

b)

Reactants — ΔH°_f — Products
$2C_{(s)} + 3H_{2(g)} + O_{2(g)} \rightarrow C_2H_4(OH)_{2(l)}$
Route 1
$+2\frac{1}{2}\ O_{2(g)}$ Route 2 $+2\frac{1}{2}\ O_{2(g)}$
$2 \times \Delta H^\circ_{c[C]}$
$3 \times \Delta H^\circ_{c[H_2]}$
$\Delta H^\circ_{c[C_2H_4(OH)_2]}$
$2CO_{2(s)} + 3H_2O_{(l)}$
Combustion products

Using Hess's Law: Route 1 = Route 2, so:
$\Delta H^\circ_f + \Delta H^\circ_{c\ [C_2H_4(OH)_2]} = (2 \times \Delta H^\circ_{c\ [C]}) + (3 \times \Delta H^\circ_{c\ [H_2]})$
$\Delta H^\circ_f + (-1180) = (2 \times -394) + (3 \times -286)$
$\Delta H^\circ_f = -788 - 858 + 1180 = \mathbf{-466\ kJ\ mol^{-1}}$.

c)

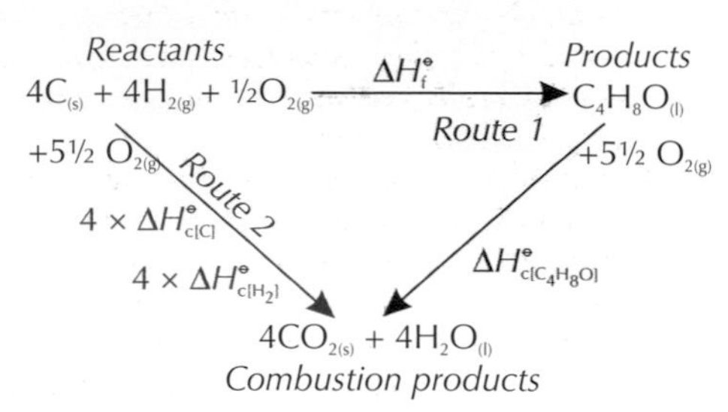

Using Hess's Law: Route 1 = Route 2, so:
$\Delta H^\circ_f + \Delta H^\circ_{c\ [C_4H_8O]} = (4 \times \Delta H^\circ_{c\ [C]}) + (4 \times \Delta H^\circ_{c\ [H_2]})$
$\Delta H^\circ_f + (-2442) = (4 \times -394) + (4 \times -286)$
$\Delta H^\circ_f = -1576 - 1144 + 2442 = \mathbf{-278\ kJ\ mol^{-1}}$.

Q3 First label the reaction scheme with the known enthalpy changes, and the chosen routes:

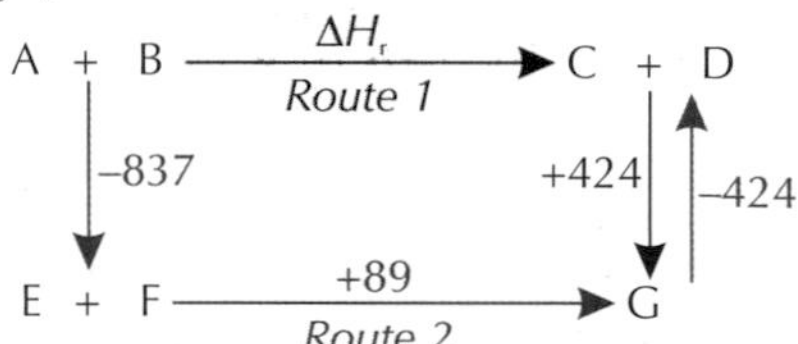

Using Hess's Law: Route 1 = Route 2, so:
$\Delta H_r = -837 + 89 + (-424) = \mathbf{-1172\ kJ\ mol^{-1}}$.

Exam-style Questions — page 121

1 a) $q = mc\Delta T = 50 \times 4.7 \times 1 = 235\ J = 0.235\ kJ$

$$\Delta H = \frac{q}{n} = -\frac{0.235\ kJ}{0.005\ mol} = \mathbf{-47\ kJ\ mol^{-1}}.$$

(3 marks for correct answer, otherwise 1 mark for q = mcΔT, 1 mark for 235 J or 0.235 kJ)

You've got to remember the negative sign on your answer — the temperature rises so it's an exothermic reaction.

b) The reaction must be carried out at a pressure of 100 kPa ***(1 mark)*** with all reactants and products in their standard states at that pressure ***(1 mark)***.

c) Any two from: e.g. some heat from the reaction will be transferred to the surroundings through the beaker. / The reaction may not have taken place under standard conditions. / There could be inaccuracies due to the measuring equipment. ***(1 mark for each)***

2 a) Hess's Law says that the total enthalpy change of a reaction is always the same, no matter which route is taken ***(1 mark)***.

b) $C_8H_{18(l)} + 12\frac{1}{2}O_{2(g)} \rightarrow 8CO_{2(g)} + 9H_2O_{(l)}$ ***(1 mark)***

c) (i)

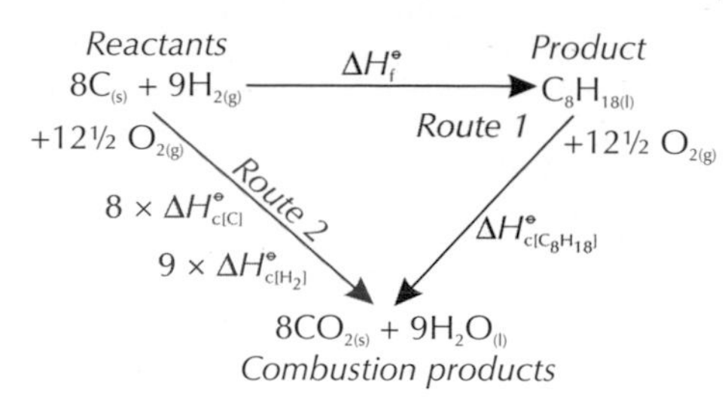

Using Hess's Law: Route 1 = Route 2, so:

$\Delta H_f^{\circ} + \Delta H_{c\ [C_8H_{18}]}^{\circ} = (8 \times \Delta H_{c\ [C]}^{\circ}) + (9 \times \Delta H_{c\ [H_2]}^{\circ})$

$\Delta H_f^{\circ} + (-5470) = (8 \times -394) + (9 \times -286)$

$\Delta H_f^{\circ} = -3152 - 2574 + 5470 =$ **-256 kJ mol^{-1}**.

(3 marks for correct answer, otherwise 1 mark for correct equation using Hess's Law and 1 mark for correct molar quantities. Allow 1 mark only for an answer of +256 kJ mol^{-1}.)

c) (ii) Exothermic ***(1 mark)***. The enthalpy change for the formation of octane is negative ***(1 mark)***.

3 a) Standard enthalpy of combustion, ΔH_c°, is the enthalpy change when 1 mole of a substance ***(1 mark)*** is completely burned in oxygen ***(1 mark)*** under standard conditions with all reactants and products in their standard states ***(1 mark)***.

b) The balanced equation for the combustion of but-1-ene is: $C_4H_8 + 6O_2 \rightarrow 4CO_2 + 4H_2O$.
Bonds broken =
(1 × C=C) + (2 × C–C) + (8 × C–H) + (6 × O=O)
So total energy absorbed =
(1 × 612) + (2 × 347) + (8 × 413) + (6 × 498)
= 7598 kJ mol^{-1}.
Bonds formed = (8 × C=O) + (8 × O–H)
So total energy released = (8 × 805) + (8 × 460)
= 10 120 kJ mol^{-1}.
Enthalpy change of combustion
= total energy absorbed – total energy released
= 7598 – 10 120 = **–2522 kJ mol^{-1}**.
(3 marks for correct answer, otherwise 1 mark for 'total energy absorbed – total energy released', and 1 mark for correct value for either energy released or energy absorbed. Allow 1 mark only for an answer of +2522 kJ mol^{-1}).

c) Some of the mean bond enthalpies are average values for the bonds in many different compounds, so they are not accurate for the specific molecules involved in this combustion ***(1 mark)***.

4 a) Standard enthalpy change of formation, ΔH_f°, is the enthalpy change when 1 mole ***(1 mark)*** of a compound is formed from its elements ***(1 mark)*** in their standard states under standard conditions
(1 mark).

b)

Reactants: $2KOH_{(s)} + H_2SO_{4(l)}$ —ΔH_r°→ Products: $K_2SO_{4(s)} + 2H_2O_{(l)}$

Route 1: $\Delta H^{\circ}_{f(reactants)}$ (from Elements to Reactants)

Route 2: $\Delta H^{\circ}_{f(products)}$ (from Elements to Products)

$2K_{(s)} + 3O_{2(g)} + 2H_{2(g)} + S_{(s)}$
Elements

$\Delta H^{\circ}_{f\ (reactants)} = (2 \times \Delta H^{\circ}_{f\ [KOH]}) + \Delta H^{\circ}_{f\ [H_2SO_4]}$

$\Delta H^{\circ}_{f\ (reactants)} = (2 \times -425) + -814 = -1664$ kJ mol^{-1}.

$\Delta H^{\circ}_{f\ (products)} = \Delta H^{\circ}_{f\ [K_2SO_4]} + (2 \times \Delta H^{\circ}_{f\ [H_2O]})$

$\Delta H^{\circ}_{f\ (products)} = -1438 + (2 \times -286) = -2010$ kJ mol^{-1}.

Using Hess's Law: Route 1 = Route 2, so:

$\Delta H^{\circ}_{f\ (reactants)} + \Delta H_r^{\circ} = \Delta H^{\circ}_{f\ (products)}$

$-1664 + \Delta H_r^{\circ} = -2010$

$\Delta H_r^{\circ} = -2010 + 1664 =$ **-346 kJ mol^{-1}**.

(3 marks for correct answer, otherwise 1 mark for correct equation using Hess's Law and 1 mark for correct molar quantities. Allow 1 mark only for an answer of +346 kJ mol^{-1}.)

Section 2: Kinetics and Equilibria

1. Reaction Rates

Page 125 — Application Questions

Q1 a)

Enthalpy (kJ mol^{-1})
456
304
112
Products
ΔH
Reactants
Progress of Reaction

Enthalpy of reactants = 112 kJ mol^{-1}.
Enthalpy of products = 304 kJ mol^{-1}.
$\Delta H = 304 - 112 = $ **+192 kJ mol^{-1}**.

b) The reaction is endothermic because ΔH is positive/the products have a higher enthalpy than the reactants.

Q2 B is the curve for the gas at a higher temperature because it is shifted over to the right showing that more molecules have more energy.

Page 125 — Fact Recall Questions

Q1 The particles must collide in the right direction (facing each other the right way) and with at least a certain minimum amount of kinetic energy.

Q2 The minimum amount of kinetic energy that particles need to have in order to react when they collide.

Q3 A small increase in temperature gives all molecules more energy, so a greater number of them have at least the minimum amount of energy to react when they collide. They will also collide more often because they will be moving about faster.

Q4 If you increase the concentration of reactants in a solution, the particles will be closer together in a given volume and so collide more often, increasing the reaction rate.

2. Catalysts

Page 127 — Application Question

Q1 a) E.g.

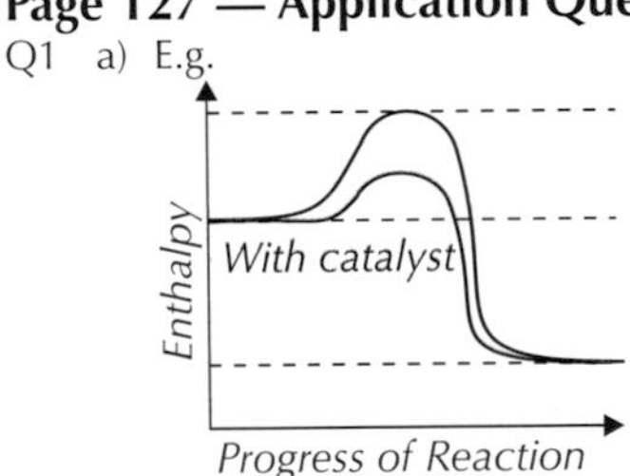

You can draw the line anywhere as long as the peak is lower than it was before and the shape of the graph stays the same.

b) Adding a catalyst would lower the activation energy for the reaction so that it would not need such a high temperature in order to take place. Being able to carry out the reaction at a lower temperature would save energy and money.

Page 127 — Fact Recall Questions

Q1 A substance that increases the rate of a reaction by providing an alternative reaction pathway with a lower activation energy. The catalyst is chemically unchanged at the end of the reaction.

Q2 Catalysts are used to speed up reactions in industrial processes that would be impossible or too slow to occur at practical temperatures and pressures. Using a catalyst means the temperature and pressure can be reduced, which saves energy and money.

Q3 A catalyst increases the rate of a reaction by providing an alternative reaction pathway with a lower activation energy. This means that more of the molecules collide with energies above the activation energy, and so can react.

3. Reversible Reactions

Page 130 — Application Questions

Q1 a) Increasing the concentration of A will shift the equilibrium to the right (favouring the forwards reaction) in order to get rid of the excess A.

b) There are 3 moles on the left and only 2 on the right. Increasing the pressure will shift the equilibrium to the right (favouring the forwards reaction) in order to reduce the number of moles to reduce the pressure again.

c) The forwards reaction is exothermic, so the backwards reaction must be endothermic. Increasing the temperature will shift the equilibrium to the left (favouring the endothermic backwards reaction) in order to remove the extra heat.

d) The reaction should ideally be performed with a high concentration of A and B, at a high pressure and low temperature.

Q2 There are the same number of moles on either side of the reaction. Increasing the pressure favours the reaction producing the fewest moles, but since both reactions are equal in this respect, increasing the pressure will not shift the position of equilibrium.

Page 130 — Fact Recall Questions

Q1 The concentrations of reactants and products are constant, and the forwards reaction and the backwards reaction are going at the same rate.

Q2 If there's a change in concentration, pressure or temperature, the equilibrium will move to help counteract the change.

Q3 The addition of a catalyst has no effect on the position of equilibrium in a reversible reaction.

4. Industrial Processes

Page 132 — Fact Recall Questions

Q1 a) A pressure of 60-70 atm, a temperature of 300 °C and a phosphoric acid catalyst.

b) A pressure of 50-100 atm, a temperature of 250 °C and a catalyst of a mixture of copper, zinc oxide and aluminium oxide.

Q2 Both reactions are exothermic, and so are favoured by low temperatures. However, at low temperatures the reaction rate drops, so the actual reaction temperatures used are a compromise between maximum yield and a faster reaction.

Q3 They can be made from renewable resources and they produce fewer pollutants than petrol.

Exam-style Questions — page 133

1 a) (i) The minimum amount of kinetic energy ***(1 mark)*** that particles need to have in order to react when they collide ***(1 mark)***.

(ii)

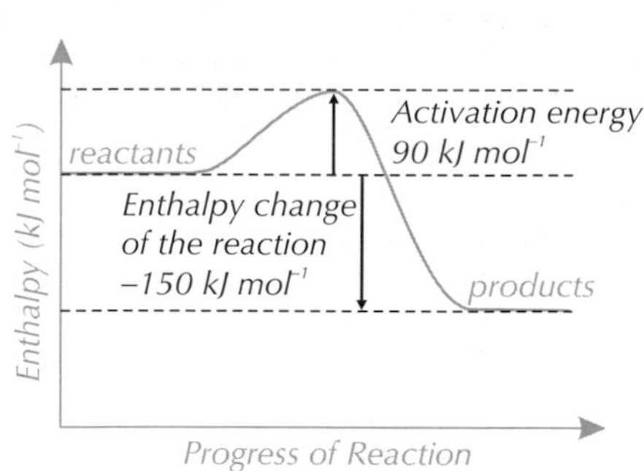

(1 mark for correctly labelled activation energy, 1 mark for correctly labelled enthalpy change of reaction.)

b) (i) A catalyst is a substance that increases the rate of a reaction without being changed or used up by the reaction ***(1 mark)***.

(ii) E.g. it will lower the activation energy so the peak of the graph will be lower ***(1 mark)***.

c) Heating the reactants gives the molecules more energy ***(1 mark)***. This means that more molecules will have an energy higher than the activation energy ***(1 mark)***, so more collisions between molecules will result in reaction, increasing the reaction rate ***(1 mark)***.

d) Lowering the pressure will reduce the rate of reaction ***(1 mark)***. This is because there will be fewer gas molecules in a given volume/the concentration will be reduced/the molecules will be further apart ***(1 mark)***, so there will be fewer collisions between molecules that result in reaction ***(1 mark)***.

2 a) In a reversible reaction, equilibrium is reached when the concentrations of reactants and products are constant ***(1 mark)***, and the forwards reaction and the backwards reaction are going at the same rate ***(1 mark)***.

b) If there's a change in concentration, pressure or temperature, the equilibrium will move to help counteract the change ***(1 mark)***.

c) The higher the pressure, the faster the reaction rate ***(1 mark)***. A high pressure also favours the forwards reaction (which produces fewer moles) so the higher the pressure, the greater the yield of ethanol ***(1 mark)***. However, high pressures are very expensive/produce side reactions/require strong and expensive equipment, so the pressure used is limited by these factors ***(1 mark)***.

d) Reducing the amount of H_2O will shift the position of equilibrium to the left ***(1 mark)*** in order to increase the amount of H_2O present ***(1 mark)***. This shift will reduce the maximum yield of ethanol from the forwards reaction ***(1 mark)***.

3 a) It has no effect on the position of equilibrium ***(1 mark)***.
Catalysts increase the rate at which equilibrium is reached but don't affect the position of equilibrium.

b) (i) exothermic

(ii) The forwards reaction is exothermic, and so the backwards reaction is endothermic. Increasing the temperature will shift the position of equilibrium to the left ***(1 mark)***, favouring the endothermic backwards reaction ***(1 mark)*** in order to remove the excess heat ***(1 mark)***.

(iii) Any two from: e.g. increasing the pressure/increasing the concentration of N_2 and H_2/reducing the concentration of NH_3 (e.g. by removing it) ***(1 mark for each)***.

Section 3: Reactions and Elements

1. Redox Reactions

Page 137 — Application Questions

Q1 a) +1
b) –1
c) +2

Q2 a) –1
b) –2
c) –1

Q3 a) H: +1, Cl: –1
b) S: +4, O: –2
c) C: +4, O: –2
Oxygen has an oxidation state of -2. There are 3 oxygen atoms here so the total is –6. The overall oxidation state of the ion is –2. So, carbon must have an oxidation state of +4 (as –6 + 4 = –2).
d) Cl: +7, O: –2
e) Cu: +1, O: –2
f) H: +1, S: +6, O: –2
Oxygen has an oxidation state of -2. There are 4 oxygen atoms here so the total is –8. The overall oxidation state of the ion is –1. Hydrogen has an oxidation state of +1. So, sulfur must have an oxidation state of +6 (as –8 + 1 + 6 = –1).

Q4 a) +2
b) +4
c) +4
d) 0
e) +4
f) –2
Hydrogen has an oxidation state of +1. So, in C_3H_6, carbon must have an oxidation state of –2 (as (6 x +1) + (3 x –2) = 0).

Q5 a) 0
b) –3
c) +6
d) +2
Fluorine is the most electronegative element so its oxidation state is equal to its ionic charge, –1. There are 4 fluorine atoms here so the total is –4. So, phosphorus must have an oxidation state of +2 (as (4 x –1) + (2 x +2) = 0).
e) +5
f) –2

Q6 a) beginning: 0, end: +2
b) beginning: +6, end: +6
c) beginning: +1, end: 0

Page 137 — Fact Recall Questions

Q1 Oxidation is a loss of electrons.
Q2 Reduction is a gain of electrons.
Q3 An oxidising agent accepts electrons from another reactant and is reduced.
Q4 A reducing agent donates electrons to another reactant and is oxidised.
Q5 0
Q6 0
Q7 –1
Q8 –1

2. Redox Equations

Page 139 — Application Questions

Q1 $Zn + 2Ag^+ \rightarrow Zn^{2+} + 2Ag$
Q2 Oxidation equation: $Ca \rightarrow Ca^{2+} + 2e^-$
Reduction equation: $Cl_2 + 2e^- \rightarrow 2Cl^-$
Q3 $2NO_3^- + 12H^+ + 10e^- \rightarrow N_2 + 6H_2O$
Q4 $Cr_2O_7^{2-} + 14H^+ + 6e^- \rightarrow 2Cr^{3+} + 7H_2O$
Q5 $H_2SO_4 + 8H^+ + 8e^- \rightarrow H_2S + 4H_2O$

Page 139 — Fact Recall Questions

Q1 An ionic half-equation shows oxidation or reduction.
Q2 B

3. Group 7 — The Halogens

Page 143 — Application Questions

Q1 a) A — bromide, B — chloride/fluoride, C — iodide
b) There would be no change in the colours of the halide solutions. Iodine is below bromine and chlorine in Group 7 so it is less oxidising than them and cannot displace them from a halide solution.

Q2 When chlorine reacts with sodium hydroxide solution it produces sodium chlorate solution. This is bleach, so it will turn the litmus paper white by bleaching it.

Page 143 — Fact Recall Questions

Q1 The boiling points increase down the group.
Q2 fluorine
Q3 bromide and iodide
Q4 a) The solution turns from colourless to brown.
b) $Br_{2(aq)} + 2KI_{(aq)} \rightarrow 2KBr_{(aq)} + I_{2(aq)}$
c) $Br_{2(aq)} + 2I^-_{(aq)} \rightarrow 2Br^-_{(aq)} + I_{2(aq)}$
Q5 a) sodium chlorate(I) solution, sodium chloride, water
b) $2NaOH_{(aq)} + Cl_{2(g)} \rightarrow NaClO_{(aq)} + NaCl_{(aq)} + H_2O_{(l)}$
Q6 When you mix chlorine with water, it undergoes disproportionation. It makes a mixture of hydrochloric acid and chloric(I) acid. The aqueous chloric(I) acid then ionises to make chlorate(I) ions.
Q7 a) Chlorine kills disease-causing microorganisms. It also prevents the growth of algae, eliminating bad tastes and smells, and removes discolouration caused by organic compounds.
b) Chlorine gas is very harmful if it's breathed in — it irritates the respiratory system. Liquid chlorine on the skin or eyes causes severe chemical burns. Accidents involving chlorine could be really serious, or fatal. Water contains a variety of organic compounds, e.g. from the decomposition of plants. Chlorine reacts with these compounds to form chlorinated hydrocarbons, e.g. chloromethane (CH_3Cl) — and many of these chlorinated hydrocarbons are carcinogenic (cancer-causing).

4. Halide Ions

Page 146 — Application Questions

Q1 He is correct for sodium chloride — it will only produce hydrogen chloride. However, the hydrogen bromide produced in the sodium bromide reaction is a strong reducing agent, so it will reduce the sulfuric acid further to sodium dioxide gas and bromine gas.
Q2 A — iodide
B — fluoride
C — bromide

Page 146 — Fact Recall Questions

Q1 How easy it is for a halide ion to lose an electron depends on the attraction between the nucleus and the outer electrons. As you go down the group, the attraction gets weaker because the ions get bigger, so the electrons are further away from the positive nucleus. There are extra inner electron shells, so there's a greater shielding effect too. Therefore, the reducing power of the halides increases down the group.

Q2 a) $NaF_{(s)} + H_2SO_{4(aq)} \rightarrow NaHSO_{4(s)} + HF_{(g)}$

b) $NaI_{(s)} + H_2SO_{4(aq)} \rightarrow NaHSO_{4(s)} + HI_{(g)}$

$2HI_{(g)} + H_2SO_{4(aq)} \rightarrow I_{2(s)} + SO_{2(g)} + 2H_2O_{(l)}$

$6HI_{(g)} + SO_{2(g)} \rightarrow H_2S_{(g)} + 3I_{2(s)} + 2H_2O_{(l)}$

Q3 a) You can use the silver nitrate test. First add dilute nitric acid (to remove ions which might interfere with the test). Then add silver nitrate solution ($AgNO_{3\,(aq)}$). Chloride ions give a white precipitate, whereas fluoride ions give no precipitate.

b) A precipitate of silver chloride will dissolve in dilute ammonia solution.

5. Group 2 — The Alkaline Earth Metals

Page 149 — Application Questions

Q1 The strontium will react more rapidly because it is lower down Group 2 than calcium so it will lose electrons more easily and is more reactive.

Q2 a) Element X has the smallest radius so will have the highest first ionisation energy. This is because the outer electron will be closer to the nucleus than in the other elements, so the attraction between the electron and the nucleus will be stronger. Also, the extra inner shells in elements Y and Z will shield the outer electrons more from the attraction of the nucleus.

b) Element Y. All three elements have 2 delocalised electrons but element Y has the largest atomic radius. So the delocalised electrons in Y will be further away from the nucleus/positive ion than in X or Z. So there's less attraction of the positive ions to the delocalised electrons and it takes less energy to break the bonds.

Page 149 — Fact Recall Questions

Q1 Atomic radius increases down the group.

Q2 Ionisation energy decreases down the group. This is because each element down Group 2 has an extra electron shell compared to the one above. The extra inner shells shield the outer electrons from the attraction of the nucleus. Also, the extra shell means that the outer electrons are further away from the nucleus, which greatly reduces the nucleus's attraction. Both of these factors make it easier to remove outer electrons, resulting in a lower ionisation energy.

Q3 less reactive

Q4 Barium has a smaller atomic radius than radium, so it's two delocalised electrons will be closer to the positive ion/nucleus. This means they will be more strongly attracted to the positive ion/nucleus than the delocalised electrons in radium. So it will take more energy to break the bonds in barium, which means it has a higher melting point.

6. Group 2 Compounds

Page 151 — Application Questions

Q1 The element with the lower ionisation energy will react more readily because it will be oxidised more easily.

Q2 There are no sulfate ions in the solution.

If there were sulfate ions in the sample, a white precipitate of barium sulfate would form.

Page 151 — Fact Recall Questions

Q1 The elements react more readily down the group.

Q2 They become more soluble down the group.

Q3 It is a suspension of barium sulfate that a patient swallows before an X-ray. It is opaque to X-rays so will show up the structure of the oesophagus, stomach or intestines.

Q4 Calcium hydroxide is used in agriculture to neutralise acid soils. Magnesium hydroxide is used in some indigestion tablets as an antacid.

7. Extraction of Metals

Page 155 — Fact Recall Questions

Q1 It's a natural substance that a metal can be economically extracted from.

Q2 a) You would roast/heat it in air.

b) It produces sulfur dioxide, which causes acid rain.

Q3 a) 700 °C in a blast furnace.

b) $2Fe_2O_3 + 3C \rightarrow 4Fe + 3CO_2$

c) $Fe_2O_3 + 3CO \rightarrow 2Fe + 3CO_2$

Q4 a) $MnO_2 + 2CO \rightarrow Mn + 2CO_2$

Don't get mixed up here — make sure you write the equation for the reaction with carbon monoxide, not carbon.

b) 1200 °C in a blast furnace.

Q5 a) $2CuCO_3 + C \rightarrow 2Cu + 3CO_2$

b) $2CuO + C \rightarrow 2Cu + CO_2$

Q6 a) The tungsten oxide is reduced using hydrogen in a furnace at temperatures above 700 °C. The reaction is:

$WO_{3(s)} + 3H_{2(g)} \rightarrow W_{(s)} + 3H_2O_{(g)}$

b) Hydrogen is highly explosive when mixed with air.

Q7 a) Aluminium is too reactive to extract using carbon — a very high temperature is needed, so extracting aluminium by reduction is too expensive to be worthwhile.

b) Cathode: $Al^{3+} + 3e^- \rightarrow Al$

Anode: $2O^{2-} \rightarrow O_2 + 4e^-$

Q8 $TiCl_{4\,(g)} + 2Mg_{(l)} \rightarrow Ti_{(s)} + 2MgCl_{2\,(l)}$

8. Recycling Metals

Page 156 — Fact Recall Questions

Q1 Advantages: e.g. saves raw materials — ores are a finite resource. Saves energy — recycling metals takes less energy than extracting metal. This saves money too. Reduces waste sent to landfill. Mining damages the landscape and spoil heaps are ugly. Recycling metals reduces this.

Disadvantages: e.g. collecting and sorting metals from other waste can be difficult and expensive. The purity of recycled metal varies — there's usually other metals and other impurities mixed in. Recycling metals may not produce a consistent supply to meet demand.

Q2 a) Scrap iron is added to copper compounds dissolved in acidified water. The iron dissolves and reduces the copper(II) ions. The copper precipitates out of the solution.

b) low grade ore/ore that only contains a small percentage of copper

Exam-style Questions — page 158

1 a) Chlorine has a lower boiling point than bromine ***(1 mark)***. This is because chlorine atoms are smaller than bromine atoms ***(1 mark)***. So chlorine has weaker Van der Waals forces holding its atoms together ***(1 mark)***.

b) (i) Potassium bromide ***(1 mark)***. Chlorine displaces the halide ions, so the halogen must be below it in Group 7 ***(1 mark)***. However, there's no reaction with bromine water so the halide ion can't be less reactive than bromine ***(1 mark)***.

(ii) Potassium iodide ***(1 mark)***.
$Cl_2 + 2I^- \rightarrow 2Cl^- + I_2$ ***(1 mark)***

You must make sure you balance ionic equations or you won't get the marks in the exam.

c) (i) Cl_2: 0 ***(1 mark)***, ClO^-: +1 ***(1 mark)***, NaCl: –1 ***(1 mark)***

(ii) NaClO is used as bleach ***(1 mark)***.

d) (i) Dilute nitric acid is added to the solution to remove ions which might interfere with the test ***(1 mark)***.

(ii) A cream precipitate would form ***(1 mark)***.

(iii) The precipitate of silver bromide would dissolve in concentrated ammonia solution ***(1 mark)***.

2 a) D ***(1 mark)***

b) Metal E has an extra electron shell compared to metal D ***(1 mark)***. The extra inner shells shield the outer electrons from the attraction of the nucleus/the extra shell means that the outer electrons are further away from the nucleus, which greatly reduces the nucleus's attraction ***(1 mark)***. This makes it easier to remove outer electrons, resulting in a lower ionisation energy in metal E ***(1 mark)***.

c) Metal F will react more quickly with water ***(1 mark)*** because it has a lower first ionisation energy ***(1 mark)***.

d) Barium has a larger atomic radius than metal F ***(1 mark)***. So its delocalised electrons will be further away from the positive ion/nucleus than those in metal F ***(1 mark)***. This means they will be less strongly attracted to the positive ion/nucleus than in metal F so the metallic bonding is weaker ***(1 mark)***.

e) (i) It is sparingly soluble / has very low solubility ***(1 mark)***.

(ii) It will be more soluble ***(1 mark)***.

f) It is used in indigestion tablets ***(1 mark)*** to neutralise acid in the stomach ***(1 mark)***.

g) (i) $TiCl_{4\,(g)} + 4Na_{(l)} \rightarrow Ti_{(s)} + 4NaCl_{(l)}$ ***(1 mark)***

(ii) A reducing agent is something that donates electrons ***(1 mark)***.

3 a) An ore is a natural substance that a metal can be economically extracted from ***(1 mark)***.

b) Carbon monoxide is cheap but effective as a reducing agent ***(1 mark)***.

c) $MnO_2 + 2CO \rightarrow Mn + 2CO_2$

d) 1200 °C in a blast furnace ***(1 mark)***.

e) Tungsten is extracted using hydrogen ***(1 mark)*** in a furnace above 700 °C ***(1 mark)***. Hydrogen is highly explosive when mixed with air ***(1 mark)***.

4 a) $3Cl_2 + 6e^- \rightarrow 6Cl^-$ ***(1 mark)*** — reduction ***(1 mark)***
$2Al \rightarrow 2Al^{3+} + 6e^-$ ***(1 mark)*** — oxidation ***(1 mark)***

b) The bauxite is purified and dissolved in molten cryolite (sodium aluminium fluoride, Na_3AlF_6) ***(1 mark)***. An electric current is passed through the liquid ***(1 mark)***. Aluminium ions are reduced at the cathode and collect as molten aluminium metal at the bottom of the cell ***(1 mark)***. Oxygen gas is produced at the anode as oxide ions are oxidised ***(1 mark)***. The process is expensive because lots of electricity is needed to heat and melt the ore/run the electrolysis equipment ***(1 mark)***.

c) Advantages: any two from, e.g. it saves raw materials because you don't need to extract more aluminium from its ore / recycling aluminium takes less energy/money than extracting it by electrolysis / fewer aluminium cans will be sent to landfill / mining damages the landscape and spoil heaps are ugly. Recycling aluminium reduces this. ***(1 mark for each point.)***
Disadvantages: any two from, e.g. collecting and sorting aluminium cans from other waste can be difficult and expensive / the purity of recycled aluminium varies / recycling aluminium may not produce a consistent supply of aluminium to meet demand. ***(1 mark for each point.)***

Section 4: More Organic Chemistry

1. Synthesis of Chloroalkanes

Page 163 — Fact Recall Questions

Q1 Reactions that are started by ultraviolet light.

Q2 $Cl_2 \xrightarrow{UV} 2Cl\cdot$

Q3 Cl·/chlorine free radicals

2. Haloalkanes

Page 164 — Fact Recall Questions

Q1 An alkane with at least one halogen atom in place of a hydrogen atom.

Q2 Halogen atoms are more electronegative than carbon atoms and so they withdraw electron density from carbon atoms. This leaves the carbon atoms with a partial positive charge and the halogen atoms with a partial negative charge.

Q3 An electron-pair donor.

Q4 Any two from: e.g. ^-CN / NH_3 / ^-OH.

Q5 A pair of dots represents a lone pair of electrons.

3. Nucleophilic Substitution

Page 169 — Application Questions

Q1

reflux, ethanol

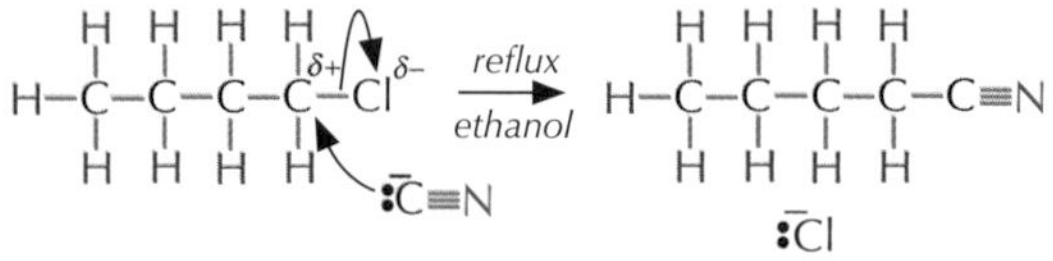

Q2 Reaction C would happen the quickest because the C–I bond has the lowest bond enthalpy of all the carbon-halogen bonds. This means that the C–I bond is the easiest to break and therefore the reaction will happen the quickest.

Q3

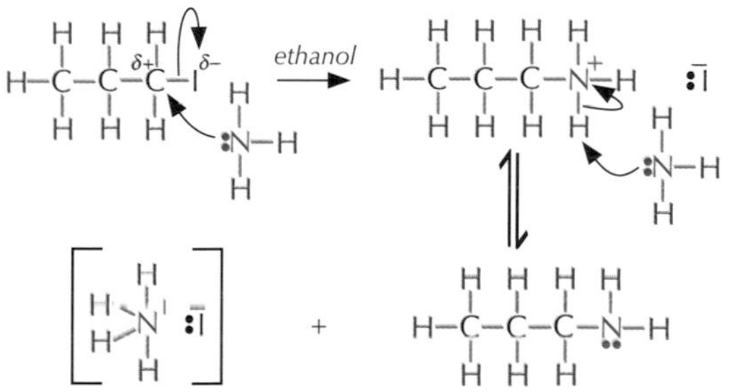

ethanol

Q4

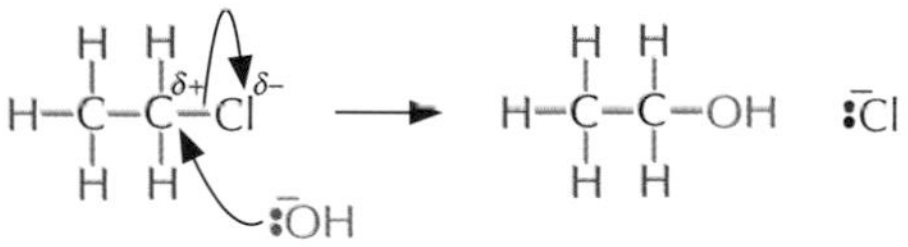

Page 169 — Fact Recall Questions

Q1 Nucleophilic substitution reactions are reactions in which a nucleophile attacks a polar molecule and replaces a functional group.

Q2 Warm aqueous sodium hydroxide or potassium hydroxide.

Q3 For a hydrolysis reaction to occur the carbon-halogen bond needs to break. The C–F bond is the strongest — it has the highest bond enthalpy. So fluoroalkanes are hydrolysed more slowly than other haloalkanes.

Q4 Heating in ethanol in a sealed tube.

Q5 e.g. ^-CN / cyanide ion

4. Elimination Reactions

Page 171 — Application Question

Q1

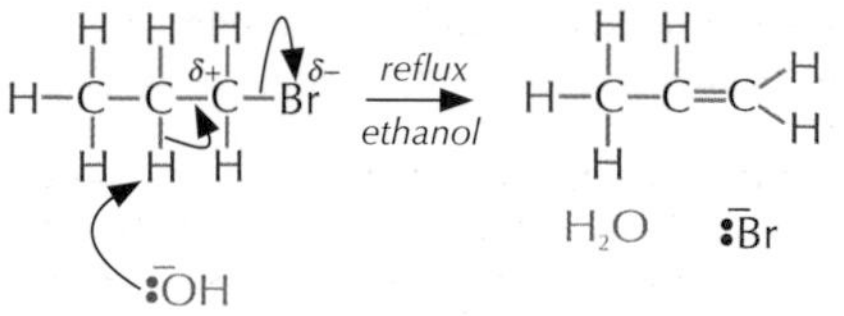

reflux, ethanol

H_2O :Br^-

Page 171 — Fact Recall Questions

Q1 An elimination reaction happens when a molecule loses atoms or groups of atoms from two neighbouring carbon atoms and forms a carbon-carbon double bond.

Q2 The ^-OH acts as a nucleophile. This is a nucleophilic substitution reaction.

Q3 The ^-OH acts as a base. This is an elimination reaction.

Q4 The elimination reaction is a good way of getting a double bond into a molecule. Loads of other organic synthesis reactions use alkenes, so the elimination reaction is a good starting point for making lots of different organic chemicals. The substitution reaction allows you to produce any alcohol molecule that you need. And alcohols can be the starting point for synthesis reactions that produce aldehydes, ketones, esters, and carboxylic acids.

5. Reactions of Alkenes

Page 176 — Application Questions

Q1

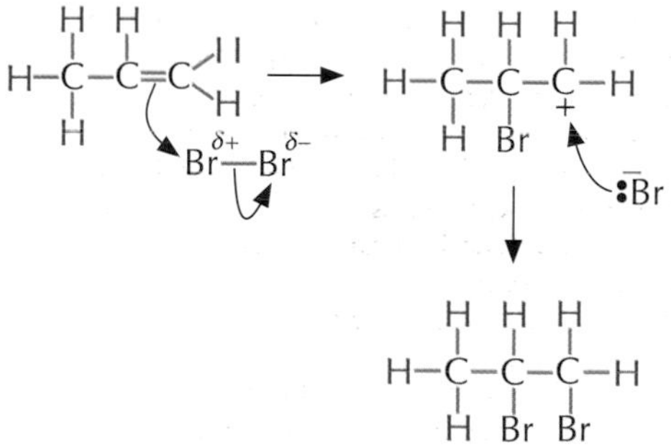

Q2

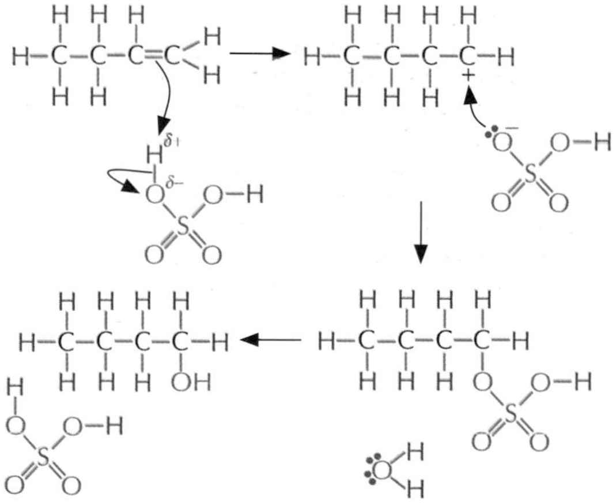

Page 176 — Fact Recall Questions

Q1 C_nH_{2n}

Q2 Alkenes are unsaturated because they can make more bonds with extra atoms in addition reactions across the carbon-carbon double bond.

Q3 Alkenes can undergo electrophilic addition reactions because they have a double bond which has a high electron density and is easily attacked by electrophiles.

Q4 Electrophiles are electron-pair acceptors.

Q5 Any two from: e.g. NO_2^+ / H^+ / CH_3CH_2Br.

Q6 Carbon-carbon double bonds/unsaturation.

Q7

$$CH_2{=}CH_{2(g)} + H_2O_{(g)} \underset{\substack{300\ ^\circ C \\ 60\ atm}}{\overset{H_3PO_4}{\rightleftharpoons}} CH_3CH_2OH_{(g)}$$

Q8 You can recycle the unreacted ethene gas.

6. More Reactions of Alkenes

Page 179 — Application Questions

Q1 a)

```
    H     H H                 H   H   H   H
    |     | |                 |   |   |   |
H - C - C=C - C - H  ---->  H-C - C - C - C-H
    |   |     |               |   |   +   |
    H   H     H               H   H       H
                                      :Br
      δ+ δ-
      H—Br
                                  |
                                  v
                              H   H   H   H
                              |   |   |   |
                            H-C - C - C - C-H
                              |   |   |   |
                              H   H   Br  H
```

It doesn't matter which carbon you add the bromine to as you'll always end up with the same product (2-bromobutane).

b) $C_4H_8 + HBr \rightarrow C_4H_9Br$

Q2 The reaction mechanism for the production of 2-bromobutane contains a secondary carbocation which is a more stable carbocation intermediate than the primary carbocation formed in the reaction mechanism for 1-bromobutane. More stable carbocations are more likely to form and so 2-bromobutane is the major product of this reaction.

Page 179 — Fact Recall Questions

Q1 hydrogen bromide

Q2 Tertiary carbocations are more stable than secondary carbocations, which are more stable than primary carbocations.

7. E/Z Isomers and Polymers

Page 181 — Application Questions

Q1 a) Z-isomer

b) E-isomer

Q2

```
  H3C       CH2CH3
     \     /
      C = C              E-isomer
     /     \
H3CH2C      CH3

  H3C       CH3
     \     /
      C = C              Z-isomer
     /     \
H3CH2C      CH2CH3
```

Page 183 — Application Questions

Q1

```
    F       H            /  F   H  \
     \     /            |   |   |   |
 n    C = C    ---->    |  -C - C-  |
     /     \            |   |   |   |
    H       H            \  H   H  / n
```

Q2

```
H       Cl
 \     /
  C = C
 /     \
H       H
```

Q3

```
   H  Cl
   |  |
 - C - C -
   |  |
   H  CH3
```

Page 183 — Fact Recall Questions

Q1 E/Z isomerism is caused by the restricted rotation around the C=C double bond. If there are different groups attached either side of the double bond then the restricted rotation of the carbon-carbon double bond means that the atoms can be arranged differently in space.

Q2 stereoisomerism

Q3 The double bonds in alkenes (monomers) open up and join together to make long chains called polymers.

Q4 Poly(alkenes) are unreactive because they have lost their carbon-carbon double bonds.

Q5 It is soft and flexible.

Q6 Any one of: e.g. bottle crates / ropes.

Q7 It makes sense to recycle polymers as they are difficult to dispose of safely and are made from non-renewable oil fractions.

8. Alcohols

Page 187 — Application Questions

Q1 a) pentan-1-ol

b) 2,2-dimethylpropan-1-ol

c) 2,3-dimethylbutan-1-ol

d) 3-ethyl-2-methylpentan-1,5-diol

That last one is a tricky one... Make sure you have the side chains in alphabetical order and the name has the lowest possible numbers in it.

Q2 a) primary

b) primary

c) primary

d) primary

Page 187 — Fact Recall Questions

Q1 $C_nH_{2n+1}OH$

Q2 A secondary alcohol is an alcohol with the –OH group attached to a carbon with two alkyl groups attached.

Q3

$$C_6H_{12}O_{6(aq)} \xrightarrow[\text{yeast}]{30\text{-}40^\circ C} 2C_2H_5OH_{(aq)} + 2CO_{2(g)}$$

Q4 If it's too cold, the reaction is slow — if it's too hot, the enzyme is denatured (damaged).

Q5 a) When the solution reaches about 15% ethanol, the yeast dies.

b) Fractional distillation can be used to increase the concentration of ethanol.

Q6 A biofuel is a fuel that's made from biological material that's recently died.

Q7 $C_2H_5OH + H_2SO_4 \rightarrow C_2H_5OSO_2OH + H_2O$

$C_2H_5OSO_2OH \rightarrow CH_2{=}CH_2 + H_2SO_4$

9. Oxidising Alcohols

Page 191 — Application Question

Q1 a)

```
    H  H  O  H
    |  |  ||  |
H—C—C—C—C—H
    |  |      |
    H  H      H
```

b)

```
    H  H  H  O
    |  |  |  ||
H—C—C—C—C—H
    |  |  |
    H  H  H
```

c)

```
    H  H  H  O
    |  |  |  ||
H—C—C—C—C—OH
    |  |  |
    H  H  H
```

Page 191 — Fact Recall Questions

Q1 Aldehydes have the functional group C=O and have one hydrogen atom and one R group attached to the carbon atom. Ketones have the functional group C=O and have two R groups attached either side of the carbon atom. Carboxylic acids have the functional group COOH.

Q2

$$R{-}CH_2{-}OH + 2[O] \xrightarrow{\text{reflux}} R{-}\overset{\displaystyle O}{\overset{\|}{C}}{-}OH + H_2O$$

primary alcohol → *carboxylic acid*

Q3 Any two from: e.g. Fehling's solution / Benedict's solution / Tollens' reagent.

10. Mass Spectrometry

Page 195 — Application Questions

Q1 E.g. CH_3^+ / $CH_3CH_2^+$ / CH_2^+ / $CH_3CH_2CH_2^+$ / OH^+.

Q2 The molecule is ethanoic acid.

```
    H  O
    |  ||
H—C—C—OH
    |
    H
```

This table shows all the m/z peaks from the mass spectrum and the fragment ions they can be assigned to:

m/z	fragment ion
15	CH_3^+
17	OH^+
28	$C{=}O^+$
29	COH^+
43	CH_3CO^+
44	COO^+ / CH_3COH^+
60	M (CH_3COOH^+)
61	M+1

Don't forget that you don't have to assign all of these peaks — just as long as you've done enough to be able to prove that it's ethanoic acid...

Page 195 — Fact Recall Questions

Q1 The one with the second highest mass/charge ratio.

Q2 The molecular mass of the compound.

Q3 CH_3^+

11. Infrared Spectroscopy

Page 198 — Application Questions

Q1 a) A (~3000 cm^{-1}) — O–H (carboxylic acid)
B (~1700 cm^{-1}) — C=O

b)

```
    H  H  O
    |  |  ||
H—C—C—C—OH
    |  |
    H  H
```

The mass of the carboxylic acid group (COOH) is 45 (12 + 16 + 16 + 1). The M_r of the molecule is 74, so the rest of the molecule has a mass of 74 – 45 = 29. This corresponds to an ethyl group (CH_3CH_2), so the molecule must be propanoic acid.

Q2 There is a strong, sharp peak at about 1700cm^{-1}, this indicates that a C=O bond is present in the molecule.

Page 198 — Fact Recall Questions

Q1 A beam of IR radiation is passed through a sample of a chemical. The IR radiation is absorbed by the covalent bonds in the molecules, increasing their vibrational energy. Bonds between different atoms absorb different frequencies of IR radiation. Bonds in different places in a molecule absorb different frequencies too. The frequencies where they absorb IR radiation are plotted to give an IR spectra.

Q2 1000 cm^{-1} – 1550 cm^{-1}

Exam-style Questions — page 200

Q1 a) $CH_3CH_2Br + OH^- \rightarrow CH_3CH_2OH + Br^-$ ***(1 mark)***

```
    H  H  δ+ δ–                      H  H
    |  |                             |  |
H—C—C—Br      ————►      H—C—C—OH   :Br⁻
    |  |                             |  |
    H  H   :OH⁻                      H  H
```

(1 mark)

The reaction of water with iodoethane would be quicker than the reaction of bromoethane with water ***(1 mark)***. This is because the C–I bond has a lower bond enthalpy than the C–Br bond ***(1 mark)***, which means it is more easily broken ***(1 mark)***.

b) $C_6H_{12}O_{6(aq)} \rightarrow 2C_2H_5OH_{(aq)} + 2CO_{2(g)}$ ***(1 mark)***
The reaction needs to be carried out in the presence of yeast and at 30–40 °C ***(1 mark)***.
In the future there will be less crude oil available to produce ethene which is used industrially to produce ethanol ***(1 mark)***. Fermentation uses renewable resources to produce ethanol and so will become more important as the amount of crude oil decreases ***(1 mark)***.

c) The hydration of ethene by steam is carried out at 300 °C and at a pressure of 60 atm ***(1 mark)***. It also needs a solid phosphoric(V) acid catalyst ***(1 mark)***. You could increase the yield of this reaction by recycling the unreacted ethene gas ***(1 mark)***.

d) A biofuel is a fuel that's made from biological material that's recently died ***(1 mark)***. Ethanol is thought of as a carbon neutral fuel because all the CO_2 released when the fuel is burned was removed from the atmosphere by the crop as it grew ***(1 mark)***. Unfortunately this isn't always the case as there are still carbon emissions if you consider the whole ethanol production process ***(1 mark)***. For example, the machinery used to produce the ethanol fuel may be powered by fossil fuels which release CO_2 into the atmosphere when they're burnt ***(1 mark)***.

Q2 a) Molecule **A** is:

```
     H  H
H\   |  |
  >C=C--C-H
H/      |
        H
```
(1 mark)

Molecule **B** is:

```
   H  H  H
   |  |  |
H--C--C--C--OH
   |  |  |
   H  H  H
```
(1 mark)

The IR spectrum of molecule **B** shows a strong, broad peak at around $3400cm^{-1}$. This corresponds to an alcohol functional group ***(1 mark)*** — hence molecule **B** must be an alcohol created from a nucleophilic substitution reaction of 1-bromopropane ***(1 mark)***. The IR spectrum of molecule **A** doesn't contain an alcohol group ***(1 mark)*** and doesn't contain bromine — hence the molecule must have been created via an elimination reaction of 1-bromopropane ***(1 mark)***.

b) Molecule **A** is propene ***(1 mark)***.
Molecule **B** is propan-1-ol ***(1 mark)***.

c) Molecule **A** is produced by reacting 1-bromopropane with ethanol and potassium/sodium hydroxide under reflux ***(1 mark)***.
Molecule **B** is produced by reacting 1-bromopropane with water and potassium/sodium hydroxide under reflux ***(1 mark)***.

Q3 a) The student could shake the alkene with bromine water ***(1 mark)***. The solution will turn from orange to colourless if a carbon-carbon double bond is present ***(1 mark)***.

b) (i) A stereoisomer is a molecule that has the same structural formula as another molecule but its atoms are arranged differently in space ***(1 mark)***.

(ii)

```
      CH3    CH3
        \   /
         C=C
        /   \
  H3CH2C     H
```
(1 mark)

```
      CH3    H
        \   /
         C=C
        /   \
  H3CH2C     CH3
```
(1 mark)

The CH_2CH_3 and CH_3 groups could also be both above the double bond for the second isomer.

(iii) The top isomer is E-3-methylpent-2-ene ***(1 mark)***
The bottom isomer is Z-3-methylpent-2-ene ***(1 mark)***

c) (i) $C_6H_{12} + HBr \rightarrow C_6H_{13}Br$ ***(1 mark)***

(ii)

```
   H  H  Br  H  H
   |  |  |   |  |
H--C--C--C---C--C--H
   |  |  |   |  |
   H  H  CH3 H  H
```
(1 mark)

(iii) This isomer is the major product of the reaction because it's formed when the reaction proceeds via the most stable carbocation intermediate ***(1 mark)***. For the major product the reaction goes via a tertiary (3°) carbocation ***(1 mark)*** and for the minor product the reaction goes via a secondary (2°) carbocation ***(1 mark)***.

d)

```
    H\     /CH2CH3          /  H   CH2CH3 \
n     C=C          ---->   |   |   |       |
 H3C/     \CH3             | --C---C--     |
                           |   |   |       |
                            \ H3C  CH3    / n
```

(1 mark for correct reactant, 1 mark for correct product.)

Q4 a) Reacting a haloalkane with ammonia produces an amine — so molecule A must be an amine ***(1 mark)***. From the mass spectrum the M peak is at 31 m/z so the M_r of the compound must be 31 ***(1 mark)***. There is also a peak at 15 m/z which indicates a CH_3 group ***(1 mark)***. So, the structure of molecule A must be:

```
   H  H
   |  |
H--C--N--H
   |
   H
```
(1 mark)

Since it's an amine, the molecule has to contain an NH_2 group. The mass of an NH_2 group and a CH_3 group is: $(14 + (2 \times 1)) + (12 + (3 \times 1)) = 31$. This is the M_r, so there are no more atoms in the molecule — the structure must be a CH_3 group attached to an NH_2 group.

b) The infrared spectrum shows a strong broad peak at about 3300 cm^{-1} which corresponds to an O–H group on an alcohol ***(1 mark)***. Acidified potassium dichromate(VI) will oxidise secondary alcohols under reflux to ketones — so molecule **B** must be a secondary alcohol ***(1 mark)***. The only secondary alcohol with an M_r of 74 is butan-2-ol ***(1 mark)***.
So molecule B is butan-2-ol:

```
   H  H  H  H
   |  |  |  |
H--C--C--C--C--H
   |  |  |  |
   H  H  OH H
```
(1 mark)

c) The infrared spectrum has a sharp, strong peak at 1700 cm^{-1}, so molecule **C** contains a carbonyl group ***(1 mark)***. It doesn't have a carboxylic acid OH peak, so molecule C must be an aldehyde or a ketone ***(1 mark)***. But molecule **C** doesn't react with Tollens' reagent which means it isn't an aldehyde so must be a ketone ***(1 mark)***. The mass spectrum shows that the M_r of molecule C is 72 ***(1 mark)***. Molecule **C** is a ketone with $M_r = 72$ — so it must be butanone:

```
   H  H  O  H
   |  |  ‖  |
H--C--C--C--C--H
   |  |     |
   H  H     H
```
(1 mark)

Glossary

Accurate result
A result that's really close to the true answer.

Activation energy
The minimum amount of kinetic energy that particles need to have in order to react when they collide.

Addition polymer
A long chain molecule made of repeating units of monomers.

Alcohol
A substance with the general formula $C_nH_{2n+1}OH$.

Aldehyde
A substance with the general formula $C_nH_{2n}O$ which has a hydrogen and one alkyl group attached to the carbonyl carbon atom.

Alkaline earth metal
An element in Group 2 of the periodic table.

Alkane
A hydrocarbon with the general formula C_nH_{2n+2}.

Alkene
A hydrocarbon with the general formula C_nH_{2n} and containing at least one carbon-carbon double bond.

Anode
The positive electrode in electrolysis.

Anomalous result
A result that doesn't fit in with the pattern of the other results in a set of data.

Atom
A neutral particle made up of protons and neutrons in a central nucleus, and electrons orbiting the nucleus.

Atom economy
A measure of the proportion of reactant atoms that become part of the desired product in a balanced chemical reaction.

Atomic number
The number of protons in the nucleus of an atom.

Avogadro's constant
6×10^{23} — the number of particles in 1 mole of a substance.

B

Barium chloride test
Test that uses acidified barium chloride to test for sulfate ions in solution.

Barium meal
A suspension of barium sulfate swallowed by a patient before an X-ray in order to show up the structure of their oesophagus, stomach or intestine.

Bauxite
An aluminium ore.

Benedict's solution
A deep blue Cu^{2+} complex, which reduces to a brick-red Cu_2O precipitate when warmed with an aldehyde, but stays blue with a ketone.

Biofuel
A fuel that's made from biological material that's recently died.

Bond enthalpy
The energy required to break a bond between two atoms. Usually given as a 'mean bond enthalpy', an average value for the particular bond over the range of compounds it is found in.

Carbocation
An organic ion containing a positively charged carbon atom.

Carbonyl compound
A compound that contains a carbon-oxygen double bond.

Carboxylic acid
A substance which has a COOH group attached to the end of a carbon chain.

Catalyst
A substance that increases the rate of a reaction by providing an alternative reaction pathway with a lower activation energy. The catalyst is chemically unchanged at the end of the reaction.

Categoric data
Data that can be sorted into categories.

Cathode
The negative electrode in electrolysis.

Causal link
The relationship between two variables where a change in one variable causes a change in the other.

Chain isomer
A molecule that contains the same atoms as another molecule but has a different arrangement of the carbon skeleton.

Charge cloud
An area in an atom or molecule where there's a really big chance of finding an electron pair.

Chloroalkane
An alkane with one or more hydrogen atoms substituted for chlorine atoms.

Closed system
A system where nothing can get in or out.

Collision theory
The theory that a reaction will not take place between two particles unless they collide in the right direction and with at least a certain minimum amount of kinetic energy.

Complete combustion
Burning a substance completely in oxygen to produce CO_2 and H_2O only.

Continuous data
Data that can have any value on a scale.

Co-ordinate bonding
A covalent bond formed when one atom provides both of the shared electrons. Also called dative covalent bonding.

Correlation
The relationship between two variables.

Cracking
Breaking long-chain alkanes into smaller hydrocarbons.

Crude oil
A mixture consisting mainly of alkane hydrocarbons that can be separated into different fractions.

Curly arrow
An arrow used in mechanisms to show the movement of a pair of electrons.

Cycloalkane
A type of alkane which has one or more carbon rings.

D

Dative covalent bonding
A covalent bond formed when one atom provides both of the shared electrons. Also called co-ordinate bonding.

Dehydration
A reaction where water is eliminated from a reactant.

Delocalised electron
An electron that is not attached to a specific atom.

Dependent variable
The variable that you measure in an experiment.

Dipole
The difference in charge between two atoms caused by a shift in the electron density in the bond.

Discrete data
Data that can only take certain values.

Displacement reaction
A reaction where a more reactive element pushes out (displaces) a less reactive element from an ionic solution.

Displayed formula
A way of representing a molecule that shows how all the atoms are arranged, and all the bonds between them.

Disproportionation
When an element is both oxidised and reduced in a single chemical reaction.

Dynamic equilibrium
In a reversible reaction, dynamic equilibrium is reached when the concentrations of reactants and products are constant, and the forwards reaction and the backwards reaction are going at the same rate.

E

E-/Z-isomerism
A type of stereoisomerism that is caused by the restricted rotation about a carbon-carbon double bond. Each of the carbon atoms must have two different groups attached.

Electron
A subatomic particle with a relative charge of 1– and a relative mass of 1/2000, located in orbitals around the nucleus.

Electron configuration
The number of electrons that an atom or ion has and how they are arranged.

Electron shell
A region of an atom with a fixed energy that contains electrons orbiting the nucleus.

Electronegativity
The ability to attract the bonding electrons in a covalent bond.

Electrophile
An electron-pair acceptor.

Electrophilic addition
A reaction mechanism where a double bond in an alkene opens up and atoms are added to the carbon atoms.

Electrostatic attraction
The force that holds positive and negative ions together in ionic compounds.

Elimination reaction
A reaction mechanism in which a molecule loses atoms or groups of atoms.

Empirical formula
The simplest whole number ratio of atoms of each element in a compound.

Endothermic reaction
A reaction that absorbs energy (ΔH is positive).

Energy level
A region of an atom with a fixed energy that contains electrons orbiting the nucleus.

Enthalpy change
The heat energy transferred in a reaction at constant pressure.

Exothermic reaction
A reaction that gives out energy (ΔH is negative).

F

Fehling's solution
A deep blue Cu^{2+} complex, which reduces to a brick-red Cu_2O precipitate when warmed with an aldehyde, but stays blue with a ketone.

Fingerprint region
The region between 1000 cm^{-1} and 1550 cm^{-1} on an infrared spectrum. It's unique to a particular compound.

First ionisation energy
The energy needed to remove 1 electron from each atom in 1 mole of gaseous atoms to form 1 mole of gaseous 1+ ions.

Fractional distillation
A method of separating crude oil fractions by boiling point.

Free radical
A particle with an unpaired electron, written like this — Cl· or CH_3·.

Functional group isomer
A molecule that has the same molecular formula as another molecule, but with the atoms arranged into different functional groups.

G

General formula
An algebraic formula that can describe any member of a family of compounds.

Giant covalent structure
A structure consisting of a huge network of covalently bonded atoms. They're sometimes called macromolecular structures.

Giant ionic lattice structure
A regular repeated structure made up of ions.

Giant metallic lattice structure
A regular structure consisting of closely packed positive metal ions in a sea of delocalised electrons.

Group
A column in the periodic table.

H

Halide
A negative ion of a halogen.

Haloalkane
An alkane with at least one halogen atom in place of a hydrogen atom.

Halogen
An element in Group 7 of the periodic table.

Hess's Law
The total enthalpy change of a reaction is always the same, no matter which route is taken.

Homogeneous catalyst
A catalyst which is in the same phase as the reactants.

Homologous series
A bunch of organic compounds that have the same general formula and similar chemical properties.

Hydration reaction
A reaction where water is added to a compound.

Hydrocarbon
A molecule that only contains hydrogen and carbon atoms.

Hydrogen bonding
The strongest intermolecular force. It occurs when polarised covalent bonds cause hydrogen atoms to form weak bonds with lone pairs of electrons on the fluorine, nitrogen or oxygen atoms of other molecules.

Hydrolysis reaction
A reaction where molecules are split apart by water molecules. The water molecules are also split into hydrogen ions (H^+) and hydroxide ions (OH^-).

Hypothesis
A specific testable statement, based on a theory, about what will happen in a test situation.

I

Ideal gas equation
The ideal gas equation is $pV = nRT$. It allows you to find the number of moles in a volume of gas at any temperature and pressure.

Incomplete combustion
Burning a substance in a poor supply of oxygen to produce carbon monoxide, water and sometimes carbon and carbon dioxide.

Independent variable
The variable that you change in an experiment.

Infrared (IR) spectroscopy
An analytical technique used to identify the functional groups present in a molecule by measuring the vibrational frequency of its bonds.

Intermediate
A short-lived, reactive molecule that occurs in the middle of a step-wise reaction mechanism.

Intermolecular forces
Forces between molecules, e.g. van der Waals forces, permanent dipole-dipole forces and hydrogen bonding.

Ion
A charged particle formed when one or more electrons are lost or gained from an atom or molecule.

Ionic bonding
The bonding in a compound made up of positive and negative ions.

Ionisation
The removal of one or more electrons from an atom or molecule, resulting in an ion forming.

Isomer
A molecule with the same molecular formula as another molecule, but with the atoms connected in a different way.

Isotope
An atom with the same number of protons as another atom but a different number of neutrons.

Isotopic abundance
The amount of each isotope present in a sample.

K

Ketone
A substance with the general formula $C_nH_{2n}O$ which has two alkyl groups attached to the carbonyl carbon atom.

L

Lattice
A regular structure made up of ions.

Le Chatelier's principle
If there's a change in concentration, pressure or temperature, the equilibrium will move to help counteract the change.

Lone pair
A pair of electrons in an atom that is not shared.

M

Macromolecular structure
A structure consisting of a huge network of covalently bonded atoms. They're also called giant covalent structures.

Mass number
The total number of protons and neutrons in the nucleus of an atom.

Mass spectrum
A chart produced by a mass spectrometer giving information on relative isotopic mass and relative abundance of isotopes.

Maxwell-Boltzmann distribution
A theoretical model that describes the distribution of kinetic energies of molecules in a gas.

Mean bond enthalpy
An average value for the bond enthalpy of a particular bond over the range of compounds it is found in.

Model
A simplified picture or representation of a real physical situation.

Molar ratio
The ratio of the moles of each reactant and product in a balanced chemical equation.

Mole
The unit of amount of substance. One mole is roughly 6×10^{23} particles (Avogadro's constant).

Molecular formula
A way of representing molecules that shows the actual number of atoms of each element in a molecule.

Molecule
The smallest part of a compound that can take part in a chemical reaction.

Monomer
A small alkene which is used to make an addition polymer.

Monoprotic acid
An acid that can only release one H^+ ion from each molecule (e.g. HCl).

Neutron
A subatomic particle with a relative charge of 0 and a relative mass of 1, located in the nucleus of an atom.

Nitrogen oxides
A series of toxic and poisonous molecules which have the general formula NO_x.

Nomenclature
A fancy word for naming organic compounds.

Nucleophile
An electron-pair donor.

Nucleophilic substitution reaction
A reaction mechanism where a nucleophile attacks a polar molecule and replaces a functional group in that molecule.

Nucleus
The central part of an atom or ion, made up of protons and neutrons.

Orbital
A region of a sub-shell that contains a maximum of 2 electrons.

Ordered / ordinal data
Categoric data where the categories can be put in order.

Ore
A natural substance that a metal can be economically extracted from.

Oxidation
Loss of electrons.

Oxidation state
The total number of electrons an element has donated or accepted. Also called an oxidation number.

Oxidising agent
Something that accepts electrons and gets reduced.

Ozone layer
A layer of ozone (O_3) found in the Earth's upper atmosphere which protects the Earth from ultraviolet radiation.

Peer review
The evaluation of a scientific report by other scientists who are experts in the same area (peers). They go through it bit by bit, examining the methods and data, and checking it's all clear and logical.

Percentage yield
A comparison between the amount of product that should form during a reaction and the amount that actually forms.

Period
A row in the periodic table.

Periodicity
The trends in physical and chemical properties of elements as you go across the periodic table.

Permanent dipole-dipole forces
Intermolecular forces that exist because the difference in electronegativities in a polar bond causes weak electrostatic forces of attraction between molecules.

Petroleum
A mixture consisting mainly of alkane hydrocarbons that can be separated into different fractions.

Photochemical reaction
A reaction started by ultraviolet light.

Polar bond
A covalent bond where a difference in electronegativity has caused a shift in electron density in the bond.

Polar chemical
A chemical containing bonding electrons with different electronegativities, so the electrons in the bond are pulled more towards one atom than the other and a dipole is created.

Positional isomer
A molecule with the same molecular formula as another molecule but with the functional group in a different position.

Precise result
A result taken using sensitive instruments that measure in small increments.

Protocol
An accepted method to test a certain thing that all scientists can use.

Proton
A subatomic particle with a relative charge of 1+ and a relative mass of 1, located in the nucleus of an atom.

Proton number
The number of protons in the nucleus of an atom.

Redox reaction
A reaction where reduction and oxidation happen simultaneously.

Reducing agent
Something that donates electrons and gets oxidised.

Reduction
Gain of electrons.

Refluxing
A method for heating a reaction so that you can increase the temperature of an organic reaction to boiling without losing volatile solvents, reactants or products. Any vaporised compounds are cooled, condense and drip back into the reaction mixture.

Relative atomic mass
The average mass of an atom of an element on a scale where an atom of carbon-12 is exactly 12.

Relative formula mass
The average mass of a formula unit on a scale where an atom of carbon-12 is exactly 12.

Relative isotopic mass
The mass of an atom of an isotope of an element on a scale where an atom of carbon-12 is exactly 12.

Relative molecular mass
The average mass of a molecule on a scale where an atom of carbon-12 is exactly 12.

Reliable result
A result that can be consistently reproduced in independent experiments.

Saturated hydrocarbon
A hydrocarbon with no carbon-carbon double bonds.

Silver nitrate test
Test that uses silver nitrate to identify halide ions in a solution.

Simple covalent compound
A compound with strong bonds within its molecules but weak forces between its molecules.

Standard conditions
100 kPa (about 1 atm) pressure and a stated temperature, usually 298 K.

Standard enthalpy change of combustion
The enthalpy change when 1 mole of a substance is completely burned in oxygen under standard conditions with all reactants and products in their standard states ($\Delta H_c^{\ominus}$).

Standard enthalpy change of formation
The enthalpy change when 1 mole of a compound is formed from its elements in their standard states under standard conditions ($\Delta H_f^{\ominus}$).

Standard enthalpy change of reaction
The enthalpy change when a reaction occurs in the molar quantities shown in the chemical equation, under standard conditions with all reactants and products in their standard states ($\Delta H_r^{\ominus}$).

State symbols
Symbols placed after the chemicals in an equation to tell you what state of matter each one is in.

Stereoisomer
A molecule that has the same structural formula as another molecule but its atoms are arranged differently in space.

Structural formula
A way of representing molecules that shows the atoms carbon by carbon, with the attached hydrogens and functional groups.

Structural isomer
A molecule with the same molecular formula as another molecule, but with the atoms connected in a different way.

Sub-shell
A sub-division of an energy level (shell). Sub-shells may be s, p, d or f sub-shells.

Synthesis
A step-wise method detailing how to create a chemical.

Theoretical yield
The mass of product that should be formed in a chemical reaction.

Theory
A possible explanation for something. (Usually something that has been observed.)

Titration
A type of experiment used to find the concentration of a solution. It involves gradually adding one solution to a known volume of another until the reaction between the two is complete.

Tollens' reagent
$[Ag(NH_3)_2]^+$. It's reduced to silver when warmed with an aldehyde, but not with a ketone. The silver will coat the inside of the apparatus to form a silver mirror.

Unsaturated hydrocarbon
A hydrocarbon with a carbon-carbon double bond.

Valence-Shell Electron-Pair Repulsion Theory
The theory that in a molecule lone pair/lone pair bond angles are the biggest, lone pair/bonding pair bond angles are the second biggest and bonding pair/bonding pair bond angles are the smallest.

Valid result
A result which answers the question it was intended to answer.

Validation
The process of repeating an experiment done by someone else, using the theory to make new predictions, and then testing them with new experiments, in order to prove or refute the theory.

Van der Waals forces
The weakest intermolecular force, caused by temporary dipoles, which causes all atoms and molecules to be attracted to each other.

Variable
A factor in an experiment or investigation that can change or be changed.

Yield
The amount of product you get from a reaction.

Z-/E-isomerism
A type of stereoisomerism that is caused by the restricted rotation about a carbon-carbon double bond. Each of the carbon atoms must have two different groups attached.

Acknowledgements

Photograph acknowledgements

Cover Photo **Laguna Design**/Science Photo Library, p 1 **Charles D. Winters**/Science Photo Library, p 2 Science Photo Library, p 3 **Robert Brook**/Science Photo Library, p 4 (top) **David R. Frazier**/Science Photo Library, p 4 (bottom) **Martin Bond**/Science Photo Library, p 8 Science Photo Library, p 9 (top) **Prof. Peter Fowler**/ Science Photo Library, p 9 (bottom) **Charles D. Winters**/Science Photo Library, p 11 **Carol & Mike Werner/ Visuals Unlimited, Inc.**/Science Photo Library, p 13 **Science Source**/Science Photo Library, p 14 (top) **James Holmes/Oxford Centre For Molecular Sciences**/Science Photo Library, p 14 (bottom) **James Holmes/Oxford Centre For Molecular Sciences**/Science Photo Library, p 15 **NASA**/Science Photo Library, p 29 **Andrew Lambert Photography**/Science Photo Library, p 39 **Charles D. Winters**/Science Photo Library, p 41 **Andrew Lambert Photography**/Science Photo Library, p 44 **Martyn F. Chillmaid**/Science Photo Library, p 48 **Martyn F. Chillmaid**/ Science Photo Library, p 57 **Charles D. Winters**/Science Photo Library, p 58 (top) **Charles D. Winters**/Science Photo Library, p 58 (middle) **Andrew Lambert Photography**/Science Photo Library, p 58 (bottom) **Bill Beatty, Visuals Unlimited**/Science Photo Library, p 59 (top) **GIPhotostock**/Science Photo Library, p 59 (bottom) **GIPhotostock**/Science Photo Library, p 60 **Charles D. Winters**/Science Photo Library, p 61 **Sheila Terry**/Science Photo Library, p 62 **Lawrence Lawry**/Science Photo Library, p 68 **Dr Tim Evans**/Science Photo Library, p 69 **Dr Tim Evans**/Science Photo Library, p 71 **Paul D Stewart**/Science Photo Library, p 72 **Emilio Segre Visual Archives/American Institute of Physics**/Science Photo Library, p 73 **Martyn F. Chillmaid**/Science Photo Library, p 75 **Richard Treptow**/Science Photo Library, p 76 **Charles D. Winters**/Science Photo Library, p 78 (top) **Ria Novosti**/Science Photo Library, p 78 (middle left) **Charles D. Winters**/Science Photo Library, p 78 (middle right) **Charles D. Winters**/Science Photo Library, p 78 (bottom) **E. R. Degginger**/Science Photo Library, p 81 (top) **Martyn F. Chillmaid**/Science Photo Library, p 81(bottom) **Andrew Lambert Photography**/Science Photo Library, p 82 (top) **Andrew Lambert Photography**/Science Photo Library, p 82 (middle) **Charles D. Winters**/Science Photo Library, p 82 (bottom) **Charles D. Winters**/Science Photo Library, p 88 **Laguna Design**/Science Photo Library, p 100 **Martyn F. Chillmaid**/Science Photo Library, p 101 **Paul Rapson**/Science Photo Library, p 103 (top) **Astrid & Hanns-Frieder Michler**/Science Photo Library, p 103 (bottom) **Simon Fraser**/Science Photo Library, p 113 **Charles D. Winters**/Science Photo Library, p 114 **Martyn F. Chillmaid**/Science Photo Library, p 124 (top) **Sheila Terry**/Science Photo Library, p 124 (bottom) Science Photo Library, p 126 **Emilio Segre Visual Archives/ American Institute of Physics**/Science Photo Library, p 129 Science Photo Library, p 131 **Deloche**/Science Photo Library, p 132 **Vanessa Vick**/Science Photo Library, p 141 (top) **Andrew Lambert Photography**/Science Photo Library, p 141 (middle) **Andrew Lambert Photography**/Science Photo Library, p 141 (bottom) **Charles D. Winters**/Science Photo Library, p 142 (top) **CC Studio**/Science Photo Library, p 142 (bottom) **P. Hattenberger, Publiphoto Diffusion**/Science Photo Library, p 146 (top) **Andrew Lambert Photography**/Science Photo Library, p 146 (bottom) **Andrew Lambert Photography**/Science Photo Library, p 148 (top) **Charles D. Winters**/Science Photo Library, p 148 (bottom) **Martyn F. Chillmaid**/Science Photo Library, p 151 **Miriam Maslo**/Science Photo Library, p 153 **Crown Copyright/Health & Safety Laboratory**/Science Photo Library, p 154 **Dirk Wiersma**/ Science Photo Library, p 155 **Ria Novosti**/Science Photo Library, p 156 **Silvere Teutsch/Eurelios**/Science Photo Library, p 162 **Andrew Lambert Photography**/Science Photo Library, p 163 **NASA**/Science Photo Library, p 173 **Andrew Lambert Photography**/Science Photo Library, p 175 **Dr Mark J. Winter**/Science Photo Library, p 182 **Astrid & Hanns-Frieder Michler**/Science Photo Library, p 183 **James Holmes/Zedcor**/Science Photo Library, p 185 (top) **Power And Syred**/Science Photo Library, p 185 (bottom) **Ed Young**/Science Photo Library, p 186 **Victor De Schwanberg**/Science Photo Library, p 189 (top) **Harvey Pincis**/Science Photo Library, p 189 (bottom) **Andrew Lambert Photography**/Science Photo Library, p 190 (top) **Andrew Lambert Photography**/ Science Photo Library, p 190 (bottom) **Martyn F. Chillmaid**/Science Photo Library, p 191(top) **Andrew Lambert Photography**/Science Photo Library, p 191 (bottom) **Andrew Lambert Photography**/Science Photo Library, p 192 **Gustoimages**/Science Photo Library, p 198 **Photo Researchers Inc.**/Science Photo Library, p 204 **Martyn F. Chillmaid**/Science Photo Library, p 205 **Garry Watson**/Science Photo Library, p 208 **Monty Rakusen**/Science Photo Library, p 209 Science Photo Library, p 213 **Dr Tim Evans**/Science Photo Library, p 215 **Jon Stokes**/Science Photo Library.

Index

P

Q

R

S

T

U

V

W

Y

Z

The Periodic Table

Relative Atomic Mass (A_r) → top number in each box; Atomic (proton) number → bottom number in each box.

Periods	Group 1	Group 2											Group 3	Group 4	Group 5	Group 6	Group 7	Group 0
1								1.0 H Hydrogen 1										4.0 He Helium 2
2	6.9 Li Lithium 3	9.0 Be Beryllium 4											10.8 B Boron 5	12.0 C Carbon 6	14.0 N Nitrogen 7	16.0 O Oxygen 8	19.0 F Fluorine 9	20.2 Ne Neon 10
3	23.0 Na Sodium 11	24.3 Mg Magnesium 12											27.0 Al Aluminium 13	28.1 Si Silicon 14	31.0 P Phosphorus 15	32.1 S Sulfur 16	35.5 Cl Chlorine 17	39.9 Ar Argon 18
4	39.1 K Potassium 19	40.1 Ca Calcium 20	45.0 Sc Scandium 21	47.9 Ti Titanium 22	50.9 V Vanadium 23	52.0 Cr Chromium 24	54.9 Mn Manganese 25	55.8 Fe Iron 26	58.9 Co Cobalt 27	58.7 Ni Nickel 28	63.5 Cu Copper 29	65.4 Zn Zinc 30	69.7 Ga Gallium 31	72.6 Ge Germanium 32	74.9 As Arsenic 33	79.0 Se Selenium 34	79.9 Br Bromine 35	83.8 Kr Krypton 36
5	85.5 Rb Rubidium 37	87.6 Sr Strontium 38	88.9 Y Yttrium 39	91.2 Zr Zirconium 40	92.9 Nb Niobium 41	96.0 Mo Molybdenum 42	98 Tc Technetium 43	101.1 Ru Ruthenium 44	102.9 Rh Rhodium 45	106.4 Pd Palladium 46	107.9 Ag Silver 47	112.4 Cd Cadmium 48	114.8 In Indium 49	118.7 Sn Tin 50	121.8 Sb Antimony 51	127.6 Te Tellurium 52	126.9 I Iodine 53	131.3 Xe Xenon 54
6	132.9 Cs Caesium 55	137.3 Ba Barium 56	138.9 La Lanthanum 57	178.5 Hf Hafnium 72	180.9 Ta Tantalum 73	183.8 W Tungsten 74	186.2 Re Rhenium 75	190.2 Os Osmium 76	192.2 Ir Iridium 77	195.1 Pt Platinum 78	197.0 Au Gold 79	200.6 Hg Mercury 80	204.4 Tl Thallium 81	207.2 Pb Lead 82	209.0 Bi Bismuth 83	209 Po Polonium 84	210 At Astatine 85	222 Rn Radon 86
7	223 Fr Francium 87	226.0 Ra Radium 88	227.0 Ac Actinium 89	267 Rf Rutherfordium 104	268 Db Dubnium 105	271 Sg Seaborgium 106	272 Bh Bohrium 107	270 Hs Hassium 108	276 Mt Meitnerium 109	281 Ds Darmstadium 110	280 Rg Roentgenium 111							

The Lanthanides	140.1 Ce Cerium 58	140.9 Pr Praseodymium 59	144.2 Nd Neodymium 60	145 Pm Promethium 61	150.4 Sm Samarium 62	152.0 Eu Europium 63	157.3 Gd Gadolinium 64	158.9 Tb Terbium 65	162.5 Dy Dysprosium 66	164.9 Ho Holmium 67	167.3 Er Erbium 68	168.9 Tm Thulium 69	173.1 Yb Ytterbium 70	175.0 Lu Lutetium 71
The Actinides	232.0 Th Thorium 90	231.0 Pa Protactinium 91	238.0 U Uranium 92	237.0 Np Neptunium 93	244 Pu Plutonium 94	243 Am Americium 95	247 Cm Curium 96	247 Bk Berkelium 97	251 Cf Californium 98	252 Es Einsteinium 99	257 Fm Fermium 100	258 Md Mendelevium 101	259 No Nobelium 102	262 Lr Lawrencium 103